THIS LAND IS OUR LAND

Aspects of Agriculture in English Art

An exhibition organised for The Royal Agricultural Society of England
by Demelza Spargo

Mall Galleries, London
5th-29th January, 1989

159

An Exhibition to celebrate:

 sponsored by Phillips Auctioneers

The R.A.S.E. is also grateful to Her Majesty's Government for its help in agreeing to indemnify the exhibition under the National Heritage Act, 1980 and to the Museums and Galleries Commission for their assistance in this connection.

THIS LAND IS OUR LAND

Aspects of Agriculture in English Art

Edited by Demelza Spargo

with contributions by: William Vaughan, C. M. Ann Baker, Brian Stewart, Roy Brigden

Photography by James Austin

The poem 'Selling The Cows at Bridgetown Farm, Iddesleigh' specially commissioned from the Poet Laureate, Ted Hughes by the Royal Agricultural Society of England

Acknowledgments

J. S. Blomfield, F. Jolly, H. B. Carter, Peter de Francia, Nick Dolan, A. P. Voce, J. D. Sykes, D. Michinson, J. M. Briscoe, Wendy Sheridan, A. Laing, C. Jane Baker, W. P. N. Crewdson, Hilary Woolley, Edwin Green, Elizabeth Conran, David Coke, Geoffrey Yeo, Stephen J. G. Hall, Jane Farrington, Dr. Peter Mathias, I. Rutherford, Sheila McGregor, Warren Newman, Vera Beale, Jill Mata, Peyton Skipwith, D. T-D. Clarke, Philip Ryder-Davies, Lorna Marshall, Peter Brears, John Gall, Lt. Col. M. G. A. Young, Michael Day, Sylvia Thomas, Victoria Slowe, Vivien West, Susan Hartley, Clifford Ellison, Ivison S. Wheatley, Angela Weight, Rosemary Ransome Wallis, Richard de Peyer, Marie Hartley, Edmund Vestey, John Halkes, Judith Palmer, Lavinia Wellicome, Wendy Rose, Peter Day, Sir Oliver Millar, Charles Noble, Amanda Kavanagh, Marita Prendy, Ian Dejardin, M. A. St. John Hollis, Frank Atkinson, Sheila Edwards, Kenneth Reedie, Rosemary Eady, D. G. C. Allan, Professor G. H. Peters, Mr. Fenelon, J. K. Royston, David Beevers, J. A. McGuirk, Patrick Bond, Wilfred Shirley†, David McNeff, Alistair Penfold, Jill Betts, I. McCabe, Julia Knight, Dr. J. M. L. Booker, E. Shepperd, A. Lawson Johnstone, R. J. Wilkins, Joan Jones, Robert Sharp, Michael Goodall, R. B. Garwell, Penny Johnson, Kai Kin Yung, John Culverhouse, Nicholas Wadham, Andrew Hemingway, Sophie Weeks, Alison Awcock, John Green, Christopher Mendez, Angela Small, Lord Miles.

To Brian Stewart for help with several entries, to H. B. Carter for the entries on Merino Sheep, to W. A. D. Donaldson for help on the entry related to Sir George Stapledon, to Hugh Cheape of The Royal Museum, Edinburgh for his contribution to the entries related to the paintings of William Shiels. To Nigel Harvey for numerous imaginative contributions. To Paul Giudici, Giudici-Martin Conservation Services, Northamptonshire.

And to all lenders without whose generosity and imagination the exhibition could not have taken place.

Contents

Catalogue

1989 is the 150th anniversary of the first show organised by the Royal Agricultural Society of England and it is also the centenary of the creation of the Ministry of Agriculture, Fisheries and Food. This happy coincidence is being celebrated by a whole series of events within British Food and Farming Year.

One of those events is this exhibition of art "This Land is Our Land". In 1947, Guy Paget wrote in 'Aspects of British Art'; "With so much wealth and talent at their disposal it is a pity that the Royal Agricultural Society (of England) does not arrange an exhibition of cattle pictures. A single ox or pig may not be of much interest, but a comprehensive exhibition, where comparison is possible would be . . . There are few country houses where the family have been rooted for two hundred years which do not boast at least one monstrosity of an ox. . .".

This is that exhibition—expanded far beyond Paget's suggestion. It is made possible by the generosity of the owners of farms and country houses, and by the great institutions linked with agriculture and art. The 'monstrosities' are here, but there is much else besides, and it reflects the pride of landowners and farmers in their agricultural achievements and their pleasure in the countryside.

The majority of the British landscape may have been fashioned by agriculture, but the rural scene has always attracted artists and it is through their eyes that we can trace the social and technical changes and the influence they have had on the look of the countryside.

I am sure that this exhibition will give visitors a great deal of pleasure and I hope it will also give them a better insight into the history and development of the first of all industries.

1988

Introduction

The Royal Agricultural Society of England, British Food and Farming Year and ''This Land is Our Land''

The decision to create an English Agricultural Society was made on 9th May 1838 at a meeting at The Freemasons' Tavern, London, chaired by Earl Spencer. Those were days of turmoil as a growing population in England made the maintenance of a protected agriculture increasingly impossible to defend. The Corn Laws were soon to be repealed, but it was not for such purposes that the Society was formed, and indeed our 1840 Charter reads:

''And know ye further, that in granting this our Royal Charter to the said Royal Agricultural Society of England, we do hereby declare it to be our full and entire will and pleasure that we extend our Royal protection to its national objects, under the condition that a principle of its constitution shall be the total exclusion of all questions at its meetings, or in its proceedings, of a political tendency, or having reference to measures pending, or to be brought forward, in either of our Houses of Parliament, which no resolution, bye-laws, or other enactment of the said body politic and corporate, shall on any account or pretence whatsoever be at any time allowed to infringe.''

The language is very strong, and inevitably there have been many occasions in the past 150 years when we *have* become involved in matters of ''a political tendency'', but our independent and charitable status is greatly treasured and we seek to abide by the principles on which we were founded.

The planning of British Food and Farming Year, of which ''This Land is Our Land'' is the first important manifestation, started in 1982, with consideration of the Society's 150th anniversary and how it should be recognised. Simultaneously, and this has a nice relevance to the exhibition, quite separate discussions that had started with thoughts of a ''Visions of Art in Agriculture'' exhibition had broadened into considerations of a Year of Agriculture. When it was realised that 1989 would be the centenary of the Ministry of Agriculture, Fisheries & Food (the old Board of Agriculture was abolished as no longer needed after the Napoleonic wars had ended) everything fell into place.

There are many obvious ways of bringing the character and achievements of our food and agricultural industry to the attention of an often ill-informed general public—be it through presentations in supermarkets or by taking children onto farms—and these will all happen throughout the year. However they cannot tell the whole story. The physical and cultural separation of the bulk of our urban population from the fields whence comes its food has resulted in a lack of understanding of the way in which the food on which we depend for life is produced, and of the climatic and other hazards to which such food production is subject. Of no less importance it has created a gulf in understanding of much of our history and culture. The country's 'first industry', in the words of Prince Philip, has shaped not only our beautiful landscape but also, historically, our trading patterns, the location and appearance of our cities, our architecture and much else besides.

It is for this reason that we turned to Art to redress the balance and tell the story. Agriculture has never been far from controversy; even the title of this exhibition was thought in some quarters to have a political connotation (it is adapted from a poem by Robert Frost). The surpluses created by the Common Agricultural Policy cause dissension that is as nothing compared with the debates on the Enclosures of the 18th Century. All that, however, is for the political arena; art can lead us to underlying truths, albeit with differing interpretations of these truths. It is our great good fortune that artists have faithfully recorded the history of this 'first industry' of ours. They have done so, of course, so often and so well, that many great paintings and other works of art are *not* here. However, an unrivalled collection, in terms both of intrinsic quality and artistic interest, has been brought together from the four corners of England. From Richard Ansdell's great painting of the Country Meeting of the Society in Bristol in 1842 to the carved pig that decorated the shop front of Fletchers' pork butchers in Grimsby; from mediaeval misericordes portraying the day-to-day activities of the fields to the painting of prisoners of war helping with the harvest in the First World War—'all human life is here'.

We are immensely grateful to all who have loaned exhibits, to Michael Rosenberg who has made it all possible, to our sponsors Phillips the auctioneers, and to all who have helped in so many ways. To one person above all, however, credit is due. It was our great fortune to find Ms Demelza Spargo, the art historian who has put together the exhibition for us. It has taken 15 months of hard work, imagination, tact, perseverance and no little management skill to make it happen. When it is over, and she takes up her Rome scholarship to study the work of Renato Guttuso we hope that this catalogue, and the memories of all who have visited the Exhibition, will be both record and recompense.

John Hearth
Chief Executive, Royal Agricultural Society of England
Chairman, Policy & Co-ordinating Committee British Food & Farming Year.

24.10.88

SELLING THE COWS AT BRIDGETOWN FARM, IDDESLEIGH

They're all still here. Same weather. Primaeval
Colour-jumble of a washed world
Under ice-cliffs of cloud.
Same small hunters in the same mud circle.

Now, from a webby cave of cob, launched
Into lungings, the Devon cow,
Overfed wallower, in her daubed reds,
Splashes into the ring, under the sticks.

All eyes on the beast. She's the same
Three, four, five years old—the genes fixed.
And the hunters' faces are unaltered.
If they've aged, it's an old oak's

Hiding another decade. It's water
At a weir. It's a shagginess of the same.
A river-lens warping the bed-rock of sameness.
Their eyes, like the voice of the Auctioneer,

Only seem to move. Wince and dazzle
Of what is unmoving. The cow's bellow and plunge
Is the fixity in the day's crystal.
In her eye—the same revelation

As the oldest fire, that feasting flame
Reflected in the eyes of the hunters
Who close round, sinking their stares, rapt
Into the dark bulk of beast.

TED HUGHES

Leisure and Toil

Differing Views of Rural Life *c.* 1750 – 1850

Agricultural activity has been a prevalent topic in British landscape painting since the 18th Century. It has, as well, figured large in animal portraiture and in that domestic form of subject painting usually referred to as 'genre'. During this long period there have been many different types and approaches. But there have as well been some remarkably consistent and dominating attitudes. The predominant one has been that of seeing the farming community and its activities as representing health, calm and well-being. At a time when the British economy and British population have been becoming increasingly less rural, there has been a corresponding increase in the desire to see the country way as the 'good life' that everyone would like to live, if only circumstances would allow them to.

This growing urban need to find such virtues in the country has, of course, presented a whole set of problems—many of which are rarely out of the papers these days. The indigenous rural population increasingly feels itself threatened by the interests of the city—whether these be the manipulations of big business, the 'interference' of settlers, or simply the irritation of day trippers walking across fields of growing crops. Something of this feeling, indeed, might have crept into the title of this exhibition, with its reference to ownership. Although they might vigorously reject the association, most depicters of the rural world these days tend to look at things from the urban point of view—never so much so as when they are insisting on timeless tranquility and banishing all images of the contemporary world. Painters of the rural scene in the 20th Century have been notorious for their inability to see pylons and silage towers. "Discussing the Milk Quota" and "Artificial Insemination Day" are still, I believe, subjects awaiting their debut at the Royal Academy.

This, then, has been the general course of things. It is one that is hardly surprising, considering the predominantly urban nature of art institutions and art patronage. But it is not totally the case. During the first century of the development in particular—the century in which I am primarily interested in this article—the rural community itself was making a strong demand and input. In the 18th Century farming constituted a highly significant—possibly predominant—part of the general economy. If anything, its role was expanding. It is widely held that it was the 'agrarian revolution' that occurred in the middle years of the century that started that economic upturn that was to fuel the industrial revolution later on. Agriculture remained a powerful factor in Britain in the early 19th Century—greatly stimulated by the reliance on its resources necessitated by the Napoleonic Wars. Comparative decline after that was slow. In 1851 the Population Census showed that a majority of Britons no longer lived and worked in the country. But it was not until the 1870s that any serious signs of major agricultural retreat became clear. A broad section of the traditional rural community were patrons of pictures in the late 18th and early 19th Centuries—and their tastes and requirements had an influence in shaping the depictions of rural life and agricultural activity.

But how great an influence? Was it as strong as that of the city dwellers? Did it lead to distant and different types of art being produced? As with most questions of patronage answers to these questions cannot be precise. But there is often evidence of a distinct rural voice being heard. One broad division in the representation of the countryside at this time is that between 'idyllic' scenes—which suggest a life of ease and innocence— and 'working' scenes—which show agricultural activities taking place or celebrate their produce. In critical terms these different types might be seen as corresponding roughly to the 'pastoral'—the world of arcadian shepherds and restful glades—and the 'georgic'—the poetic tradition that followed Virgil's description of the countryside as a place made prosperous through toil. By and large the 'pastoral' tradition was favoured by those who viewed the country from the city, and the 'georgic' by those who lived and worked in the country. But of course the division was never absolute. There were many complexifying factors. One of these was class. There was a tendency for the wealthier members of society to favour the 'pastoral' view no matter whether they lived in the city or the country. Another was the changing role played by agriculture itself. During the Napoleonic Wars, for example there was a more general sympathy for the 'georgic' approach than during preceding or subsequent decades.

Noticeable in both these attitudes is a relative lack of criticism. Studies in recent decades—notably Raymond Williams' classic *The Country and The City* (1973)—have drawn attention not only to the projective nature of the sense of rural idyll, but also to the massive exploitation of country workers during the period. Undoubtedly this happened. The increasing capitalization of the land—the consolidation of large estates, introduction of new farming methods, enclosure of common land—led to the dispossession and degradation of traditional labourers. An increase in the number of vagrants and paupers, and periodic bouts of rioting and destruction of property were amongst the most visible consequences of this process. Yet such matters hardly figure at all in the paintings of the period. There is not really much mystery about this. These pictures were, after all, bought or commissioned by the 'haves'—even if some of these were still relatively modest farmers. Such people did not, on the whole, wish to adorn their walls with reminders of contemporary rifts and problems. If one wants any sense of these in visual terms one has to turn to caricature. But even here the comment is limited by the traditional licence given to the jester. There is none of the hard hitting 'serious' criticism that one finds, for example, in contemporary poems by Crabbe or Goldsmith—or a little later in the *Rural Rides* of Cobbett. The division between art and literature on this issue merits reflection. Perhaps it was due to the fact that art at that time was so much more directly dependent upon patronage and ownership than was writing. Perhaps, too, there is a more fundamental requirement for visual art to provide delight, to satisfy the 'scoptophilic' drive. Be that as it may, it remains a fact that criticism of social conditions was less evident in the pictures than in the literature of the period. Even those artists—like Constable—who made a great issue about the 'truthfulness' of their paintings, were highly selective in this respect.

The issue of 'art' raises another interesting complication. For the period is rich in representations of rural themes by painters who fall outside the academic tradition. One of the great strengths of the current exhibition is that it places both types of work side by side. Traditionally art historians have tended to consider so-called 'naïve' art as falling outside their terms of reference and as being irrelevant to the discussion of 'high' art. Aesthetic changes in this century have made us more susceptible to the charms of such work. Yet we have tended to see them as the products of some timeless consciousness. Only recently has serious attention been given to their importance as historical records and to the part they play in the visual culture of a specific period. Indeed—as this exhibition should help to make clear—the division between 'sophisticated' and 'naïve' art is a gross over-simplification—one brought about largely by the barrier set up by the academic artist between his art and that of other practitioners. In reality there is a broad range of artists and of pictorial types. Furthermore, the divisions between them are often unclear, or made for arbitrary reasons. In the case of animal portraiture, for example, some painters—like Stubbs or Herring—are seen as being 'sophisticated'; others—like Pollard or Bradshaw—are considered 'naïve'. Yet these artists worked for a similar clientele and shared a pictorial tradition. In the place of the image of a divided practice—two groups working according to different criteria on opposing sides of a frontier—it might be helpful to put that of a broad, continuous terrain. Each artist has a different place in this landscape. But there are paths between them and few of these are impassable. This point is important for the history of art in general. But it has particular application in the field of rural art. For it is here that the patronage of those artists so frequently called 'naïve' had a particularly strong basis—both in views of places and in the detailed portrayal of animals and farm produce.

In the second part of this article, I want to look at some of the dominant types of rural imagery of the period. Three of these will be types that suggest country interests—namely the view of the estate, the 'working' landscape and animal portraiture. Three will suggest city views—that is the pastoral idyll, the rustic in the city, and finally an attempt to re-interpret the country under the influence of that high urban tendency, Realism.

1. The view of the estate

The view of the estate represents first and foremost the interests of those in authority. Aesthetically it took its rationale in the first place from the *Georgics* of Virgil, with their emphasis on the importance of farming for the wealth of society at large. Already in the late middle ages this interest could be personal and specific. In the celebrated *Tres Riches Heures* of the Duc de Berry in the early 15th Century the rich man's castle is shown underpinned by the rural economy that surrounds it. During the Renaissance the cyclical image of farming that the books of hours could provide was replaced by perspectival vistas. These could make different points through their ordering of space. No artist during this period came closer to a detailed sense of peasant life than the Flemish painter Pieter Bruegel. Yet while peasants dominate the foreground, there are views in the background of the wider world order into which they fit. His celebrated *Summer*—one of a series of paintings now in the Kunsthistorisches Museum in Vienna gives a marvellously precise account of harvest time in a farm on the outskirts of a village. Some products are already fully gathered and are being carried along the road that leads from the foreground to a distant town and the sea beyond. Even this small corner, Bruegel seems to be saying, has its place in the world order and is a significant part of the economy. Bruegel often shows his peasants hard at work. But there is a compensatory image of the leisure that they can also enjoy. In *Summer* for example, there are signs of a festival being prepared in the village. Later artists tended to find even this compensatory representation of work problematic, and would tend to make it look less back-breaking. An important figure for 18th Century artists was the early 17th Century Flemish artist Pieter Paul Rubens. Rubens retired to an estate after his highly successful career at the Flemish court. Paintings done on his estate—notably the *Chateau de Steen* (National Gallery) emphasize more the fruitfulness of the country rather than the toil necessary in producing it.

The English Estate view followed on such traditions—though with a characteristic greater emphasis on the topographical. Images began to proliferate around 1700—the time when the political upheavals of the earlier Stuart period seemed to be at an end and new wealth was being injected into the country. The artists who first produced these views were largely of Flemish origin (often political and religious refugees); figures such as Jan Sibberechts and Leonard Knyff. Knyff is remembered in particular for his detailed 'bird's-eye' views of great estates—in which agriculture plays its part along with all other activities of the lordly demesne. Such grandiose overviews soon gave way to more specific vistas. George Lambert was one of the first to specialize in these. As well as views of country houses, he also did direct views of the land. His *Hilly Landscape with a Cornfield* (Tate Gallery) of 1773 is a representation of the countryside around Box Hill. What is remarkable about this work is the combination of detailed topography with an image of rural plenty. The cornfield attests to the latter. It is being reaped by a solitary worker; presumably a more realistic inclusion of a team of reapers would have made work too obtrusive in this idyll. In the foreground there stands a figure who appears to be directing the work of the artist. It is unclear if he is actually the owner of the land. But he certainly represents authority and those who are benefiting from the plenty behind. Thomas Gainsborough's *Mr and Mrs Andrews* (National Gallery) represents ownership of farming land in a particularly direct way. Mr and Mrs Andrews are shown on their estate, with a rich cornfield beside them. Here, however, there is no farm work evident. The main point here seems to be to emphasize the wealth of their possessions.

These pictures of owners standing proudly in their productive fields seem to be more of a characteristic of the early than the later 18th Century. With the increase in wealth it seems that those in possession of larger estates wished to distance themselves from the activities that provided their wealth. Later portraits by Gainsborough—for example the *Morning Walk* of 1786 in the National Gallery—show figures walking in a generalized nature, without any hint of agricultural activity going on. It is interesting to note that, at a more modest level, the 'estate' view continued to flourish. Many detailed records of farms by 'naïve' artists can be found, for example the *South View of Fen End Farm* (1790) and the *Country Fete* (c. 1800) from the Mr and Mrs Andras Kalman Collection. Such images emphasize plenty and possessions in a very detailed way. Such farm portraiture, of course, continued up to the present day, when it usually takes the form of the aerial photograph.

2. The 'Working' Landscape

As opposed to the view of the estate, the 'working' landscape emphasizes some aspect of rural activity. Such images occur in the 18th Century—though usually in the guise of the portrayal of 'rural types' as in the *Milkmaid* by Gainsborough. During the last part of the century however, interest shifted more towards the activity itself. An early example can be found in the *Reapers* of George Stubbs, where the figures are shown at work in a factual, unsentimental way. Stubbs' unromantic view was perhaps too much for his contemporaries. For apparently his subject was poorly received when it was turned into a mezzotint[1]. Far more popular in the 1790s were the romanticized scenes of rural life by George Morland, in which smallholders were shown in picturesque squalor. The real vogue for 'modern' farming scenes occurred during the Napoleonic Wars. One of the first artists to exploit the genre was Turner, who included figures working the land in his views of the Thames Valley around 1810. Over the next few years a large number of young landscape painters essayed the genre-notably William Henry Hunt, William Mulready, John Linnell and George Frederick Lewis. Their views of modern English scenery were given a greater actuality by being based on oil studies made out of doors.

It seems that this vogue was fuelled in the first place by the propagandist emphasis on English scenery and English agricultural prosperity in a period when the country was at war with France. Turner—an intensely ambitious and competitive artist—seems to have been attracted to the genre for this reason. But many of the other artists seem to have gone beyond this original aim into a more detailed evocation of the 'real' landscape. On the whole their work in this direction was not appreciated. Most of them subsequently abandoned such work for more profitable idealizations.

The exception to this rule was John Constable. Constable is now regarded as being unique in his pursuit of 'real' landscape in the early nineteenth century. But it would be perhaps truer to say that he was the one who persisted with it longest and brought it to the most successful result. Part of the reason may have been his deep personal involvement. The son of a Suffolk miller and landowner, he recorded obsessively his native territory. Like Hunt, Lewis and Linnell, he did this using direct oil sketches. However, his knowledge of country ways meant that he could do this with an unique understanding of the crafts and farming techniques he was portraying. He showed such features as a 'runover dungle', and the building of barges on the River Stour. His most detailed pictures are painted before 1816—significantly a period when he was working almost exclusively for a local Suffolk clientele. Although Constable was at this time already keen to succeed in London, he was still drawing his strength from his native environment. It is interesting to note that his first teacher had in fact been a local craftsman, John Dunthorne. Like many other local artists of the period—for example the animal painter William Bradshaw—Dunthorne was a plumber and glazier by profession. Constable was later to replace Dunthorne's painting methods with those of his London teachers. Yet he remained a confidant of Dunthorne's, would sketch in his company when in Suffolk, and discussed his artistic ideas with him.

After 1816 Constable became more and more of a 'London' artist. His later pictures become more grandiose, and increasingly replace detailed records of local scenery and activities with dramatic atmospheric effects. Undoubtedly this change can be related to his ambition to become a Royal Academician—something that he finally achieved in 1828. It is significant that his patrons now tended to come increasingly from the city. Constable himself played down the local element in his work and emphasized it more as a generic representation of England. This can be seen in the title that he gave to the series of mezzotints after his work published from 1830 onwards, *English Landscape*.

Constable's move away from his native world can be seen in personal terms. However, it is also interesting to see that it takes place at the same time that any 'city' interest in the working landscape goes underground. For after the Napoleonic Wars the interest in seeing a vigorous productive land as an image of England declines. In the country itself there is a period of great unrest—sparked off by the decline in agriculture that followed the wars. The 'reality' of the rural world in the early 1820s was one of vagrancy and rick burning. Not surprising, perhaps, that people turned their backs on this and sought instead images of timeless ease.

As with views of estates, however, images of 'working' landscapes did continue but in a more specialized context. Increasingly these related to the growth of professional agricultural organizations, the movement that gave birth to the R.A.S.E. itself. The *'Match Ploughing Scene'* of Thomas Smythe is an example of this kind of work.

3. Animal Portraiture

Like portraiture of estates, portraits of animals in the eighteenth century came out of a venerable tradition. By and large it was one connected with sport, and the great animal painters of the period—Wootton, Seymour and Stubbs—all had work in this area as their basis. But a significant feature of the growing strength of farming at this time is the development of new breeds and the wish to celebrate these by portraiture. Stubbs becomes involved in this as part of his wider practice of animal painting. But it became more and more a specialist activity in the nineteenth century—as can be seen in the career of artists like James Pollard.

One of the striking features for us is the gross shape of so many of these animals. Sometimes it seems hard to believe that the animals could in fact have been bred to assume such shapes. There is, indeed, some evidence to suggest that farmers encouraged exaggeration. The great wood engraver Thomas Bewick records such a circumstance in his *Memoir*. As a young man he was asked to do such work. But, as he said "I objected to put lumps of fat here and there where I could not see it." (Memoir, 1862, p. 183)[1] Despite this, there is clear documentary evidence that animals were bred at that time to be excessively fat. Some were even so large they had to be supported by wooden props when they stood. It is probably true that artists like Pollard and Bagshaw heightened this effect in their work. But in doing so, they were responding to a very specific kind of aesthetic demand. Even more than the 'working landscape', this kind of painting was for strictly rural clientele—being of more interest to the producers rather than the consumers of livestock.

4. The Rural Idyll

The idyllic 'pastoral' view of rural life seems to have had its origins at Court, and to have been used largely as a contrast to conditions there. At that time its artificiality was clear. But in the eighteenth century it took on a greater urgency. As city life became more distant from that of the country, it was possible to confuse the boundaries of fantasy and reality and to come to believe that the 'pastoral' world was in fact that of the true countryside. Some such transformation seems to have taken place in Gainsborough after he left his native Suffolk in 1760. Such later pictures as the *'Market Cart'* contrast strongly to his early detailed landscapes and portraits. The treatment has become generalized, the colours have gained a soft nostalgic glow. The figures in his pictures are no longer specifically modern. They could almost be confused with arcadian shepherds. This tendency was one encouraged by the 'picturesque' movement of the period. Although held in check to some extent in the early nineteenth century, when the 'working' landscape briefly came into vogue, it reasserted itself in the 1820s. Samuel Palmer's 'visionary' portrayals show an intensely literary approach to rural life, which emphasized the archaic and pastoral. Although Palmer and his friends settled in the Kent village of Shoreham their depictions bear little sense of being actual records of what they saw. Eventually, in the 1830s, Palmer left Shoreham, disillusioned at not being able to find there the primeval world he sought. In later years he painted increasingly wistful representations of a fantasy pastoral world. His friend and mentor John Linnell took a similar path. In Linnell's case, the choice is particularly striking because, during the Napoleonic period, he had been one of the pioneers of tough, accurately observed rural scenes. Over the years Linnell's technique became broader and his subjects more idyllic. Eventually he was to take the process to its logical conclusion. In 1851 he retired to Redhill in Surrey. Here he acquired eighty acres of woodland which he kept in a wild state, rarely felling a tree. It was the paintings of nature that he produced based on this 'unspoilt' terrain that turned him into the most popular of all Victorian landscape painters.

5. The Rustic in the City

As the City became more remote from the country, the views of rural life craved by those who lived in the city became more idyllic and distanced from contemporary events. But there was one area in which the town dweller still retained a direct link with agriculture. This was through the market, where produce was brought to be sold, often by the farmers themselves. Here there was less scope for sentimentalization—and it is no surprise to find that market scenes gave rich material to the caricaturist. Thomas Rowlandson's vigorous portrayal of *'Smithfield Market'* falls into this genre. The earthiness suggested by the rural presence—together with the commercial nature of the transactions taking place often provided scope for erotic commentary. The cartoon of the *"Sale of a Wife"* at Smithfield may be on one level a dig at an obsolete outlandish custom. But it also gains a certain poignancy from the existence of a 'marriage market' in high society in the form of the 'season' and of the common sight of the country girls who become prostitutes in London. Hogarth's *"Harlot's progress"* of 1731 had played on this theme (the first scene of the series shows the 'heroine' of the story arriving from the country). It remained a dominant image in the nineteenth century. For even after it fitted the facts less exactly, it had a potency as suggesting the 'innocence' of the countryside being corrupted by the wickedness and unnaturalness of the city. When the Pre-Raphaelite Dante Gabriel Rossetti wished to paint a 'realistic' modern subject he settled upon this theme. His unfinished picture *"Found"* shows a fallen country girl being discovered in the streets of London by her former rustic sweetheart. The young man is up in London on his way to market—something that is made clear by the calf in the cart he has been driving. This 'trapped' calf is a symbol of the plight of the girl herself. Such—Rossetti seems to be saying—is the fate of all things brought from the country to the city.

6. An Attempt at Realism

Despite being presented as a 'modern' subject, Rossetti's picture seems to be drawing on an old tradition and to show very little sign of direct observation. But other members of the Pre-Raphaelite brotherhood were more innovative in this respect. When the Brotherhood was established in 1848 it took 'truth to nature' as one of its central tenets. For a brief period it embodied something of the directness of approach found earlier in the century in Constable and the other explorers of 'working' landscapes. Like these artists, the Pre-Raphaelites promoted working directly from nature. The most consistent in this principle was Holman Hunt. Although perhaps the least appealing of the group, Hunt was the most radical in his search for literal truth. This tendency can be seen in his most important treatment of a rural theme, the *'Hireling Shepherd'* of 1851. The picture was painted on a farm at Elwell, south of London. The principle figures were studied directly from farm hands. In painting the picture Hunt was characteristically aiming at both a visual and a moral truth. The visual truth was to show shepherds and shepherdesses as they really were rather than as they were portrayed in the conventions of the pastoral. The moral truth was to use this rural scene as a commentary on the religious controversies of the time. It seems that the image of the young couple dallying was intended to remind contemporaries of 'muddle-headed pastors' who disputed obscure issues of doctrine rather than looking after their flock. Certainly this meaning can be discovered in the work. The swain is showing his girl a Death's Head Moth while the lamb she is meant to be nursing eats a green apple, and the flock he is meant to be tending strays into the corn. But more shocking for contemporaries was the rude health and erotic earthiness of the couple themselves. Whatever the intended moral of the piece, Hunt was visually presenting a bucolic world in a vigorous and unvarnished manner. Significantly, Hunt was asked by a patron to do another painting that showed only the sheep and left out the disturbing rustic lovers altogether.

It might seem that Hunt's vigorous portrayal of farm hands was a prelude to later 'Realist' art—such as that produced by Herkomer, and Clausen later in the century. But I think that it represents a unique moment—and one that was not likely to recur as the rural world became a relatively less central part of the economy. In a recent article in *Art History* (2) Kay Dian Kriz has shown how Hunt's rustics 'of the coarsest breed' gave offence as much to urban radicals as to urban conservatives. Both groups wanted the image of a timeless, virtuous rural world as a contrast to the modern city. And it is the traditional nature of rural society that is explored by later realists—whether to celebrate it or to show it under threat from the modern world.

Hunt's refusal to accept this convention closes a vigorous chapter of English art in which rural and urban voices could be heard in dialogue.

William Vaughan

Notes

1. Quoted in James Ayres *English Naive Painting*, 1980, p. 111.
2. Kay Dian Kriz "An English Arcadia revisited and reassessed: Holman Hunt's *The Hireling Shepherd* and the rural tradition." in *Art History*, December 1987, pp. 475-491.

Mr. and Mrs. Andrews, Thomas Gainsborough

The Artist as Witness

The Evolution of Livestock in England

The early history of English livestock is sparse. Mediaeval art illustrates the uses and husbandry of animals; and, in some species (notably the dog and the sheep) incipient breeds can be identified. During the next 200 to 300 years animals appeared in portraits of their owners as pets or as indicators of rank, but rarely as livestock.

There are some drawings of farm animals in the surviving work of Francis Barlow (1626-1704). Then, from the latter part of the eighteenth century, both written and artistic information increases considerably. Inevitably, most of the pictures in this exhibition are associated with the rise and progress of the major breeds of the more common species, but a number of less commonly recorded species and breeds have been represented to provide a balanced view. Each species and, where appropriate, breed is considered in turn.

Cattle

"Keeping Cattle in a Forest", (162) refers to a common practice, but appears to also carry allusions to the belief that the cattle preserved in some parks were the relicts of wild herds. The cows have the typical markings of white with black muzzles, ears and feet. There were also herds in which these points were red; some herds were polled. The bull represents the atypical animals which sometimes occur and are usually culled. Many herds have become extinct in the last 200 years, but that at Chillingham (163) still exists.

It is of interest that the first notable historian of White Cattle, the Reverend John Storer, was an early advocate of using art to trace breed history.

Illustrations of mediaeval cattle provide more information on husbandry and techniques than on incipient breeds. These are hinted at in the 16th and 17th Centuries and appear as accepted facts in the 18th Century.

The Longhorn entered history as a group of breeds, extending from the northern end of the Pennines and the adjacent western districts through to the centre of England. William Marshall (1745-1818) stated that the Midland breeds of Longhorns differed from each other as much as a Hereford differed from a Gloucester. Some of the variation in the Northern breeds can be seen in "The Painter's Home, Ambleside" (217a) and "Windermere from Troutbeck" (310). In the latter work, one animal appears polled; a variant of the Longhorn mentioned by writers from the 1780s to the 1860s.

The early development of the modern Longhorn is usually associated with Robert Bakewell and Robert Fowler. However, neither concealed that he had bought in stock which had been improved earlier (albeit by breeders who had not received national publicity). Both Bakewell and Fowler obtained some foundation cows from Mr. Webster of Canley. Bakewell also based his early breeding on the method of Webster: i.e., he used bulls from other breeds of Longhorn, mainly from the North. Thus, part of his early success was due to hybrid vigour from the cross. The selection and inbreeding, emphasised by so many writers, came later.

Fowler hired bulls from Bakewell. One was called Twopenny. Another bull was Twopenny's inbred grandson, called simply "D" (or the Mad Bull). This bull, mated to a cow by Twopenny got Fowler's bull Shakespear, calved c. 1778.

Fowler had many of his herd painted (173-180). All confirm comtemporary observations that, like Webster's foundation cows, Fowler's herd was predominantly red, in contrast to the general fashion for lighter-coloured Longhorns. Unfortunately it is not possible to identify all the individuals unequivocally. For example, Brindled Beauty (175) resembles the portrait which Trow-Smith said was of Rollright Beauty. Shakespear (174) does not match William Marshall's observation that ". . . he scarcely inherits a single point of the long-horned breed; his horns excepted . . . he had every point of a Holderness or a Teeswater bull." But, while Shakespear has little in common with Garrard's Teeswater ox (83), neither is he very like Garrard's Longhorned bull (82). Both these animals were scale representations based on actual measurements, so it could be that the portraits of Fowler's stock are idealized. The cow-like heads and necks of the bulls (173, 174, 178) also suggest stylization, as these were not mentioned by contemporary observers.

It is also possible that Shakespear (174) is the son of Shakespear out of Young Nell.

Fowler's herd was praised by his contemporaries. William Marshall gave Shakespear a high reputation as a stock-getter; and, Arthur Young noted that many considered Lady Washington ". . . the finest cow in England". At Fowler's dispersal sale in 1791, Brindled Beauty made 260 guineas; and, 205 guineas were paid for Garrick (177), son of Shakespear out of Horned Beauty.

There were also criticisms. One complaint—the neglect of milking ability—was supported by the inclusion of "3 Welch cows, used as nurses" in Fowler's sale.

The Shorthorn provides some interesting parallels and contrasts with the Longhorn. The former occurred along the North-East coast from Northumberland to Lincolnshire as a group of breeds. Some of these breeds, such as the Teeswater (83) and the Holderness were known nationally before *the* Shorthorn became fashionable. Glover's bull and cows (185) belong to this group.

Much credit for the early development of the present Shorthorn breed is given to Robert and Charles Colling and the latter's wife Mary (née Colpitts). In 1782 Charles spent 3 weeks with Bakewell, so it is not surprising that the Collings followed similar methods of breeding.

The Collings bought-in stock gave rise to several tribes (i.e., female lines). The Duchesses originated from the yellow-red roan Duchess bought for £13 in Darlington Mart in the early 1780s. In 1810, one of her descendants, Young Duchess, was sold for 183 guineas to Thomas Bates to become his Duchess 1st. The Wildairs were derived from a cow of that name bought by Robert Colling. A descendant Wildair (37) by Favourite 252 put back to Favourite bred Juno (36).

Charles and Mary's best known bulls were Favourite 252 and his son Comet 155 (33). The latter was the first bull to sell for 1,000 guineas. One of Robert's best known bulls was another son of Favourite: the White Bull 151 (31).

Some contemporary critics of the early Longhorn breeders commented on a "lack of oxen". This implied that there was no demonstration of the commercial end-product, and that so many males were kept as bulls that selection was relaxed. Shorthorn breeders, on the other hand, had a tradition of producing and celebrating fat oxen. One of the earliest mentioned is the Newby Ox, c. 1700, with a total deadweight of 145 stone 6lb. The Blackwell Ox (166), Howick Mottled Ox (161), Howick Red Ox (160), and the Whitley Ox (138a) were all commemorated in the late 18th Century. However, the most important advertising came from the Ketton Ox, later exhibited as the Durham Ox, bred by Favourite 252 out of a common cow. The tradition was continued well into the 19th Century.

Shorthorn breeders also fed heifers. A roan 3-year-old by Favourite was exhibited and sold for beef at Darlington in 1799. Robert Colling's famous female, who acquired the name "White Heifer that Travelled", also sired by Favourite, represented less of a sacrifice as she was a freemartin (i.e., a heifer born twin to a bull and sterile because anastomosis of the foetal circulatory systems exposed her, in utero, to the hormones of her brother).

The Craven Heifer (172) represents another aspect of breed evolution, namely breed replacement by grading up. The original Craven heifers were Longhorns, but the repeated use of Shorthorn bulls eventually resulted in a Shorthand type, currently represented by the few surviving Northern Dairy Shorthorns.

The spread of the Shorthorn was facilitated by the appearance of Coates Herd Book in 1822 (186a). This was compiled by George Coates of Carlton, near Pontefract, the breeder of the 500 guinea bull Patriot (181). The herd book had a special appeal to wealthy landowners and stockbreeders, who were familiar with the uses of the General Stud Book, first published in 1791.

Coates Herd Book also provided the information used by Sewall Wright as the basis of some of the most important genetic research of the 20th Century. Wright's research has practical implications, as in the genetic analysis of breed structure. For example, by 1920, the Shorthorn breed as a whole had an average relationship to the bull Favourite 252 (calved in 1792) of 55.2%. (The relationship between parent and offspring, or between full sibs, is 50%.) This high degree of relationship to a single individual is remarkable as, like other breeds, Shorthorns had been selected in the intervening period for different aims, and specialised beef and dairy types had emerged.

In the late 18th Century there was a group of breeds extending from Dorset and Somerset to the Cornish border. One breed, the North Devon (commonly just called "the Devon") was well known because of its long tradition of being sent as beef cattle to London. The (North) Devon was also valued for draught, and its work oxen were reported being used in many districts throughout England.

There was a brief vogue among improvers for feeding Devons, as shown by Coke's obese ox (62). However, the local breeders of North Devon regarded their stock as a "tenant farmer's breed"; their more typical animals improved for beef are those recorded by Ward (186b), by Garrard (83) and with Francis Quartly (285). Many examples of the more general type of cattle and their colour variation appear in Devon landscapes of the era (212). There were also polled strains.

The North Devon continued to be important locally, and many were exported successfully to developing countries and colonies. Improved North Devon bulls were used in herds of other breeds in the same general breed group. The appearance of Davys' Devon Herd Book in 1851 facilitated the absorption of the West Devon, the East Devon, and the Somerset into the (North) Devon. However, the South Devon remained apart. Partly because of isolation, and partly because of different markets, it evolved along separate lines. The South Devon attained its own herd book in 1891. Today the breed is expanding as a producer of quality beef, with the added advantages of a large size and the existence of naturally polled strains.

The Hereford was never considered anything but a single breed, native to the county of the same name. While best known for meat and draught, early Herefords were also kept in dairies and one won the dairy class at the 1839 Royal Show. The early Hereford breed was variable for colour and pattern: individuals could be red, brown, grey, or spotted; faces could be coloured, mottled, or white (280). The change to the unvarying pattern of red with a pure white face is comparatively recent. It illustrates the importance of colour and other markers to breeders.

The basic use of markers is to identify individuals. (In some breeds with variable patterns the registration forms include standardised outlines of an animal so that details of its pattern can be drawn and, thus, recorded.) As a corollary, colour is associated with relationship. In the Hereford, some superior herds were characterised by white faces and, through the sale of bulls and selection, the trait spread to become the trademark of the whole breed. In other breeds with the same trait, such as occurred in some individuals of the South Devon and the Welsh Black breeds, breeders selected *against* the white face in case crossbreeding with Herefords was suspected.

Hereford cattle spread early. One is recorded in Garrard's picture of the 1811 Woburn sheep shearing (73). The breed became important internationally, especially in the developing colonies.

The Gloucester is usually considered to be a close relative of the Hereford. It is interesting to contrast the divergence of the two breeds in pattern and in purpose. The Gloucester is typically red with white finching and was selected for milk; the breed has never been numerous. The cow Blossom (105), who belonged to a Mr. Dean of Berkeley, was used by Edward Jenner in his development of vaccination to confer immunity to smallpox. Blossom gave cowpox to her dairymaid, Sarah Nelmes. Jenner transferred serum from Sarah Nelmes to 8-year old James Phipps on the 14th May, 1796. Part of Jenner's success may have been due to his fortuitous choice of a Gloucester as, in at least one molecular system, Gloucester cattle do not show the same immune reactions as other breeds.

Blossom was rewarded by an honourable retirement. After her death her hide (105b) hung in Jenner's coach house until 1857. Then Jenner's family gave it to St. George's Hospital, where Jenner had been a student. The horns are not the originals, which were taken as souvenirs, as were many of her tail hairs.

The Suffolk (80-81) was well known in the late 18th Century for its milking qualities. The breed was variable in colour (but typically dun) and was polled. The Suffolk was interbred with the Norfolk until the two breeds lost their identities in a new breed, the Red Poll (292) in the latter part of the 19th Century.

The Norfolk resembled the Devon in being typically red and usually (but not always) horned. The cattle head on tins of Colman's mustard is of a Norfolk bull.

The Sussex was also similar to the Devon but larger: e.g., the Burton Ox was 16.2 hands. The breed did not lack improvers, including John Ellman of Glynde, but has never been of more than local importance in England. The breed has done well in South Africa.

The three plough oxen (211) could be Sussex as they appear heavier and bigger boned than the Devon. However, the team is not harnessed with the typical Sussex yoke.

Despite the variety of native breeds, English farmers have imported cattle from other countries. Some of these breeds have become well established here. An early example was the Channel Island breeds from Jersey (165), Guernsey and Alderney (164 a & b). They were followed by the Kerry and the Dexter from Ireland. The Ayrshire became known mainly because it accompanied Scottish farmers migrating to England; but, the Aberdeen Angus (284) spread largely through the efforts of Clement Stephenson, a veterinary surgeon who had a herd near Newcastle upon Tyne in the late 19th Century.

Pied Lowland cattle became naturalised in the early twentieth century, as the British Friesian, and now constitute the bulk of the national dairy herd. Since 1955 there has been an influx of continental breeds, here represented by the Simmental (538). It remains to be seen how many of these more recent immigrant breeds will become established. There has been renewed interest in native breeds, especially for beef, and several of our English minority breeds, including the British White, Longhorn, Sussex and South Devon, have done very well in recent MLC trials.

Finally, in respect to bovines, mention must be made of the interest shown by early English stock importers in other species: e.g., Water Buffalo *Bubalus bubalis* L. (79); the American "buffalo" *Bison bison* L.; and the Zebu *Bos indicus* L. Although much of the initial interest faded, it was the forerunner of the 20th Century development of the many *taurindicus* breeds which have improved the efficiency of beef and dairy production in hot climates.

Ovicaprines (Sheep and Goats)

England has numerous, locally adapted breeds of sheep. These are grouped by habitat into *hill* and *lowland* breeds. The latter are subdivided into *longwools* and *shortwools*. During the 18th Century a dominant breed arose in each of the lowland groups.

The Leicester (a longwool) was developed from an existing Leicester sheep by Bakewell. Some of his contemporaries suggested that there had been crossing: breeds mentioned included the Lincoln, the Warwick and sheep from the Yorkshire Wolds. Whatever the means, the resulting Leicester had heavy fleeces and carcases. One of the most famous Leicester sheep was the ram Two Pounder (28), named because his body was the shape of a two-pound cannon.

Bakewell promoted his sheep, letting rams at high prices[1]. Bakewell founded the Dishley Society, a group of élite breeders who agreed to maintain high prices. These included Thomas Coke (64). The breed became fashionable, and, as witnessed by the portrait (296), remained so for many years.

It was claimed that the Leicester was used to improve many breeds, especially other longwools. Some, such as the Warwickshire, seem to have been absorbed by the Leicester. Others, such as the Cotswold (305, 308), Lincoln, Romney Marsh, Teeswater (297), and South Devon (297), remained distinct. The Leicester also contributed to new breeds: the Border Leicester, the Blue-faced or Hexham Leicester and the Wensleydale (in Britain); the Columbia and the Targhee (in the U.S.A.); and, the Ile de France.

The main role of the modern Leicester, and other longwools, is to produce speciality wool and to provide sires for crossing.

The Southdown was originally a small, active, hardy shortwool, native to the Suffolk Downs. After selection by John Ellman of Glynde (cf 242) the breed spread rapidly. Breeders on better land practised further selection, emphasizing size and early maturity. Jonas Webb of Babraham (242) was especially successful in these respects and the breed assumed a tubby shape. It also became less hardy.

The Southdown made two major contributions to English (and other) sheep. It was (and is) used to sire fat lambs, and from the crosses made for this purpose in the early 19th Century, a new category of breeds arose: *the Down breeds*.

The Hampshire Down (315) was based on Berkshire Knott, Wiltshire Horn and Southdown. The Oxford Down was derived from crosses between the newly-formed Hampshire Down and the Cotswold. The Shropshire Down arose from crosses between the Southdown and several breeds from the Welsh Border country. These breeds probably included the now-extinct Worcester (196), a small, hardy, polled sheep with a mottled face and short, soft, silky wool.

The Down breeds became important for wool and fat lamb production, both from pure flocks and, through sires, from crossbreds. Today many Down breeds, including the parent Southdown, are of minority status. An exception is the Suffolk breed (derived from the Southdown and the Norfolk Horn) which provides some 46% of all British rams, mainly as sires of crossbreds.

In the late 18th Century there were many breeds of hill, heath and moorland sheep. The examples exhibited include the Herdwick of the Lake District (319), the Swaledale (317), and the Cheviot (317), which evolved on the Scottish Border.

Hill sheep had (and still have) considerable local importance as the main or sole means of exploiting some land, but they were little valued by the leading improvers of livestock. Although many writers extolled the excellence of hill mutton, the small size was associated with small profits. Prices for the wool from hill breeds were low, partly because of fashion and partly because of husbandry methods. One, the northern practice of salving (199) with a mixture of butter and tar to protect sheep against ectoparasites and the weather, disappeared in the early 19th Century. The use of tar for owners' marks of identification continued into the 20th Century and caused many fleeces to be downgraded.

Attempts to use crossing to improve flocks which had to live on the hills raised mortality. Throughout the 19th and 20th Centuries, the 'improvement' of heaths and moors was accompanied by breed replacement, as in Norfolk and in parts of the north-east Yorkshire moors, and the borders of Scotland and Wales. There was also the expansion of the traditional practice of selling cast hill ewes to farmers on lower ground for crossing with tups of lowland breeds. The cross-bred ewe lambs are usually retained for a further cross, often with a Down ram as the terminal sire. In this way, hill breeds provide about a third of the genetic contribution to the present day supply of lamb meat.

Apart from flying flocks of hill ewes from Scotland and Wales, England has imported relatively few breeds of sheep. One was the Spanish Merino (51, 52) at the instigation of George III. The Merino became fashionable and is well in the foreground of the Woburn Sheep Shearing (73) but only a few flocks persisted into the late 19th Century in England. The most important outcome of "His Majesty's Spanish Flock" was the diffusion of the breed to Australia, where the Merino withstood arid conditions better than did the British breeds.

Recently there has been interest in continental sheep as terminal sires, and a few flocks of Charollais, Ile de France, Bleu du Maine, and Texel have been established. Another recent development has been the import of the Friesland Milksheep for dairy purposes.

The goat is undeservedly neglected in the English farming record. The species has been important as a source of meat and meat for humbler rural families. Higher in the social scale, goats' milk was prescribed for invalids. For example, around 1800 many people stayed in Rothbury to partake of the goats' milk plentiful in that district. Chevon (goat meat) has never become popular despite sporadic attempts at marketing, such as the Kid Dinner held by the British Goat Society in 1880.

Many farms used to include a few goats among their stock. This was supposed to be beneficial to the health of cattle, horses and sheep, and there was the tangible advantage of milk for orphan lambs or for calves. Another use was to provide companionship for solitary horses, especially racehorses. Goats, especially wethers, were sometimes used to draw small carriages.

The early English goats approximated to the type now known as Old English (a type which has almost disappeared except in feral populations). This is small and compact with a dense hairy coat, polymorphic for colour; both sexes are horned and bearded (200).

Various breeds of goats have been imported. The Bagot is reputed to have been brought to England in the 14th Century. The Angora (200) was known to Bewick and kept by the Duke of Wellington in the 1880s. Cashmere goats were imported in the 1820s and a herd was established at Windsor by George IV.

In the 19th Century several breeds were formed by crossing British goats with imported stocks. The Anglo-Nubian included various types of middle eastern and Indian goats, many of which came as milch goats carried by P and O boats. The British Alpine, British Saanen and British Toggenburg were all established by grading up to the continental breeds.

At present there is some revival of interest in goats. Goats' milk, cheese, yoghurt and butter are carried by many speciality food shops. The world boom in mohair, made from the fleece of the Angora Goat has led to further imports of this distinctive breed.

Pigs

Mediaeval representations of the English pig give the impression of a homogenous type, similar to but smaller than, the wild pig *Sus scrofa* L. By the late 18th Century there is ample evidence of several breeds. The most common type seems to have been the tall, heavy white pig which William Marshall considered to be the "original" English breed. Pigs of this type are represented by the Curly Coated pig (332) and in the landscapes by Leakey (212) and Ibbetson (217). Many were fed to enormous weights. The Yorkshire Hog (193) was 12.2 hands high, nearly 10 feet long and weighed 12 cwt., at four years of age. Such a size makes credible the early anecdotes of pigs being used for pack, draught, and even riding.

The Berkshire (333) was known by name in the late 18th Century. By that time it had spread as far as Yorkshire because of its reputation as an improved breed. It has undergone many changes of shape, size and colour during its development. The Gloucester Old Spot (327) and what may be the Oxford Dairy Pig (190) are close relatives of the Berkshire and of each other. Slut (192) appears to be of a similar type. She started life as a free-range pig in the New Forest and was tamed and trained to retrieve by a keeper. She lived to be over 10 years, when she weighed in at over 700 pounds.

During the late 18th and early 19th Centuries, English pigs were altered by crosses with imported breeds, mainly Chinese and Neapolitan (334). The aim of these crosses was to produce earlier maturing pigs. The crosses also produced fatter, smaller animals. Existing breeds were changed, as can be seen by comparing the group of Berkshires (314) with their less 'improved' relatives (e.g., 189, 190). Many new breeds arose from the crossing. Some were ephemeral, but others, such as the Small White persisted into the 20th Century. Despite this extensive crossing, recent estimates of genetic distance do not reveal a close relationship between English and Asiatic breeds.

The next major external influence upon English pigs came with the import of Swedish Landrace swine after the Second World War. The breed is now popularly (but incorrectly) known as *the* Landrace. (A landrace is a breed of any domesticated species which has evolved in a particular district, and so the term should be used in conjunction with the names of the species and district concerned.)

The Swedish Landrace pig has been used widely, both as a pure breed and for crossing. However, there have been negative effects, occasionally resulting in a commercial catastrophe. In spite of quarantine precautions, it is thought that the Swedish Landrace introduced atrophic rhinitis into England. The Swedish Landrace breed is characterised by a fairly high gene frequency for a syndrome variously called "porcine stress syndrome", "pale soft exudative muscle", or "malignant hyperthermia". Expression of this unfavourable genetic condition depends upon exposing the pig to certain stresses (which have become much more common in modern intensive pig-keeping). Most English breeds have low frequencies of these stress-susceptibility genes. It is unfortunate that the publicity which accompanied the imports of the Swedish Landrace caused many English breeds to be neglected, some to the extent that they are extinct, like the Lincoln Curly Coat and the Cumberland.

Horses and other Equids

Power for medieval husbandry was provided by both oxen and horses. Illustrations suggest that usually (but not exclusively) the latter were used for light tasks, such as harrowing, and for haulage. Horses were also important for riding and as pack animals.

Donkeys were used by humbler people until well into the 20th Century. The more affluent sometimes kept donkeys to carry children or for light harness work. A small luxury market for asses' milk persisted into the 19th Century.

In contrast to the European continent, there has never been much interest in the mule, bred from Jackass x Mare. The hinny is bred from the reciprocal cross and was even rarer in England.

As most agricultural writings emanated from improved districts, there is comparatively little record of the pack transport which was once common. The Bell Mare (203) commemorates the trains of pack horses which carried goods in the Lake District and the Pennines. The bell was used to keep the train together and to warn oncoming road users. The Bell Mare (possibly an Early Dales or Fell pony) and the horse (possibly a Devon Packhorse) in Leakey's landscape (212) also represent the many smaller breeds and crosses which did so much work until the first quarter of the 20th Century.

By the 18th Century there were several recognised breeds of larger horses, suitable for riding, driving and farm work. One group, centred on Yorkshire, but extending up into Northumberland and down into Lincolnshire, was characteristically bay with black points. The type is now represented by the Cleveland Bay.

Ploughboy (187) painted c. 1795 is a further example of the general utility farm horse common at the time. He also illustrates some of the complexities of the artistic record: he is described as a Suffolk Punch, a breed which was then (as now) characterized by chestnut colour; and, he is not the same animal as the Suffolk stallion painted by Sartorius which Trow-Smith identified as ". . . probably Ploughboy, foaled in 1795". This does not mean that either attribution is incorrect: there are many examples of different animals with the same name; and, there are pre-studbook records of introgression from the Norfolk Trotter to the Suffolk which could account for the atypical colour.

Many farmers continued to favour the active type of farm horse. Others, because of the heavy nature of their soil, and the demand for powerful horses for town haulage, selected for increased size and strength. The early Black Horse, or Shire, which even after Bakewell's attentions was not much heavier than Ploughboy, changed to the type represented by the mare and fillies painted by W. A. Clark (322, 323). However, the greater size and weight resulted in less activity, and the fashion for profuse feather increased susceptibility to grease and to cracked heels. Reaction to these disadvantages, and observation of the Percheron in France during the First World War, led to imports and the establishment of the latter breed in England.

Motorisation caused a decline in horse numbers. The continued interest in riding as a recreation meant that lighter types were less affected. This made it possible for some of our mountain and moorland breeds to survive. Heavier breeds nearly disappeared but have been saved by the revival of interest during the past decade.

The most important imports of horses were the eastern stallions which contributed to the foundation of the Thoroughbred in the seventeenth and eighteenth centuries. One breed, the Arab, became established in its own right. Various other light breeds have been absorbed into English stocks. At present there is a vogue for several continental breeds, most of which were improved in the nineteenth century by the Cleveland Bay.

Importations of heavy breeds include the Flanders (mentioned throughout the sixteenth to eighteenth centuries); the Belgian (in the late nineteenth to early twentieth centuries); the Percheron (495); and, recently, the Ardennes.

Apart from the donkey and the mule, the only other equines to receive serious consideration as work animals were various zebras. It was hoped to use these to breed zebra mules, suitable for use in the colonies.

Because of the great variety of recreational human needs which the horse fulfils, the horse is *today* a significant economic factor.

Dogs

The iconographic record of the dog is extensive, but largely illustrates either pets or the sporting dogs of the rich. There were also less fashionable types of sporting dogs, here represented by a water dog (300), possibly an early Newfoundland, judging from its Spitz-like tail; and, by the Devon Spaniel in Leakey's landscape (212). Many districts had local breeds of dogs used for work with livestock (299). The dog, painted by Ibbetson (217a), could be the now rare Cumberland Sheepdog.

Widdas's "Terrier with Rat in a Cage" (251) is a reminder that dogs contributed to pest control. This painting also demonstrates the darker side of man-animal relationships: a theme which concerned several artists of the period.

Cats

Powerful interests in the medieval church condemned cats by associating them with the Devil; as a result, bubonic plague spread as rodents multiplied unchecked by feline predators living with man. Many medieval artists expressed a dissenting view from church authority; these artists depicted the role of the cat in rodent control and as a loved companion. A similar appreciation of the cat as a guardian against the pilfering and spoilage of stored grain by rodents is shown in the inclusion of cats in many scenes of farm yards or buildings.

Ferret

References to ferrets in England occur as early as the 14th Century. Originally the ferret was used in managed warrens, as illustrated by James Ward's "Ferrets in a Rabbit Warren". In the 19th Century, warrens ceased to exist and the ferret was relegated to the control of rats and feral rabbits—and to being an accessory of poachers.

Rabbits

The first illustrations of rabbit farming in warrens appeared in medieval times. The practice was of economic importance until the 19th Century. By this time, several breeds, such as the Silver Sprig, were available for warrens; further breeds were kept intensively, mostly in back-yards.

Many specialised breeds have been developed for meat, pelts or fancy. The Angora, introduced in the early 18th Century, produces wool. Most rabbit production is still on a small scale, although larger commercial enterprises exist.

Poultry

At least ten species of birds have been bred as farm animals in England. The goose, *Anser anser,* the duck, *Anas platyrhynchos,* and the pigeon, *Columba livia,* are natives of the British Isles. Imported species include: the peacock, *Pavo cristatus,* bred for the table from Norman to Stuart times; the turkey, *Meleagris gallopavo,* the Guinea Fowl, *Numida meleagris,* and the *Muscovy Duck, Cairina moschata.* These three imported species were mentioned as new arrivals in England in the 16th Century. In addition, there is the Chinese Goose, *Anser cygnoides,* which probably came in the 18th Century, and there is the Japanese Quail, *Coturnix coturnix japonica,* which was introduced after the Second World War.

The origin of English domestic fowl, *Gallus gallus,* is not clear. They are usually regarded as pre-Roman imports. Whatever their origin, domestic fowl are the most common of our poultry and represent the class in this exhibition. Two types, Barnyard Fowl (314) and Game Fowl were recorded in the 16th Century but had probably diverged from each other much earlier.

The original Game type produced many varieties. An early use of these was to distinguish the birds of different owners: e.g., Red Pile was once associated with Charles II. The pair here (270a) were obviously in provincial ownership, but are typical of the breed and the variety. The cock has been dubbed (i.e., his comb has been removed). This operation was performed in order to deny opponents a hold during cock-fights. Dubbing also prevented injury to the comb by frost bite; cocks with frost-damaged combs sometimes became infertile.

Cockfighting was made illegal in 1849, but Game continued to be bred for table and exhibition purposes. Today it is known as the Old English Game to distinguish it from derived and imported game breeds. Game were often crossed with Barnyard fowl to improve the table qualities of the latter. However, the Barnyard fowl of different districts developed distinguishing features, and different breeds arose. Until show standards were laid down, some of these breeds contained considerable variation.

Yorkshire, Lancashire and Derbyshire gave rise to breeds of the Hamburgh breed group (268). The spangled birds shown here have many characteristics of the Lancashire Crescents of Half Moonies, except the sickle feathers of the cock are not the clear white with black moon tips specified by Mooney clubs (but difficult to attain). The size of the centre bird suggests it is a hen-feathered cock. By the late 19th Century most of the breeds in this group had been lumped with foreign breeds with similar markings as "the" Hamburgh.

In the southeastern counties there was another breed group, consisting of the Kent, the Sussex, the Surrey, and the Dorking. Many individuals in these breeds had five toes. There was also polymorphism for colour, as in the chickens which inhabit La Thangue's "Sussex Farmyard" (271). The trio of five-toed silver-grey birds (269) might well belong to this breed group, although their legs are longer and their carriage more upright than would now be considered typical. Early this century the breed group was reduced to two breeds: the five-toed Dorking and the four-toed Sussex. The Dorking and the Sussex also differ from each other in body shape and in the range of colour varieties, another case of character displacement.

Probably the most influential import of foreign breeds was the 1843 gift to Queen Victoria of some Asiatic clean-shanked fowl, described as Cochins. This had several major consequences: poultry breeding, especially for exhibition, became fashionable; further breeds were imported; and, new breeds were synthesized. In particular, brown-shelled eggs, characteristics of Asiatic breeds, were introduced. The original British and European breeds were all characterised by white or creamy egg-shells.

Crawhall's "Cock and Hens" (266) are of the Asiatic type. It is not possible to determine the breed with certainty: Asiatic fowl were extremely variable and names abounded. Experts argued for many years about the identity and correct type of the Shanghai, the Cochin, and the Cochin China. Today, they are only remembered in the modern Cochin. There was similar confusion in other cases, such as the Brahma Pootra and the Chittagong. The most lasting contribution of Asiatic fowl was to new utility breeds. These remained popular until the late 1950s.

After the Second World War, several factors caused the poultry industry to expand. Many returned servicemen and women invested their gratuities in smallholdings; materials which had been required for the war effort needed new markets; and research successes, such as antibiotics, radar, and the atom bomb, raised expectations that science would have a dramatic effect on the efficiency and prosperity of agriculture.

One of the best known ways in which large intensive poultry enterprises sought to use science was by trying to exploit hybrid vigour from crossbreeding. Geneticists identified fast growth, early sexual maturity, and high egg production as important requirements. The White Leghorn has all these traits and so was widely used in breeding programmes.

The White Leghorn is a Mediterranean breed and thus is also characterised by white egg shells. But many customers liked brown eggs. Continued marketing of white eggs did not alter consumer preference. Instead, consumers began to inquire into the methods associated with the production of white eggs. Today in England most birds kept for commercial egg production lay brown eggs.

Bees

Since the 18th Century beekeeping (446) has been recognised as an important minor industry. It has been encouraged by classes at agricultural shows (including the Royal) for beeswax, honey and mead. Bees are also appreciated for increasing the yields of some crops by improving pollination.

Despite the utility of photographs, animals are still painted and modelled, both as individuals and as components of scenes. Not surprisingly, many of these representations contain traditional elements. However, there is a major difference between the work of the late 20th Century and that of earlier artists. The latter placed their animals in a variety of typical settings, thus providing a record of the environment in which evolution occurred. Modern artists avoid many recent developments: there are no scenes of animals in the intensive commercial conditions which are characteristic of modern agriculture and which provide new evolutionary pressures.

Commercial artists are even more misleading. Many devise or copy anachronistic rural scenes and livestock to market the products of modern agricultural technology. Quite apart from the historical inaccuracies, the association of intensive products with extensive husbandry has other implications. For example, town dwellers are given a false picture of animal production as an idyllic, low input occupation, rather than the reality of an expensive commercial enterprise, sometimes in unpleasant conditions.

For artists there are further challenges in the immediate future. For example, there is the domestication of new species, including fish and molluscs. There will be more drastic changes made to the appearance and behaviour of the 'Classical' domesticates. Will we need to return to the fertile imagination of Hieronymus Bosch to depict the future of man-animal relations as modified by genetic engineering?

C. M. Ann Baker © 1988

1 As shown in the painting by Thomas Weaver "The Ram Lefting at Dishley" by Thomas Weaver, Tate Gallery, London.

A Farming Perspective

Farming is surely unmatched as an industry so deeply rooted in the past and yet so characterised by change. It is about 5,000 years since settled agriculture began to take over, in lowland parts of Britain at least, from the previously nomadic forage style of food gathering where man hunted and scavenged in the wild as best he could. The onset of a warmer climate probably accompanied this development for it has the effect of drying the soil and making more viable the laborious clearance of native forest to make way for cultivated land.

Everything and nothing has changed over the course of the intervening millennia. From the evidence available, it seems likely that those early farmers practised a mixed system in which both crop production and animal husbandry played a part. A range of cereals could be grown, with emmer wheat and barley being the two most prominent, and excavation records have suggested the presence of cattle, sheep and pigs. Then, as now, much depended on climate, geography and good management. The efficiency of existing plant and breed varieties, the technology and the social structure of the day would have acted as further constraints on output.

If all farming, whether ancient or modern, can be distilled down into these same basic elements then it ought to be possible to categorise the causal factors that bring about significant landmarks of agricultural change which in turn have had far-reaching consequences for the development of society as a whole. This has long been a matter of debate amongst historians and has centred around the relative importance of a number of inter-connecting factors. One that has already been mentioned is climate and the extent to which even quite small shifts in temperature and rainfall can have extensive knock-on effects for output and practice. In the more distant past these are difficult to detect with any great certainty but it does seem, for example, that the period 700-1100 AD is distinguished from the centuries that preceded and followed by virtue of slightly higher harvests that resulted were instrumental in sustaining the marked increase in population that was occurring at this time.

Throughout history, times of significant population growth have been accompanied by an extension of agricultural activity. Of course, the reason is clear: the more mouths there are to feed, the more food has to be produced and the more people there are to produce it. Which came first, the people or the food, is more complex but need not detract from the point that the two occur together. It is also true, certainly up to the 17th Century, that when population growth outstripped the capacity of the food supply to keep up, then malnutrition and greater susceptibility to disease followed. The Black Death of 1347 which carried off perhaps a third of the country's people is the most dramatic demonstration of this principle.

Early on, agricultural output could be raised by simply clearing some more forest and extending the area given over to active farming. But this could only go so far with the technology and labour available; thereafter, the solution lay in more intensive working of the land already in cultivation. In the 12th Century, this was represented by the emergence of the classic three field rotation in which only one third of the land was in unproductive fallow at any one time as opposed to one half in more basic on-off systems where land was under the plough one year and not the next.

The second half of the eighteenth century saw the culmination of a long chain of developments now collectively known as the Agricultural Revolution and can be interpreted in a similar vein. Population growth was running at about 60,000 a year during the period and by 1800 the total had reached 9 million, probably more than 50% higher than the figure of a hundred years before. In spite of this daunting trend, which continued on into the nineteenth century, the country succeeded in gearing up its agricultural output to carry on producing most of its own food requirements. This had been accomplished in part by a further extension of the cultivated acreage with a lot more waste and marshy land being cleaned, drained and put under the plough. The gradual adoption of more productive methods was also taking effect by this period. Replacing the fallow with a root crop such as turnips meant that more stock could be maintained on the extra feed and more manure directed onto the arable land which in consequence was in better shape to produce the ensuing crops of cereals. The continuing process of enclosing what remained of the open fields facilitated more efficient land use and allowed large tracts of previously unimproved common and waste to be brought into the mainstream of production. As a result, total corn production was higher by 25% in 1800 and 70% in 1820 than it was in 1750. Stock numbers also rose considerably over the same period with about 9 million sheep and perhaps a million cattle being added.

For the last hundred years or so the population—production equation has ceased to be so decisive in this country because, as an industrial nation, we have had the wherewithal to import huge quantities of foodstuffs from new agricultural territories overseas. Indeed, the free flow of cheap imported food has at times, notably in the last quarter of the nineteenth century and again in the 1920s, pushed domestic farming into almost complete disarray and depression. Two World Wars, the Second in particular, demonstrated the strategic and economic importance of having a healthy agricultural industry at home so that from the 1940s state assistance and protection for farmers has been a feature of the peacetime era.

Since Britain's entry into the Common Market, this structure of governmental support has been subsumed within the Common Agricultural Policy. The difficulty, not to say the price, of regulating agricultural production on a European scale has become a prominent issue publicly and politically so that the talk now is how to produce less rather than more without the whole farming infrastructure tumbling to the ground. Since the introduction of milk quotas in 1984 the UK butter mountain, which peaked at 250,000 tonnes, has fallen to much more manageable levels although many producers are left counting the cost. Attention is shifting now to finding a workable way of curbing cereal production that would not send unsettling ripples through other sectors of the industry.

This apparent problem of how to limit agricultural output is unique in our history and a consequence not simply of state subsidies but of the ever onward and upward march of scientific progress over the last hundred and especially the last forty years. John Bennet Lawes, whose former family estate at Rothamsted in Hertfordshire still houses the most famous agricultural research station in the world, started to manufacture superphosphate on a factory scale in the early 1840s. It was the first beginnings of a commercial fertiliser industry that has come to revolutionise agricultural practice, make traditional rotation patterns redundant and bring hitherto unimaginable yields. In the control of pests and plant diseases, and the breeding of more efficient and productive livestock, science has made further dramatic progress. One hundred years ago the average yield per hectare for wheat was just over 2 tonnes. Although this was more than double the best efforts of a medieval farmer, it rather pales beside modern figures which can range between 4 and as much as 9 tonnes.

It is a remarkable fact that even today this country is able to produce, from a slowly shrinking farmland acreage, 80% of its needs in temperate foodstuffs. The process will not stop here. There will always be scope for squeezing a little bit more out of the soil but increasingly the gains have to be weighed against the economic, environmental and social costs. Although the countryside is the farmers' factory it is also much more than that as well. The challenge now is how best to strike the right balance so that we have a profitable farming industry producing the kind of food that people want and can afford to eat from a rural landscape that we can still admire and enjoy.

No mention has yet been made of technology in the assessment of agricultural change partly because the path of progress in this area is not as straightforward as might first appear. Victorian farm workers, for example, were assisted by all manner of new powered machinery at the same time as they were using some hand tools that had barely altered since Roman times. Every schoolboy knows that Jethro Tull built a seed drill in the early eighteenth century but the textbooks omit to mention that another hundred years had elapsed before it made any significant impact upon general agricultural practice in this country.

Time and again the mere existence of a new and in some respects better way of doing something was no guarantee of immediate success. It is not just that farmers were notoriously slow to take to new-fangled ideas, although there have always been some who fit the description, but rather that the benefits of change had first to outweigh the sometimes considerable disadvantages or costs. A new implement or machine requires an additional outlay; it will probably need extra skills, accessories and perhaps a different form of power to operate effectively; it may depend on the services of a specialist for its maintenance and repair. Usually the perceived gains to the farmer had to be substantial to convince him to go ahead and buy. The motivating force was often a need to increase output per man on the farm either because there was an economic incentive to work more land or because labour was scarce and therefore more expensive.

The earliest farmers would have used hand tools, similar to what we know as mattocks or spades, to break up the soil for seed bed preparation. Later, something over 4,000 years ago, the ox drawn ard began to appear. It was a simple kind of plough incorporating a share that was drawn through the soil. On light land one man could perhaps double or triple his daily work rate compared to hand tools, although there were the running costs of the implement and of the working oxen to take into account as well. In Britain, the ard remained in use throughout the Roman period and took in along the way steady improvements in design and materials of construction.

There is also archaeological evidence for the presence of a rather different implement, the mouldboard plough, from at least the second or third century A.D. Its new feature was that it could cut and turn a recognisable furrow slice rather than do little more than stir the soil as was the case with the ard. The ability to lay up land in furrows was important, for reasons connected with drainage and aeration, if colder, wetter and heavier soils were to be successfully cultivated. A not unreasonable assumption has been that the adoption of the mouldboard plough, a gradual process that was still working through in the early medieval period, indicates an extension of the cultivated acreage onto the heavier soils and that this in itself was a reflection of increased demand.

The heavy wooden plough, now with its wearing parts sheathed in iron and hitched to a new type of ox yoke that improved the draught, was a significant element in the intensification of agricultural practice during the thirteenth century. No examples have survived and there are few remotely contemporary illustrations apart from the very fine agricultural vignettes that enliven the pages of the Luttrell Psalter, a monastic production of about 1340 from E. Anglia. In addition to the plough, these scenes depict a horse drawn harrow, a seed box for hand sowing, scythes, harvest carts and flails, all with a precision that shows them to be little different from equipment in use four and even five hundred years later.

Clearly, the period all the way from the fourteenth to the late eighteenth century was not one of great technological innovation as far as agriculture was concerned. The more dramatic changes came in other respects and were put into practice using the basic range of equipment already available. The sixteenth century is a case in point. Population figures were rising again now that the tremendous losses caused by the Black Death had at last been made up. Measures to increase yields included more use of leguminous crops, such as clover or beans, to improve soil fertility; more varied rotations; and the introduction in some areas of ley farming in which arable land is rejuvenated by being put down to grass in a regular cycle.

The first British books on farming, beginning in 1523 with Fitzherbert's *Boke of Husbandrye,* provided a new vehicle for the dissemination of information. Anthony Fitzherbert was a landowner and judge with first-hand knowledge of agricultural practice in different parts of the country. He gives a comprehensive guide to the best principles of farming, with meticulous attention to detail on everything from the washing and shearing of sheep to the finer points of hay-rake making during the long evenings of winter in preparation for the coming year. It is also evident from the text that there was a degree of regional variation in the design of farm equipment to meet local conditions. This was still a very strong feature of the farming scene in the late Victorian period. When, for example, Fitzherbert talks about a plough with a moveable mouldboard that can turn furrows to either side he is describing the highly distinctive Kentish turnwrest plough, well suited to the downland slopes, which could still be found at work in much the same form in 1900.

Agricultural literature blossomed during the seventeenth and eighteenth centuries as the spirit of enquiry brought forth a whole spectrum of discourses on what could increasingly be called the science of husbandry. Many works discussed improvements to farm equipment but often in a largely theoretical way that had little effect upon general practice. Things began to change in the early 1800s when high food prices and labour shortages induced by the wars with Napoleon encouraged some farmers to take more interest in new devices. One example was the threshing machine which had made its debut in 1786 and was still at a fairly crude stage of development but was now beginning to appear in those areas most affected by the scarcity and cost of local labour.

The tempo quickened noticeably in the middle of the century. A growing number of specialist agricultural engineering companies were emerging able to produce by factory methods large quantities of implements and machines, stoutly constructed out of wood and iron, that were then sold and serviced by agents around the country. Competition between these firms, spurred on by the trials organised by the Royal Agricultural Society, was intense and resulted in a general rise in the standard of equipment available at a price the farmer could afford. This applied not only to field work but to the whole range of hitherto laborious processing operations, from chaff cutting to butter churning, which could now be carried out by machines driven either by hand or by horse, steam or water power. The extent to which farmers took to the new ways varied widely and was a matter not only of individual inclination but of the size, type and location of the farm. There could be few, however, that remained entirely untouched by this technological revolution.

The enthusiasm for mechanisation was fired by a shortage of farm labour that became apparent after 1850. Manufacturing industry was a voracious competitor in the labour market, siphoning people away from the rural areas, so that by 1851 more than half the population was for the first time urban based. In agriculture, this demographic transformation was felt most keenly during the peak periods of summer when all available hands were needed to bring in the corn harvest. For such a traditionally labour intensive operation, new machinery held out obvious positive benefits.

Transatlantic influences played a part for the opening up of the vast prairie lands of America to corn production created a hot-house effect on innovation and labour saving devices. The two American reaping machines that were exhibited in England at the Great Exhibition of 1851 aroused considerable interest and the similar versions that were very quickly on offer from home manufacturers found many ready buyers. The 1880s saw a new generation of machines, again of American origin, that not only cut the crop but also bound it into sheaves to thereby further diminish the labour requirement in the field. The binder, either horse or tractor drawn, was still a dominant feature of the harvest landscape in the years following the Second World War. Thereafter, it was steadily superseded by the combine harvester which goes a stage further to unite the cutting and threshing of the crop into a single operation.

The twentieth century has seen mechanisation come to dominate all branches of the farming industry through the agency of the internal combustion engine and electrical power. In 1900, over 1 million horses were at work on British farms and still as many as half this figure in 1946. There followed a precipitous and perilous decline to almost nothing. After its initial flush of success during the First World War, the tractor struggled rather to make headway in the depression years of the 1920s. Technical improvements to efficiency and reliability, together with the exigencies of another war-time emergency, however, saw it gain rapidly in favour so that when the tractor revolution really got under way it was carried through remarkably quickly.

The triumph of the machine has resulted in some remarkable productivity gains since the Second War. Today, for example, a combine harvester can, with the minimum of human labour, process around 12 hectares of corn in a single day. The army of farm workers in every village is now a thing of the past for less than 3% of the current working population is employed in what still is the country's biggest and most extensive primary industry.

Where things go from here is not entirely clear given the social and economic pressures now bearing down upon intensive high-tech agriculture. Large scale heavily capitalised enterprises will no doubt continue to push at the frontiers of science and engineering in those areas and on those holdings most equipped to do so. But there will also be a place for the small farm, worked perhaps by a part-time farmer with an income supplemented from other sources, where the operation is correspondingly geared at a lower level. After a mini-revival in recent years, there are even signs that the heavy horse, hitched to a new generation of trailed implements, may have a peripheral role to play on these farms in the future—another case of everything and nothing changing in agriculture.

Illustrations:

1. Ploughing scene from the Luttrell Psalter, c. 1340.

2. This illustration from *The Book of the Farm*, 1851, by Henry Stephens gives an idea of the manual labour required in the harvest field when hand tools alone were used.

3. Land Army girl with a Fordson tractor and two-furrow plough, 1944.

Roy Brigden

1

THE MOWING OF CORN WITH THE SCYTHE.

2

3

Landscape Painting, Livestock Portraiture and the Picturesque

Throughout the development of British landscape and animal painting there have always been 'provincial' or 'itinerant' painters who seemed to have ignored fashions and earned a steady living painting 'matter of fact' portraits of prized livestock commissioned by their proud owners.

The 18th Century saw a rapid rise in the demand for portraits of pedigree stock. Breeding techniques had improved—due largely to the influence of pioneering work by men such as Robert Bakewell. In 1710 the average weight of beeves at Smithfield was 370 lbs; by 1795 it had risen to 800 lbs[1]. Breeders at all levels were looking for artists to record new breeds or prize stock. Such paintings would often be reproduced as prints, (see 81) which also acted as a useful advertisement for the stockbreeder.

The artist would normally charge for his work according to the time it took. Often these pictures would show the animal, or animals, side-on and drawn to a scale to fill the canvas. Once the animal was completed the surrounding background would then be painted in—almost as an afterthought (see 282 and 173-7). This convention continued unchanged throughout the 18th and 19th Centuries and many of the resulting works, although often naive, are painted with a loving charm that is a delight to see.

Sometimes discerning stock breeders would pay extra for a more detailed landscape as a background to their animals (see 308 and 181), and many artists found it more profitable to specialize as both landscape and animal painters.

During the 18th Century there was a growing awareness of the beauty of the British countryside and a change in attitudes towards landscape painting. The effects of the Agrarian Revolution and the progressive enclosure of the countryside may have acted as an added impetus. At first the 'cultivated taste' derived from the Grand Tour preferred the Italianate landscapes and georgic pastorals of the old masters such as Claude and Dughet, to the exclusion of British views.

In landscape the works of Claude were held in particularly high regard. The extent to which their admiration for this master developed during this time is difficult to envisage. His paintings were collected by the aristocracy of England with a fervour that often bordered on the obsessive. Sir George Beaumont (1753-1827), now largely remembered today as Constable's patron, so loved Claude's painting of 'Hagar and the Angel' that he set it in a travelling case so that he could take it with him on journeys by coach.[2]

The insatiable demand for the artist's work was in part met by the production of *Claudian landscapes* from the hands of important early English landscape painters such as John Wootton, George Lambert, Richard Wilson and arguably the most influential of all—the Smiths of Chichester.

The Smiths produced the desired Claudian landscapes to please their patrons, but with an originality that was to play a dominant role in the development of rustic genre and picturesque landscape. They were among the first artists in England to paint local scenery peopled by British gentlemen and peasants within a typical Claudian setting. Frequently they would paint an Italianate view, perhaps featuring a Roman villa on a hill, and in the far distance an eminently English town or city—often showing Chichester with its spire protruding from the surrounding buildings. However, mostly they depicted delightful, small scale rural scenes composed from Sussex scenery.

Their reputation spread further through the reproductions of their work by the best engravers of the day such as Woollett, Elliott, Peake and Vivares. In 1762 one critic wrote that 'The superiority of the Smiths as Landscape-painters is so incontestably visible to those that have the least judgement in Painting, or in Nature, that to declare my Opinion in this matter is quite unnecessary'[3]. The publication in 1769 of 27 engravings of the Smiths' work (dating back to 1757) under the title of Picturesque Scenery of England and Wales, further increased their reputation and they became so universally admired that they were even classed by some critics in the same rank as Claude and Poussin[4]. As Luke Hermann[5] observed, the Smiths were able to enjoy a good living from painting rustic views and pastoral landscapes at a time when the genius of Gainsborough had to concentrate on portrait painting because he could not afford to devote himself to the landscape painting he loved, and Richard Wilson struggled to find sufficient outlets for his work.

Undoubtedly prints of the Smiths' work helped to make the pastime of seeking out Claudian views within the British countryside more popular. This created a climate receptive to the later theorists of the Picturesque, such as Gilpin, Price and Knight.

It became increasingly popular for the nobility and gentry to partake of pleasure tours of the British countryside, encouraged by improvements in roads and transport and by the problems of travel abroad provoked by wars on the continent. Tours of Britain rapidly took the place of the Grand Tour. One of the standard pieces of equipment often carried on such journeys was the Claude glass. This was a slightly convexed darkened mirror held up to reflect the landscape as a framed picture with subdued tones reminiscent of the paintings of Claude Lorraine. It was particularly effective for viewing sunsets. By such means the tourist continued to view the landscape as a potential painting by one of the old masters.

The growing taste for 17th Century Dutch landscapes, and the interest in British rural life encouraged and reflected in art, literature, music and philosophy provided a climate in which Dutch 'realism' and Classical 'idealism' could merge to produce a British School of landscape painting in which the genius of artists like Turner and Constable could flourish.

In a series of popular works on Picturesque travel published in the latter part of the 18th Century the Rev. Gilpin was able to marry the vogue for tourism with the great interest in aesthetics promoted by Hogarth's 'Analysis of Beauty' (1753) and Edmund Burke's 'A Philosophical Enquiry into the origin of our Ideas of the Sublime and the Beautiful' (1757). Gilpin's identification of Picturesque objects as a third aesthetic category, was not merely a classification of another existing taste, but a recognition that what might be either sublime or beautiful in nature may lose this quality when translated into paint.

Perhaps the most logical attempt at defining the distinguishing features of the Picturesque was undertaken at the end of the century by Uvedale Price in 'An Essay on the Picturesque as compared with the Sublime and the Beautiful; and on the use of studying pictures for the purposes of Improving Real Landscape' (1794). Price came to the conclusion that the Picturesque applied "to every kind of scenery, which has been, or might be represented with good effect in painting" but added the further conditions or qualities of "roughness and of sudden variation, joined to that of irregularity". Canvases containing large areas of flat colour, empty of incident were considered of little interest, and paint was regarded as visually more pleasing when it presented variety of tone and hue. The dock leaves, mosses, sticks and stones so often used by artists were useful additions to Picturesque landscape painting for they effectively broke up the uniformity and flatness of the foreground stimulating "curiosity and pleasure" (see cat 12).

Certain subjects were considered suitable for painting because of their 'roughness'. The old twisted tree was used so often that it became virtually the symbol of the Picturesque (see cat 174 and 296). In Jane Austen's *Sense and Sensibility*[6] Marianne Dashwood wished to have "every book that tells how to admire an old twisted tree".

Subjects such as cows, goats, donkeys, old cart horses, weeds, ivy and creeper, old logs, rotten posts, rickety fences. jagged rocks, ruins and old barns all gained an added popularity and were frequently used to embellish paintings and give 'Picturesque' effect. A humble cottage was also often used by artists to give their paintings more variety and interest (see cat 175 & 62).

"Sheep are considered more picturesque", wrote Price, "when their fleeces are ragged and worn away in parts, than when they are of equal thickness, or when they have been lately shorn. No animal indeed is so constantly introduced in landscape as sheep, but that as I observed before, does not prove superior picturesqueness". By such logic the fleeces of Cooper's sheep in (344) were clearly more picturesque than the sheep in (296).

The most picturesque of the human species were farm labourers, peasants, fisherfolk and gypsies. Numerous rustic scenes of farm labourers hard at work or enjoying a deserved rest were produced for the nobility and gentry by artists such as the Smiths, Gainsborough, Moreland, Wheatley, Barker, Collins, Witherington and Shayer (see Selling peas, Bell Inn at Cadnam etc).

The buyers of such pictures were generally attracted by peaceful images of social harmony. Patrons understandably did not wish to hang on their walls paintings that might remind them of the threat of revolution or disorder, nor did they wish to live with works that might prick their conscience concerning the plight of the poor. Although the standard of living experienced by the agricultural labourer varied considerably from area to area, some undoubtedly suffered severe hardship. William Cobbett in writing about the valley of the Avon in 'Rural Rides' (1830) commented:

"In taking my leave of this beautiful vale I have to express my deep shame, as an Englishman, at beholding the general extreme poverty of those who cause this vale to produce quantities of food and raiment. This is, I veryily believe it, the worst used labouring people upon the face of the earth. Dogs and hogs and horses are treated with more civility; and as to food and lodging, how gladly would the labourer change with them! This state of things never can continue many years. By some means or other there must be an end to it; and my firm belief is, that the end will be dreadful. In the meanwhile I see, and I see it with pleasure, that the common people know that they are ill used; and that they cordially, most cordially, hate those who ill-treat them".

The increase of rioting and incendiarism after 1815 must surely have given weight to the underlying fear held by many wealthy British people, of the possibility of a revolution similar to that experienced in France.

This threat was brought home to Thomas Sidney Cooper in 1848 when he was visiting Osborne to paint Queen Victoria's Jersey cow and its three calves. He was accosted by a large body of Chartists who had marched to Osborne with the intention of entering the house and grounds. They were eventually dispersed by an army of men and sent back to Southampton.

Cooper's painting of The Victoria Jersey Cow (273) was admired for the skilful and natural arrangement of the animals. To give the work more picturesque variety and intricacy Cooper introduced a rustic cottage, and in the foreground a wooden log, dock leaves and a pool of water. This gave rise to an amusing incident, which he described in his autobiography 'My Life' (1890):

"I then thanked her Majesty for her graciousness to me, and was about to leave, when the Prince suddenly said: 'How about those dock-leaves that you are introducing into the foreground, Mr Cooper?'. I answered: 'The privilege of my branch of art, your Royal Highness, is to take advantage of objects of still life, to assist the composition of a work, and for pictorial combination; and such accessories as dock-leaves are considered allowable, to avoid the monotony, as much as possible, of grass and earth'. 'Well,' said the Prince jocosely, 'they are beautifully painted, but they do not give evidence of good farming'.

Her Majesty smiled appreciatively, and, shaking her finger at the Prince, said: 'How about the little pool of water in which the heifer's hindlegs are standing?'.

'Oh,' said his Royal Highness, laughing, 'I think it is a beautiful artistic idea, and gives a stamp of nature to the scene'.

'Yes, Albert,' said the Queen, 'and I like its introduction much; but it is not evidence of good draining'.

Upon this they both laughed heartily, and I confess I could not help joining in myself. I could see then, and afterwards heard as a fact, that her Majesty was very fond of farming, and that the Prince was endeavouring to make a complete work of the drainage throughout the whole estate."

Cooper was England's most accomplished cattle painter and through his art became an extremely wealthy man, owning over 400 acres of valuable land in Canterbury. In 1873 he was able to command a record £2,500 for a cattle picture, at a time when the average wage of the agriculture labourer looking after such cattle was then £35 per year. Cooper successfully continued painting until his death in 1902. His life had spanned most of the nineteenth century and he carried the principles of picturesque cattle painting into the twentieth century.

Brian Stewart

Notes:

1. Stella A Walker; Sporting Art England 1700-1900; London 1972; p. 164
2. Michael Clarke; The Tempting Prospect; London 1981; p. 133
3. Anonymous; An Historical and Critical Review of the Painting, & c. Now exhibiting in the Great of the Society instituted for the Encouragement of Arts; London 1762
4. Richard & Samuel Redgrave; A Century of British Painters; London 1866; p. 37-38
5. Luke Hermann; British Landscape Painting of the Eighteenth Century; London 1973; p. 24
6. Jane Austen; Sense and Sensibility; Begun 1797 pub. 1811

Pictures of War and Peace

"The trouble about war paintings of agriculture is that they are rather hard to distinguish from peace pictures."

This was not the remark of a common-or-garden Philistine. It was made by Sir Kenneth Clark during the course of World War II when he was Chairman of the War Artists' Advisory Committee. His comment is thought provoking, particularly when one looks at the paintings included in this exhibition, but requires some background information prior to an examination of its implications.

An important factor in the history of 20th Century depictions of agricultural and rural subjects was the establishment in 1930 of The Pilgrim Trust. A substantial sum was bequeathed by the late Edward Harkness, an American citizen, as a mark of his "admiration for the part Britain had played in the 1914-18 War and for the courage with which her people had sustained a grievous burden in the years that followed." Harkness wanted his gift to be used for some of the country's 'more urgent needs' and 'to promote her future well-being'. The Trust decided to devote their attention to the national heritage of historic architecture, works of art, historical records, humane learning, the countryside and coast. But at the same time, in the 1930's, massive unemployment was perhaps the most pressing of Britain's more urgent needs and during these years the Trust expended their income about equally between the preservation of the historic heritage and schemes for the welfare of the unemployed.

With the outbreak of war in 1939, unemployment came quickly to an end; work on the repair of buildings virtually ceased; learned bodies had to suspend or curtail their activities. The trustees turned their attention to schemes for the welfare of the forces or of others engaged in the war effort, and to the alleviation of hardship caused by the war. In order to give employment to artists and at the same time to make a record of historic buildings and places liable to destruction by enemy action, they instituted a scheme known as Recording Britain. Artists were commissioned to make drawings or paintings of scenes that might disappear for ever.

Between 1940 and 1943 thirty-two English counties and four Welsh counties were recorded. Herbert Read wrote about the aims of the scheme: "Photography can do much, but it cannot give us the colour and atmosphere of a scene, the intangible genius loci. It is this intangible element which is so easily destroyed by the irresistible encroachment of what we call civilisation: schemes of development, the growth of industry, the building of reservoirs and aerodromes, by motor roads and—for the present—by bombs . . . This is not fiddling while Rome burns; it is Rome itself. Better than the wordy rhetoric of journalists or politicians, it shows us exactly what we are fighting for—a green and pleasant land, a landscape whose features have been moulded in liberty, whose every winding lane and irregular building is an expression of our national character. We are defending our very possession of these memorials; but when we have secured them from an external enemy, the existence of these drawings may serve to remind us that the real fight—the fight against all commercial vandalism and insensitive neglect—goes on all the time. There will be little point in saving England from the Nazis if we then deliver it over to the jerry-builders and the development corporations'.

The Trust made it known that it might be prepared to offer financial assistance to help artists during the war and in late December 1939, plans for a committee to deal with such a scheme were drawn up, based largely on a document produced by T.E. Fennemore, Secretary of the Central Institute of Art and Design, then based in the National Gallery. A C.I.A.D. memorandum from 1939 recommended that 'artists should be appointed to make drawings, paintings and prints at the war fronts, in factories, workshops, shipyards and on the land, and of the changed life of the towns and villages, thus making a permanent record of life during the war which would be a memorial to the national effort and of particular local value.'

Artists were employed to depict the civilian effort on the land. Mona Moore, Archibald Hartrick, Nora Lavrin, James Bateman, Evelyn Dunbar and Thomas Hennell covered a wide range of agricultural subjects in works which demonstrated clear stylistic differences from those works produced during World War I. On the strength of such results the Ministry of Agriculture urged the W.A.A.C. to authorise greater coverage of agricultural topics but the response, sadly, was that of Clark quoted at the beginning of this essay.

It was probably Lady Norman who was responsible for the inclusion of the fine paintings by Evelyn Dunbar of the work done by women on the land. Early in December 1939, Lady Norman made a firm request for the inclusion of this category of work in subjects to be covered by the project. She believed that such paintings could provide an important comparison with works produced during the Great War.

More than one implication is carried in Sir Kenneth Clark's statement. The principal implication refers to the way in which he appears to have believed people looked at paintings of agricultural subjects, in a way which divorced history (or never even considered it), from the image. It would also suggest that from time immemorial and stretching infinitely into the future, paintings of work on the land would consist of a similar approach to the subject, any variation being related purely to individual artistic style or to period or national style. Such an interpretation is restrictively narrow and severs all connections between the painting and the time in which it was made.

Artists painting during times of peace have frequently used agricultural subjects purely as a vehicle for their artistic interests. Images of subjects which were seen as being restful to the mind or amusing anecdotes of rural life; such images were closely related to the demands of contemporary society as any basic examination will reveal. A painting made because it would sell was, at a very simple level, responding to a demand. The existence, or frequent absence of images of agriculture in high art must ultimately relate to such demands.

Other artists were commissioned to record animals and activities. The resultant works often demonstrate the dominance of subject over style. Occasionally a painter would transcend the documentary element, a pre-eminent example is the work of Thomas Weaver. His painting of the ram letting at Dishley, the home of Robert Bakewell [Tate Gallery] is a compelling image which not only conveys information to the spectator with a heart-felt vigour but also controls the gaze through the severity and awkward perspective of the background. It stands as a painting worthy of contemplation and because of its very specific nature demands that the spectator looks into the historical background which gave rise to its existence.

Some knowledge of the practice of letting rams from an improved breed, or more precisely of the achievements of Robert Bakewell and his importance in the society of his time enhances the experience of looking.

When thinking of war and peace, it is worth remembering that the greater part of the age of the improvers of agriculture, those figures of the late eighteenth and early nineteenth centuries and the painters and sculptors who worked for them, were at their most active during a period of conflict: the Napoleonic Wars [1799-1815].

It seems more than likely that the economics of such a situation set up certain priorities amongst artists' patrons who demanded works which were capable of consolidating their own economic achievements. Such paintings or sculptures were more than pictorial advertisements, they were a visual affirmation of the values of a sector of society. Most societies at one time or another have depicted the things upon which its prosperity depends, although historically there is a major difference between English and (to generalise) ancient Egyptian or Greek society, in that in these nations such depictions often contained a dual narrative; the secular accompanied frequently by the religious, which suggested that it was through the grace of God that their prosperity continued.

One of the peculiarities of English paintings of agricultural subjects is that, where one exists, the dual narrative is frequently vague. It is suggested but rarely explicit. Such a quality may be discerned in Sir George Clausen's 'Digging Potatoes at Sunset' of 1900. Seated amidst sacks of potatoes, a young woman rests for a moment, her face illuminated by the gentle light; a man continues to turn the earth and drop the freshly dug vegetables to one side. Behind them a fire burns dead vegetation. This is a peacetime painting of labourers, of 'the bottom crust of society', as the artist has been reported as describing his subjects. It is suffused with the light of the setting sun, it has a tender, non-specific melancholy and an inference of harmony between man and the land. Timeless and tranquil it speaks softly of the sublime.

Casting one's mind farther afield, how very different this is from the clarity and vigour of Breugel and Millet, both of whom brought together agricultural and religious imagery which shares a language involved with the description of life and death and how the human being endures his earthly existence. Emile Zola's great novel *La Terre,* written around 1880 stands as a masterpiece of description of the very subjects which gripped Millet. Taking what could have been a medieval table of the occupations of the seasons and the human cycle of birth, marriage and death Zola, as Douglas Parmeé writes in the introduction to his translation of *La Terre,* produces:

"a detailed, concrete and vivid observation—not necessarily, be it noted, of significant detail, but frequently of meaningless detail, all the more effective and real because of its apparently random nature—and creates a solid, satisfying effect of immediacy and plausibility."

Zola's novel was written precisely at a time when, across the Channel, in England, a massive agricultural depression was setting in. When Gauguin and Van Gogh were painting in the agricultural surroundings of Brittany, English agriculture was firmly in the grasp of the depression which would continue up to and beyond World War I. Gauguin wrote that in Brittany "I find the savage, the primitive. When my clogs ring out on this granite soil, I hear the tone which I seek in my painting." This was a Post-Impressionism far removed from that of Clausen.

The differences between French and English agricultural and art history are marked and clearly go far beyond the scope of this essay. From 1871 there was effective universal suffrage in France, a situation which arrived rather more slowly in England, although Gladstone introduced an act which extended the electorate to about five million which made the rural electorate as democratic as the urban. *La Terre* ends as the time for French enfranchisement has arrived. Zola casts before his reader in his portrait of Beauce, the great grain growing region of France, the enduring symbol of the sower:

"That morning, Jean had slung a blue canvas seedbag round his middle, and was holding it open with his left hand, whilst with his right he took out a handful of wheat and at every third step scattered it broadcast with a sweep of his arm. His heavy shoes sank into the rich, thick soil which clung to them as he strode along rhythmically swaying his body . . . The weather had suddenly turned cold and windless and a pitch-black sky spread a sombre, even light over this still ocean of land. They were sowing everywhere: another sower was working three hundred yards away to the left and yet another further along to the right; and for miles around, others and yet others could be seen sinking from sight and receding into the distance over the level ground ahead, tiny black figures, mere lines which grew thinner until they were finally lost from view."

Between them Zola and Millet gave the world a final and potent view of a way of life which stretched back to ancient times. Views which derive from periods of both peace and war. The images given to us by life which was already impossible to sustain without radical change.

During the course of World War I it became clear that England was not capable of producing enough food to sustain itself and certain changes came about to rectify the situation. However, much remained as it had been at the onset of the depression. Mechanisation spread very slowly, horses still pulled thousands of ploughs, rural craftsmen still carried out many of the services which were available from a more efficient source, the industrialised manufacturers of implements and components. Nevertheless it was clear that things were changing, if very slowly.

It was this fact which was recognised by The Pilgrim Trust and also by many individuals such as Thomas Hennell who not only travelled the country recording scenes of threatened crafts but also wrote extensively about them: "As common crafts grow scarce and die out, it occurs vividly to some people, that here is something precious; though hitherto it has always been taken as a matter of course, and of little consequence to any save those whose living it has been. But now it will be missed, for nothing of the same kind is growing up to fill its place. The old tree is half-dry and tottering; a few hands would pluck the branches of experience to strike them, if possible, in some sheltered spot."

And so we find in the twentieth century agricultural paintings which are closely involved with this concept of recording for posterity something which is on the verge of disappearing forever. Briefly, during the period 1939-45, this process halts and paintings emerge which show real work being done for real and pressing reasons.

Following the war which had witnessed an intensification of agriculture sufficiently great to introduce throughout the country all the advances in mechanisation which had been available since the 1870's but had not been taken up [possibly through the financial restrictions imposed by the depression] the recording tendency re-emerged, as for example in the work of S. R. Badmin, who had also worked during the inter-war period on such subjects.

It may well be true that some, if not most, of the finest works of art with agricultural content have their foundation in times of war, or at the very least times of great conflict and uncertainty. Virgil, whose epic poem The Georgics so often comes to mind when considering the relationships between agricultural, art and literary history ends his verses with a reference to war:

> "This song of husbandry of crops and beasts
> And fruit-trees I was singing while great Caesar
> Was thundering beside the deep Euphrates
> In war. . ."

Demelza Spargo

Reginald Fairfax Wells, Man with a Staff   461a

The Long, Slow Centuries

c. 1000-1500 and 1500-1700

These were centuries of extremely gradual change in agriculture. Chaucer (1340-1400) and Shakespeare (1546-1616) could have changed ages and each would have found much that was familiar and unaltered.

Appearances, however, are notoriously deceptive and these apparently uneventful seven hundred years contained economic forces which would bring about the beginning of the modern age!

Amongst the earliest, and most important changes, was the break-up of the feudal system; its demise closely connected with the Black Death which swept through England in 1349. The severe loss of life, up to 50% in some communities, affected bargaining positions between landlord and tenant with resultant change in both the English land system and practice of husbandry. The Black Death accelerated change which had already begun; for example the liberation of the Villein previously tied to the land, who began to receive payment for his labour. Towns increased in number, as did the urban population. A Villein who could escape from his lord for a year and a day could hide in a town and once free sell his labour.

In 1360 the Statute of Labourers was intended to control rising labour costs caused by that same depletion of the workforce and an altering agricultural structure, but its harshness precipitated the Peasants' Revolt during which the rebels, led by Wat Tyler, captured London and forced their demands on the Government. The Government subsequently rescinded on their agreements, but change had taken a firm grasp and was unstoppable.

Agriculture was not uniquely in the hands of the secular community. Vast Monastic agricultural empires existed; such as the upland sheep empires of the Cistercians, whose Pennine abbeys often housed huge wool stores and monks wore habits of untreated wool.

It was in the monasteries that the masterpieces of illumination were created. Those of special relevance to agriculture are the Luttrell Psalter c. 1340 and the Holkham Bible. Attention to detail in these works is moving. Human relationships are indicated between figures who work stacking sheaves or heaving laden carts; physical effort is emphasised and repose wittily observed; figures lean on their tools; agriculture and nature are combined in images of crows dipping greedily into unattended sacks of corn while others are chased off by a dog; the activities are precisely recorded; weeding, breaking clods, reaping, herding sheep, ploughing and sowing seed. These Occupations of the Months appear not only in the finest illuminated manuscripts but also in humbler calendars and astrological pieces. They also provided the subject matter for ornamental carving in churches on misericords, poppyheads and corbels.

By the end of the Middle Ages wool was the most important commodity, apart from food, which derived from the land. This is something testified to by a merchant of Coggeshall who c. 1400 inscribed on his house "I praise God and ever Shal it is the Shepe that pays for al". A tremendously important industry, the wool trade left its stamp on English culture and institutions: the Lord Chancellor takes his seat on the Woolsack; the 'wool churches' of the Cotswolds contain carvings of sheep; brass memorials which often depict a lord and lady not with the customary hound, lion or helm at their feet, but a sheep.

The economic importance and associated power of the wool market led to the first great movement of enclosure, in the Tudor period. A million acres would be enclosed, and fifty thousand people lose their work, in the interests of the better management of sheep. In parts of England it brought to an end the agricultural system which had emerged as dominant at the end of the Dark Ages, that of Open Fields. This form of land management may still be seen today in the Parish of Laxton in Nottinghamshire, England's last open field village, which retains its Court Leet, the authority over the annual farming calendar, to which all the village farmers adhere.

Virgil, author of *The Georgics* (which stood for many years as the most important alternative interpretation of the land to that represented by chivalric romances) wrote:
"Felix qui potuit rerum cognoscere causas"
"Happy is he who has been able to learn the cause of things."
His aphorism is of some relevance to the late 16th and the whole of the 17th Century, when a totally new concept, that of improvement began, during a brief period, to be urged by agricultural authors. Prior to this the only available literature concentrated on what was known. The impetus for this innovation came from necessity: increasing population and urbanisation led to a greater demand for food. This was partly to be met by reclamation of land—as in the farms—and also partly by improvement in farming methods.

Seventeenth Century

"Man who is the servant and interpreter of Nature, can act and understand no further than he has observed, either in operation or in contemplation of the method and order of nature."

So wrote Sir Francis Bacon (1561-1626) in his *Novum Organum* of 1620. Bacon was the first British scientist to concern himself with agriculture, working at his home at Verulam on experimental studies on the effects of various agents on the germination and growth of wheat.

This was an age of experiment; incorrect deductions were frequently made by the original researchers, but the publication of their work enabled subsequent scientists to consider alternative deductions.

The Civil War of the 1640's sent a number of English landowners abroad, for example, Sir Richard Weston to Flanders, where he learned from a Flemish merchant, in 1644, why farmers on poor soil between Ghent and Antwerp were so prosperous. They rotated their crops: first flax, then turnips, then oats undersown with clover. The turnips and clover provided large quantities of food for the livestock, enabling a larger number to be kept; these provided greater amounts of manure which led to still larger crops. In 1645 Sir Richard wrote an account of what he had seen, *A Discours of Husbandrie used in Brabant and Flanders,* noting "what a huge <u>IMPROVEMENT</u> I might make on my own estate . . . "

These years then marked the beginnings of the "Age of Improvement". Farmers and scientists had not yet begun to work together to this end. However, in 1660 a *Philosopher's Society* was formed; in 1662 the Society received Royal patronage and became the *Royal Society*. From the outset this society was interested in agriculture; the Georgical Committee was devoted to this end.

In 1681 Christopher Wren was elected President of the Society, and overhauled its organisation. The Georgical Committee at this point urged the Fellows to plant potatoes as a valuable crop and suggested that they encouraged their friends to do the same. The Committee was also responsible for the drawing up and sending out of a questionnaire to "experienced Husbandmen in all the Shires and Counties of England, Scotland and Ireland". Their aim was to make known "what is knowne and done already, both to enrich every place with the aides, that are found in any place, and withall to consider, what further improvements may be made in all the practice of husbandry".

Two members of this committee, Robert Boyle (1627-1692) and John Evelyn (1620-1706) made substantial contributions to this early period of agricultural science. John Evelyn, the diarist, wrote the first English book on the soil: "*A philosophical discourse of earth, relating to the culture and improvement of it for vegetation.*" This book remained popular throughout the 18th Century.

> "It is verily almost a miracle to see . . . that
> the bare raking and *combing* only of a Bed of
> Earth, now one way then another, as to the
> *Regions* of Heaven, and *Polar* Aspects, may
> diversify the annual *Production,* which is a
> *Secret* worthy to be considered."

The 17th Century was still a time when there was not enough food to last all the animals through the winter and many had to be slaughtered as it set in:

> "At hallontide, slawten time enterith in
> and then doth the husband mans feastinge begin.
> From thence unto shroftyde, kill now and then some:
> their offal for howsold, the better will come."
>
> Thomas Tusser 1573

Autumn fairs, feasts and wakes testify, particularly in the north, to the deeply rooted ritual of the winter killings. The result of the slaughter of livestock was very meagre production of manure during the winter months.

Detail from the Luttrell Psalter, British Museum

Medieval Occupations of the months from a manuscript in the Bodleian Library

The Long Slow Centuries c. 1000-1500 and 1500-1700

1

Facsimile of 1599 Map: 'Plan of Manour and Lordship of Rock', 1885
64 x 73cm.
C. J. Bosanquet, Esq.

Villages were, in Medieval England, frequently divided between one or more manors. In most villages peasants lived in small dwellings, placed side by side often with a small enclosure adjacent to it. Around and beyond the village lay the common fields—arable land which formed, perhaps, the most characteristic of the manorial organisation. Besides the common fields were the meadows. Then came the commons of which the villagers had grazing rights, beyond these lay the 'waste', and the woods and forest.
No hedges divided one part from another, but the common fields were divided up into a furlong which was further divided into strips or selions. At right angles to the strips ran the 'headlands', unploughed for access.

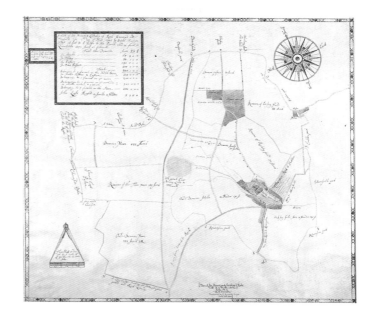

2

Encaustic tile with beast's face from Malmesbury Abbey, Wiltshire, 13th Century
12.5 x 12.5cm.
Athelstan Museum, Malmesbury (North Wiltshire District Council)

One of 36 tiles from the cloisters of Malmesbury Abbey, many of which depict beasts, mythical or actual.

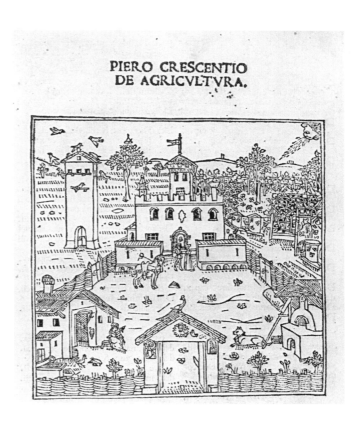

PIERO CRESCENTIO DE AGRICVLTVRA.

3

De Agricultura, 1495
PETRUS CRESCENTIUS
16.5 x 23cm.
Lawes Agricultural Trust. Rothamsted Experimental Station.

The first printed book on agriculture was by Petrus Crescentius, the *Liber ruralium comodorum,* printed by John Schussler of Augsburg in c. 1471. From the time of this volume all agricultural books were beautifully made, for fifty years they continued to have elaborately drawn capital letters, coloured by hand showing the craftsmanship of the Renaissance. After Augsburg, Italy led the way in early agricultural publications.

4

Boke of Husbandry, 1534
SIR ANTHONY FITZHERBERT
Lawes Agricultural Trust. Rothamsted Experimental Station

The first English book on farming to be printed was Sir Anthony Fitzherbert's *Husbandry* of 1523.

3

5

Corbel from the Parish of Bibury, with carved head of a sheep
The Parish Council of Bibury

Sir Thomas More (1478-1535) wrote in 'Utopia' (Book 1):
  "Your sheep, that were won't to be so meek and tame and so small
  eaters, as I hear say, be become so great devourers, and so wild,
  that they eat up and swallow down the very men themselves."
Wool prices, during the late 15th Century boom in the wool
trade, reached their highest level in 1480. By the time the Tudors
came to the throne, great personal fortunes had already been
amassed. The Cotswolds were the centre of the industry.
The monuments of this age are the churches of Fairford,
Cirencester, Northleach and Chipping Campden. Their
benefactors, such as the Grevilles and Hicks of Chipping
Campden, the Celeys and Forteys of Northleach and the Tames
of Fairford, probably did not own their own flocks but rather
bought and packed wool on a huge scale.

An accurate description of the 15th century Cotswold breed
does not exist. In the nave of Northleach Church there are three
brasses that depict sheep and woolpacks at various of the
benefactors' feet.

A smallish, clean-faced sheep with long-stapled wool, shown
in the various engravings in Cotswold Churches, is indicated
and is reminiscent of the present Cotswold breed in all but size.

6

Misericord: Killing the Pig, 15th Century
40 x 50cm.
By permission of the P.C.C. of Ripple

A misericord is a ledge projecting from the underside of hinged
seat of a choir stall in a church, on which the occupant may
support him or herself while standing.

7

Misericord: Sowing Seed, 15th Century
40 x 50cm.
By permission of the P.P.C. of Ripple

The venerable Bede (c. 673-735 A.D.) described an abbot:
  "Who being a strong man and of an humble disposition used to
  assist his monks in their usual labours, sometimes guiding the plough
  by its handle, sometimes winnowing corn, and sometimes forging
  implements of husbandry with a hammer upon an anvil."
Depictions of agricultural activities in churches continued well
into the 15th Century, particularly in carved misericords and
poppyheads.

8

Misericord: Mowing, 14th Century, 1397
30 x 60cm.
By courtesy of the Dean and Chapter of Worcester

The Misericord from Worcester Cathedral shows three men
mowing with scythes; supporters of a robed fox preaching and
a rabbit riding a hound.

9

Plan of Hatfield Broadoak, Essex, 1587
RALPH TRESWELL
Parchment, 44 x 67cm.
St. Bartholomew's Hospital, London.

10

Book of Plans, 17th Century
Anon. Possibly Martin Llewellyn
Paper in buckram binding, 43 x 30cm.
St. Bartholomew's Hospital, London.

11

Five hundred points of good Husbandrie, 1585

THOMAS TUSSER

18 x 13.5cm.

Lawes Agricultural Trust. Rothamsted Experimental Station.

Thomas Tusser (1524 - c. 1580) was born at Riverhall in Essex. His book contains directions and axioms for good farming. Reprinted many times, as late as 1723 Lord Molesworth suggested that

> "I should humbly propose that a school of husbandry were erected in every country, wherein an expert master of the methods of agriculture should teach at a fixed yearly salary, and that Tusser's *Old Book of Husbandry* should be taught to the boys, to read, to copy, and to get it by heart, to which end it might be reprinted and distributed."

12

The First Book of Cattel, 1587

LEONARD MAXALL

Lawes Agricultural Trust. Rothamsted Experimental Station

Maxall wrote two other books related to farming, the first on the cultivation of trees and the second on poultry. His work was based largely on classical authors and since he was from Sussex, for the local red cattle. Choose a beast he suggested where:

> "His belly bigge compasse in falling deepe, his ribbes to be wide and open, his vaines large, his back streight and flat, with a little bending towards the rumpe, his thighs round, his legs streight and well trust, rather somewhat short than large . . .''

13

The Newe and Admirable Arte of Setting of Corn, 1600

SIR HUGH PLAT

17 x 13.25cm.

Lawes Agricultural Trust. Rothamsted Experimental Station

This book deals with the new idea of setting corn seed at equal distances apart, both in row and between the rows, so that seed might be conserved and the crop enhanced.

Plat made his most valuable contribution in another work, 'Jewel House', in suggestions for the use of manure, in which an illustration depicts a movable roof on a barn which allowed a dung heap to be raised while always under cover.

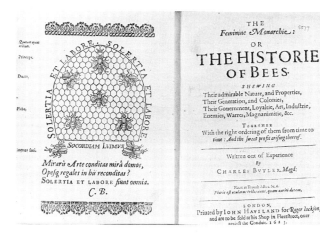

14

14

'The Feminine Monarchy' or 'The Historie of Bees', 1623 (2nd edition)

THE REV. CHARLES BUTLER

14.5 x 19cm.

Lawes Agricultural Trust. Rothamsted Experimental Station

Charles Butler, M.A. of Magdalen College, Oxford, the Vicar of Wotton in Hampshire, was the first person to discover that bees really were a feminine monarchy and to discern the true uses of the queen and drones.

11

13

15

Gerard's Herbal, 1633

33.7 x 21.5cm.

Lawes Agricultural Trust. Rothamsted Experimental Station

In one of the standard reference works on the potato Redcliffe Salaman noted that the first recorded mention of the potato in print (so far discovered) is that made by John Gerard in his catalogue of plants in the gardens under his control in Holborn in 1596. In his *Herbal* of 1597 Gerard gave the potato a chapter to itself. On the frontispiece Gerard displayed his exclusive knowledge of the potato in English circles, by causing his portrait to be executed with a spray of potato foliage with flower and berry in his hand.

Salaman also notes that the potato came from Virginia when all evidence confirms that it came from Peru. The error is investigated by Salaman who notes:

"In 1585, Thomas Harriot (agent to Sir Walter Raleigh) accompanied Sir Richard Grenville on the second expedition to Virginia, or rather to the Island of Roanoke, planned and financed by Sir Walter Raleigh. A year later, Harriott and most of his companions were taken off by Sir Francis Drake and brought back to Plymouth. In 1588 Harriot wrote an account of the Virginia Settlement and the 'commodities there found and to be raysed'. Amongst these, he described three different edible roots under their native Alonquin names—*Openauk, Okeepenauk* and *Kaishcucpenauk.* The latter is our Jerusalem artichoke and the second, identified as the truffle-like fungus *Pachyma Fries,* was not favoured by the settlers and only eaten by the natives when other 'bread' was scarce. It is with the first-named root that we are concerned. The description given by Harriott runs: 'a kind of root of round form and of the bignes of walnuts, some far greater, which are found in moist and marish grounds growing many together, one by another, in ropes or as they were fastened with a string. Being boiled or sodden they are very good meat.'

These roots are the well-known *Glycine apios,* a staple food of all native tribes in eastern North America from the Gulf of Mexico to the St. Lawrence River. The French likening them to a rosary, called them *Chapelets.* The English spoke of them as Indian potatoes, bog potatoes or ground nuts.

Clusius in his account of the potato (*Solanun tuberosum*) remarks that 'not wholly dissimilar there appear to be those roots which the Virginians named *Openauk*—a perfectly correct and legitimate remark. It may be that Gerard, either in that same year or a little later, had received a tuber of the potato from Clusius or, Harriott may have given him in addition to his Virginian specimens a potato tuber from the cookhouse stores of Drake's ship. In either case he would doubtless have planted both in his Holborn garden. It is probable that the *Glycine apios* or *Apios tuberosa* failed to grow but the plant which flourished was the common potato. This might well have been accepted as one of Harriott's Virginian collection. It is not impossible that Gerard was the more readily confused by his desire to ingratiate himself with Elizabeth by being able to announce that this new food plant, the importance of which he had the good sense to recognize, was the first fruit of the colony which had been established at so great a sacrifice by her favourite Raleigh and named after the Virgin Queen herself."

16

The English Husbandman, 1635

GERVASE MARKHAM

19 x 15cm.

Lawes Agricultural Trust. Rothamsted Experimental Station

The most prolific writer of the period 1600-1640 was Gervase Markham (1568-1637) born at Cothan, near Newark, Nottinghamshire.

"The English husbandman, drawne into Two Bookes, and each Booke into Two Parts. The First Part contayning the Knowledge of Husbandry Duties, the Nature of all Sorts of Soiles within this Kingdome, the Manner of Tillage, the diversity of Ploughes, and all other Instruments. The Second Part Contayning the Art of Planting, Grafting and Gardening, the Vse of the Vine, the Hopgarden, and the preservation of all Sorts of Fruits, the Draught of all sorts of Knots, Mazes, and other Ornaments. London: Printed for Henry Taunton, and are to be sold at his Shop in Saint Dunstans Churchyard in Fleet Street."

15

Plough-foot, there you shall place a little paire of round wheeles, which bearing the Beame upon a loose moving Axletree, being just the length of two furrows and no more, doth so certainly guide the Plough in his true furrow that it can neither lose the land by swerving (as in these light soiles every Plough is apt to doe) nor take two muchland, either by the greedinesse of the Plough, or sharpnesse of the Irons, neither can it drowne through the easie lightnesse of the earth, nor run too shallow through the stiffinesse of the mould, but the wheeles being made of a true proportion, which should not be above twelve inches from the centre, the Plough with a reasonable hand of government shall runne in a direct and even furrow: the proportion of which Plough is contained in this Figure.

The Plough with Wheeles.

This Plough of all others I hold to bee most ancient, and as being the modell of the first invention, and at this day is preserved both In *France, Germany,* and *Italy,* and no other proportion of Ploughes knowne, both as we perceive by our experience in seeing them plow, and also by reading of their writings: for neither in *Virgil, Columella Xenophon,* nor any old Writer; nor in *Heresbachius, Stevens,* nor *Libault,*

16

34

17

The English Improver or a New Survey of Husbandry, 1649
WALTER BLITH
Lawes Agricultural Trust. Rothamsted Experimental Station

The most instructive of the mid-17th Century works. Lord Ernle
wrote of Blith:

> "In other ways Blith's work is significant of the era of the Civil
> War. He himself beat his plough share into a sword, became a
> Captain in the Roundhead Army, dedicated his introduction to the
> Rt. Hon. the Lord General Cromwell, adorns it with a portrait of
> himself arrayed in full military costume, and adds to the legend,
> *Vive La Re Publick*."

18

A discourse of Husbandrie. Used in Brabant and Flanders, 1650
DEL. SIR RICHARD WESTON (published by Samuel Hartlib)
14 x 18.5cm.
Lawes Agricultural Trust. Rothamsted Experimental Station

Samuel Hartlib who published the work, published and edited
many agricultural volumes. He came to London in 1628 and
is responsible for the promotion of much important material
which might otherwise never have been printed and distributed.
Sir Richard Weston derived his theory on a four-course rotation
system from farming he had observed between Dunkirk and
Antwerp and as George Fussell remarks in the 'Old English
Farming Books' it had some of the elements of Sir George
Stapleton's renowned ley farming. It was flax, turnips, oats,
with clover bush-harrowed in and grazed until the following
Christmas, mowed three times the following year, and then left
down as a ley for four or five years until exhausted.

A

DISCOURS
OF
HUSBANDRIE
USED IN
BRABANT
AND
FLANDERS;
SHEWING
The wonderfull improvement of Land there ; and
serving as a pattern for our practice in this
COMMON-WEALTH.

LONDON,
Printed by *William Du-Gard*, Anno Dom. 1650.

18

19

England's Improvement by Sea and Land, 1677-1681
ANDREW YARRANTON
Lawes Agricultural Trust. Rothamsted Experimental Station

The volume deals with many subjects, viz. National Granaries,
Land Banks, Cutting of Canals to allow agricultural produce
to circulate freely. Yarranton was also the author of a volume
dealing with the improvement of lands by Clover, c. 1663.

THE
SOYLS, HUSBANDRY, and USES
Proper for
CYN-FOYLE
With the several Manners of its Improvement; Fit to be known
by all that delight in *HUSBANDRY*.

20

20

Document: Tract on 'The Soyle, husbandry and uses of Cyn-foyle', 1669
36 x 24cm.
Unit of Agricultural Economics, Oxford

Cyn-foyle = Sainfoin, *Onobrychis Vicii folia*, which is now
widely grown as a forage crop. It has pale pink flowers and
curved pods. The name derives from 17th Century French and
Medieval Latin *sanum faenum*, meaning wholesome hay.
Sainfoin is one of the crops undersown with corn. (Cyn-foyle
sounds similar to Cinquefoil, but this is in fact a weed).

21

Systema Agriculturae, 1668
JOHN WORLIDGE
18 x 28.5cm.
Lawes Agricultural Trust. Rothamsted Experimental Station

John Worlidge's *'Systema Agriculturae'* ran to five editions in
his lifetime. The title page is engraved by 'F/H Van Horne,
Sculp.' One of its most outstanding features is the design for
a seed drill. It also deals with new field crops, turnips and new
grasses, clover, lucerne and sainfoin.
The frontispiece is matched with an extensive verse that explains
its content:

> "First cast your eye upon a Rustick Seal,
> Built strong and plain, yet well contrived and neat,
> And situated on a healthy soyl,
> Yielding much wealth with little cost, or toyl . . ."

The frontispiece and an explanation of it are reproduced on
the following two pages.

Systema
Agriculturæ.
Being
The Mystery Of Husbandry
Discovered and
laijd Open
by
J: W:

H Van Hoie fecit

Sould By Samuel Speed Neere yᵉ Inner Temple Gate In Fleetestreete. Aᵒ. 1668.

THE
EXPLANATION
OF THE
Frontispiece.

First cast your eye upon a Rustick Seat,
    Built strong and plain, yet well contriv'd, and neat,
    And scituated on a healthy Soyl,
Yielding much Wealth with little cost, or toyl.
Near by it stand the Barns fram'd to contain
Enriching stores of Hay, Pulse, Corn, and Grain;
With Bartons large, and places where to feed
Your Oxen, Cows, Swine, Poultrey, with their breed.
On th'other side hard by the House, you see
The Api'ary for th' industrious Bee.
Walk on a little farther, and behold
A pleasant Garden from high Windes and Cold
Defended (by a spreading, fruitful Wall
With Rows of Lime, and Fir-trees streight and tall,)
Full fraught with necessary Flow'res and Fruits,
And Natures choicest sorts of Plants, and Roots.
Beyond the same are Crops of Beans and Pease,
Saffron, and Liquorice, or such as these;
Then Orchards so enrich'd with fruitful store,
Nature could give (nor they receive) no more,
Each Tree stands bending with the weight it bears
Of Cherries some, of Apples, Plums, and Pears:
Not far from thence see other Walks and Rows
Of Cyder-fruits, near unto which there flows
A Gliding Stream; the next place you discover.
Is where St. Foyn, La Lucern, Hops, and Clover
Are propagated: Near unto those Fields,
Stands a large Wood, Mast, Fewel, Timber yields.
In yonder Vale hard by the River stands
A Water-Engine, which the Winde commands
To fertilize the Meads, on th'other side
A Persian Wheel is plac't both large and wide
To'th same intent; Then do the Fields appear
Cloathed with Corn, and Grain, for th'ensuing Year.
The Pastures stockt with Beasts, the Downs with Sheep,
The Cart, the Plough, and all, good order keep;
Plenty unto the Husbandman, and Gains
Are his Rewards for's Industry and Pains.
    Peruse the Book, for here you onely see
    Th' following subject in Epitomy.

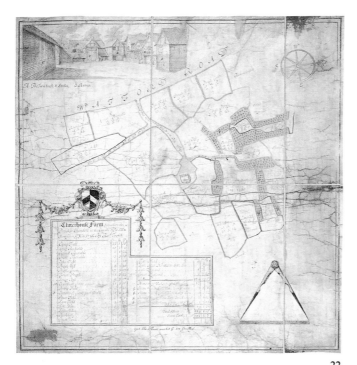

22

Map including Clitterhouse Farm, Hendon, 1715
ROBERT TREVITT
Paper, 64 x 60cm.
St. Bartholomew's Hospital, London

This map contains what is believed to be the earliest surviving depiction of an English farmstead.

22

Comet

33

The Age of the Agricultural Improvers

c. *1750-1820*

With a constantly increasing population and land worth reclaiming running out, the improvement of land already under cultivation became essential. Reclamation during the last years of the 17th Century had been massive; the Restoration of the monarchy in 1660 saw the foundation of the Bedford level corporation which continued and extended the drainage of water-logged land in the Fens.

Two developments stand out in this period: Jethro Tull's horse-drawn seed drill and the establishment of the four-course or Norfolk rotation, perfected by Charles, 2nd Viscount Townshend.

Jethro Tull (1674-1744) devoted his life to improving his land at Prosperous Farm, near Hungerford in Berkshire. The drill which he invented enabled plants to be sown at a regular distance apart which greatly facilitated the removal of weeds and hoeing to maintain a fine tilth around the growing plants. His drill was the first machine of modern mechanization. His book *The new horse hoeing husbandry, or an essay on the principles of tillage and vegetation* was published in 1731.

From 1730-38 Charles Townshend worked on his remote Norfolk farm on the four course rotation which transformed the husbandry of the eastern counties and benefited the whole of English agriculture. Following the advice of Sir Richard Weston he introduced folded turnips in place of fallow. He also adopted Tull's method of drilling turnips instead of broadcasting them achieving better tilth and control of weeds—his yields increased dramatically.

The second great movement of Enclosure began around 1760 and continued into the 1830's. Oliver Goldsmith in *The Deserted Village* wrote of its effects:

> ". . . a bold peasantry, their country's pride
> When once destroyed, can never be supplied.
> A time there was, ere England's griefs began,
> When every rood of ground maintained its man . . . "

Grazing rights were at the heart of the problems thrown up by enclosure. Under the Open Field System a farm, in addition to its measured acreage included rights of turning stock onto the common and stubbles of arable fields. A villager by grazing his stock on such land could accumulate agricultural capital by running stock throughout the year without cost to himself. These rights vanished with the coming of hedges.

The period 1780-1800 has been described as one of the most lively in the history of agriculture anywhere; a time when "great landowners set an example to those of lesser degree". In 1776 Thomas Coke of Holkham succeeded to his estate in Norfolk, where 'two rabbits were fighting for every blade of grass''. Coke was a great experimenter and innovator and from an annual rent roll in 1776 of £2,200 he increased it to £20,000 in 1816. His fame also derives from the annual demonstrations at the Holkham Clippings or sheep shearings; an event taken up by the Dukes of Bedford at Woburn.

In 1793, The Board of Agriculture was set up by Pitt. Its first secretary, Arthur Young had collected information about farming in the different English counties and a large part of France and together with the first President of the Board he organised a series of county agricultural surveys. From 1800-12 under the auspices of the Board of Agriculture Sir Humphry Davy delivered annually a course of lectures on agriculture. Published in 1813 under the title *Elements of Agricultural Chemistry*. Davy defined the science:

> "Agricultural science has for its objects all those changes in the arrangement of matter connected with the growth and nourishment of plants, the comparative values of their produce as food; the constitution of soils; the manner in which lands are enriched by manure, or rendered fertile by the different processes of cultivation."

Another momentous development of these years, the improvement of livestock, which could not have taken place without the attendant improvements in the provision of winter fodder through agrarian improvement, produced a demand for visual records of valuable, improved breeds of animal. Many of these new, wondrous creatures travelled throughout England; the Durham Ox, the White Heifer; the Yorkshire Hog who "excited the public curiosity so much that the proprietor for admission money to see him in 3 years has received near 3,000 pounds!!!''.

The names of the Breeders are many: Robert Bakewell of Dishley Grange in Leicestershire who worked on Longhorn cattle and Leicester sheep; the brothers Collings, Robert and Charles; Coke of Norfolk; Robert Fowler; Jonas Webb; John Ellman of Glynde. All had portraits made of the animals they most prized.

During the 1790's a number of agricultural societies were established, some purely local, others related to a district. In the years which followed the conclusion of the Napoleonic wars, which had seen much prosperity in English agriculture, a severe depression set in.

23

23
Jethro Tull (1674-1741)
ARTIST UNKNOWN
Oil on canvas, 125.5 x 89.5cm.
R.A.S.E.

The author of *Horse-hoeing Husbandry* (1731), Jethro Tull, lived in Berkshire and was the inventor of the 'hoe-plough' and the turnip drill.

> "All roots" he wrote, "are as the intestines of animals and have their mouths or lacteal vessels opening on their outer spongy superfices . . . When roots are in tilled soil the greater pressure is made against them by the earth which continually subsides and presses their food closer and closer even into their mouths, until it becomes so hard and close that the weak sort of roots cannot penetrate any further into it unless reopened by new tillage which is called hoeing."

Tull's seed drill had eleven shares and would sow three different kinds of seed without mixing them. Barley was sown at seven inches apart and four inches deep; clover three inches above the barley and between every two of these rows, at half an inch deep a row of sainfoin.

The drill was also ingenious in its capacity to sow half the seed at four inches into the ground and half at half an inch. Tull also mixed old and new seed in his sowings; thus the seed would germinate and emerge at four different times 'giving it so many chances of escaping the fly.'

The seed drill derives in part from the mechanics of the organ, which Jethro Tull had played as a youth. Often exasperated with his labourers Tull resolved to quit farming unless he 'could contrive an engine to plant . . . more faithfully than such hands would do. At last he 'pitched upon a groove, tongue and spring in the sound-board of the organ. With these a little altered, and some parts of two other instruments as foreign to the field as the organ is added to them, I composed my machine.''

24
The horse-hoeing husbandry, 1733
JETHRO TULL
Lawes Agricultural Trust. Rothamsted Experimental Station.

25
Rt. Hon. Lord Viscount Townshend, (1674-1738)
PAINTED BY SIR GODFREY KNELLER c. 1646-1723
Engraving
R.A.S.E.

Charles 'Turnip' Townshend was trained for a political life. In 1721 he became Secretary of State but following a period of extreme rivalry between Townshend and Walpole he resigned from politics on May 15, 1730 and retired to his estate at Rainham.

His vigorous advocacy of the turnip and its benefits for British agriculture, through which he earned his famous nickname, was valuable in two important ways. The turnip facilitated the keeping of greater numbers of stock, especially through the winter, because there was more than just hay to feed them. The cultivation and feeding of stock also led to the increased practice of folding animals and hence a more efficient system of manure collection which, once distributed on the land led to the production of heavier crops.

Without turnip culture the improvements in stock breeding by such figures as Robert Bakewell of Dishley, Charles Colling of Ketton and his brother Robert of Barmpton would not have been possible. It is of note that in several paintings, for example Thomas Weaver's depiction of Colling's White Shorthorn Heifer of 1811, a farm labourer sits with a basket of turnips which he prepares for the gigantic creature.

Townshend's fame also lies in his development of rotation cropping. Rather than cultivating two or even three straw crops one after the other and then leaving the land fallow for a year to recover he decided to try a four course system.

The first year began with turnips, during which period the land was cleaned. The next year he sowed barley or oats and the third he planted clover and ryegrass. The clover left nitrogen in the ground for the fourth year when he sowed wheat. He would then return to turnips, manuring them fully and sometimes folding them off with sheep.

Townshend's four-course, or Norfolk rotation was soon adopted throughout the country. His success was perhaps indebted to the advice of Sir Richard Weston to use turnips and clover in place of fallow and to Tull, for drilling rather than broadcasting his turnip seed.

26
Robert Bakewell on his Cob
JOHN BOULTBEE
Oil on canvas, 104 x 84cm.
R.A.S.E.

'Improver' of the Leicester breed of sheep and of Longhorn Cattle; Robert Bakewell of Dishley Grange in Leicestershire is acclaimed as the creator of modern methods of animal breeding. Bakewell, around 1760, took the long-legged, slow-maturing animal, which was kept almost entirely for its yield of wool and began to work on it. His objectives were to produce 'a sheep possessed of the most perfect symmetry, with the greatest aptitude to fatten, and rather smaller in size'.

To the old Leicester sheep he introduced Lincoln and Hereford (Ryeland) blood. From the resultant prototype he isolated a quick-maturing, fatter type of sheep, and fixed it by inbreeding. In 1790 he formed the Dishley Society. Only members of this Society were allowed to own the improved Leicester sheep and were bound by rigid rules.

Although Bakewell's methods met with success, his objectives have been questioned and his sheep were criticized by his contemporaries. Prolificacy and milking ability were lost; wool yield was reduced, too much fat lay in the carcase, the meat was of low quality.

Similar criticisms could be levelled at his work on the original Longhorn Cattle; Bakewell 'improved' a goodle triple-purpose animal, sacrificing its milk yield in order to produce a fatter, early maturing beef animal.

27
Robert Bakewell's Chair
R.A.S.E.

Inscription on back of splat:
"This chair was made under the direction of the Celebrated Robert Bakewell of Dishley out of a willow that grew on his farm. It was his favourite seat, and the back which thus records his Memory, served as a screen when seated by his fireside, calculating on the Profits, or devising some Improvement on his farm. Thousands of pounds have been known to exchange hands in the same . . . Mr. Bakewell died in 1795".

28

27

28
'Two Pounder', 1790
J. DIGBY CURTIS
Oil on canvas 75 x 88cm.
Unit of Agricultural Economics, Oxford

Walter Shaw Sparrow, writing in 1932 in *Walker's Quarterly* (published by Walker's Galleries of Bond Street, London) said of this painting:

"By rare good luck, a portrait in oils of Bakewell's most noted ram, 'Two Pounder', that earned for his owner more than £800 in one year, has come down to our time; it belongs to Professor C. S. Orwin, and is signed 'J. Digby Curtis, 1790'. The ram is a fine fellow with slender legs, but he would have cut a much better figure if he had been painted on a larger canvas; he dominates too much over the landscape background and forefront, in which there are some translucent effects plainly suggested by watercolour drawings . . . I would wish to know more of J. Digby Curtis. In his handling of the fleece he made use of a palette knife—a novel display of technical courage in 1790. If this Curtis was the J. D. Curtis who, in 1827, sent a landscape to the British Artists, he may have been at the beginning of his career in 1790."

29
Signed Copy of Bakewell's Petition, c. 1790
24.5 x 18.5cm.
Private Collection

"To the Nobility, Gentry, and Others.
The humble Petition of Robert Bakewell, of Dishley, in the County of Leicester.
    Sheweth
That your Petitioner has for a Series of Years employed his Attention on a Plan for improving the Breed of *Horſes* for Cavalry, Harneſs and Draught, as alſo of *Neat Cattle* and *Sheep*.
That your Petitioner, in Purſuit of this Plan, had many Difficulties to furmount, having the Prejudices of other Breeders to combat, and various Experiments to make, in order to aſcertain which were the beſt Kinds to breed from; and that ſuch Experiments were attended with conſiderable Expence, and more Trouble than he can well convey a Senſe of.

. . . continues overleaf

That your Petitioner apprehends he has brought all the different Kinds of Stock above-mentioned to a greater Degree of Perfection than has been done by any other Perſon, and thereby rendered important Services to this Country; and in this Opinion he hopes he is juſtified, by the beſt Judges having purchaſed from this Stock, at higher Prices than from any other, and having ſent them into the Counties of Bedford, Bucks, Cambridge, Cheſter, Cumberland, Derby, Devon, Dorſet, Durham, Eſſex, Glouceſter, Hereford, Herts, Huntingdon, Kent, Lancaſter, Leiceſter, Lincoln, Norfolk, Northampton, Northumberland, Nottingham, Oxon, Rutland, Salop, Somerſet, Southampton, Stafford, Suffolk, Suſſex, Warwick, Weſtmorland, Wilts, Worceſter, York, into North Britain, Wales, Ireland, Germany, and Jamaica.

That your Petitioner has made conſiderable Improvements in Agriculture, Diviſion of Lands, Watering of Meadows, &c.

That your Petitioner, in Conſequence of the aforeſaid Difficulties and Expences, as well as by many great and unavoidable Loſſes, to the Amount of many Thouſand Pounds, is rendered incapable of purſuing his Plan; and as a conſiderable Part of the Stock is ſoon to be ſold, and probably will fall into the Hands of thoſe who for Want of Experience, or other Cauſes, cannot be ſuppoſed to manage it to the ſame Advantage, conſequently little if any further Improvement can be expected therefrom.

But, if the Public ſhould take his Caſe into their Conſideration, and grant him ſuch Aſſiſtance as would enable him to purchaſe the Whole, or the beſt Part of this Stock, he is fully perſuaded he could be highly inſtrumental to the general Good of this Nation, by continuing in his late Line of Breeding Buſineſs, and carrying it forward in ſuch a Manner as will be moſt conducive to the public Service; and he apprehends he could make as great Improvement from the State the Stock is now in, as he has done from the State of Stock in general at the Time he began this Buſineſs, an Object he thinks of great Importance to the Honour and Intereſt of the Britiſh Empire; for if it be allowed that the Increaſe of Herbage by Improvement in Agriculture is a real Advantage to the Public in general, he conceives the Improvement of Stock, ſo as to gain a greater Quantity and better Quality of Fleſh from ſuch Herbage, to be of equal, if not of greater Importance.

Your Petitioner therefore moſt humbly ſolicits, &c.''

Amongst subscribers were the Duke of Rutland with £200 and the Duke of Devonshire with £50.

31

permissable as against the then existing system of perpetually crossing with 'strange' breeds or 'strange' families within the breed upon which the experiment was being made. They went a stage beyond Bakewell in their application of the system of inbreeding.

It has been noted that the cattle of Robert Colling differed from those of his brother at Ketton; mostly in style and particularly in the character of the head. Families which he brought to perfection included the Princess, Wildair and Red Rose.

From the Red Rose family sprang Pilot, one of the most influential of the Booth (beef) herds and also from that family came the Cambridge Roses developed in the Bates herd. The Red Roses started a Shorthorn fashion in the pioneer meat and milk producing days of the mid-West of the United States. Two sales, one in 1818 and the other in 1820, dispersed the Barmpton herd and these produced an aggregate sum of £10,126 14s 6d, an average of £94 12s 10d for 107 animals.

30
Veterinary Chest and Contents
M.E.R.L.

A late 18th Century veterinary chest for transporting medicines.

While during the 1790's a number of agricultural societies were established, another society of that period, the Odiham Society of Hampshire concentrated on veterinary science and education. One of its members, Thomas Burgess, was responsible for the advocation on 'humanitarian grounds' of humane treatment for sick farm animals based on a fuller knowledge of their anatomy and diseases.

In 1788 the Odiham Society sent two students to the recently established Paris veterinary school. The French idea was taken up in London. The London Veterinary College opened in 1792 with Charles Vial de St. Bel, the French Veterinarian as Professor.

31
The Famous Early Bull: Property of Robert Collings of Barmpton, Darlington
ATTRIBUTED TO D. DALBY OF YORK
Oil on canvas, 65 x 76cm.
Unit of Agricultural Economics, Oxford

Robert Collings of Barmpton (brother to Charles at Ketton Hall) agreed with Robert Bakewell's view that 'calves take considerably more to the male than to the female parent.' Both the Collings brothers were convinced by Bakewell that his 'new system' was founded on two ideas. The first an ideal of small bone as against large and the second that interbreeding was

32
Catalogue of Sale of Pedigree Stock, 1810
R.A.S.E.

"A Catalogue of the Improved Shorthorn Cattle and also Leicestershire Sheep. Belonging to Mr. Charles Colling of Ketton, near Darlington, in the county of Durham which will be sold by auction on Thursday and Friday, the 11th and 12th day of October next, 1810.''

33
Comet: a light roan Shorthorn Bull in a landscape, 1811
THOMAS WEAVER
Oil on canvas, 71.1 x 91.4cm.
Beamish Museum

'Comet' was got by 'Favourite' out of 'Young Phoenix', and bred by Charles Colling of Ketton. He was sold at the Ketton sale in October 1810 for 1,000 guineas and bought by Messrs. Wetheral, Charge, Wright and Trotter of Darlington. A contemporary description of 'Comet' at the sale described him as '. . . the great attraction of the sale, and his close breeding [by Favorite, dam by Favorite, out of Favorite's dam], did not detract from his value or appearance. Charles Colling declared him to be the best bull he ever bred or saw. He was a beautiful light roan, dark [red] neck, with a fine masculine head, broad and deep breast, shoulders well laid back, crops and loins good, hind quarters long, straight, thick, and well packed, thighs, twist full and well let down, with nice straight hocks and hind legs. He had fair-sized horns, ears large and hairy, and a grandeur of style and carriage that was indescribable. It was admitted that no bull so good had ever before been seen, and eminent breeders have since said that they never again saw his equal'. He was calved 1804 and died in 1815.

34

Cup made from horn of Comet
M.E.R.L.

35

35

'The Durham Ox' in an extensive landscape, 1804
GEORGE GARRARD A.R.A.
Oil on canvas, 63.5 x 75.6cm.
Beamish Museum

This portrait was painted for the Earl of Strathmore in June 1804. Charles Colling, who had bred and fed the ox, had married Miss Colpitts, the daughter of the land agent for the Earl's estates.

The ox was got by 'Favourite' out of a 'common black and white cow', bought for the Collings by John Simpson at Durham Fair. He was bred to his greatest flesh-taking capacity and weighed 3,024 lbs. He was sold to Mr. Bulmer of Harmby in February 1801 for £140, and he had a special travelling carriage made for the ox to take him around the country. He in turn sold him to Mr. John Day, who exhibited him all over the country in numerous fairs and shows, where he was a sensation. Day wrote a pamphlet entitled 'An account of the late extraordinary Durham Ox with remarks on the great advantage to be derived by the breeder and the public from the encouragement of such a breed', which was sold wherever the ox appeared. He was said to have been good-natured and remarkably agile for his size; Day's family used to travel with him in the special carriage and generally treated him like a pet. Despite several high offers, Day always refused to sell him. He travelled several thousand miles exhibiting the animal over many years, until it dislocated its hip at Oxford in February 1807, and had to be slaughtered.

36

'Juno' a red Shorthorn Cow in an extensive landscape, 1804
GEORGE GARRARD A.R.A.
Oil on canvas, 63.4 x 76.3cm.
Beamish Museum

'Juno', a 'beautiful, improved, 4-year-old, shorthorn cow' was by 'Favourite' out of 'Wildair' bred by Mr. Robert Colling. This portrait was painted for the Earl of Strathmore in June 1804.
Garrard also produced an engraving of 'Juno', published by him on 31 May, 1813.

37

'Wildair' an eight-year-old heifer, in a river landscape, 1827
THOMAS WEAVER
Oil on canvas, 64.2 x 75.9cm.
Beamish Museum

'Wildair' was by 'Favourite': her grand-dam was by 'Ben', great-great-grand dam by 'Hubback', great-grand-dam by the sire of 'Hubback'.

38

A Shorthorned Heifer: seven years old. Bred and fed by Mr. Robert Colling in the county of Durham, 1811
T. WEAVER ENGRAVED BY W. WARD
Proof: Mezzotint
Private collection

The animal stands facing right, outside a stable. On the right a seated herdsman holds a turnip and a knife with which to cut it.

39

Part Silver gilt cup and cover with two figure handles and shorthorn knob
The Shorthorn Memorial Cup
R.A.S.E.

At the Royal Agricultural Society's Show at Newcastle in 1923 this cup was presented to the Society:

"On behalf of the County of Durham, Mr. Alderman Davis and Mr. William Parlour presented to the Society "The Brothers Colling Shorthorn Memorial Challenge Cup."
This Cup, illustrating the story of the world-famous achievement of these two brothers, has been inspired by the early English Founders' Cups, in which symbolism is bent to the purpose of design. Beginning at the foot of the Cup, one sees the land, furrow, rig and root, from which rise trunk and branch encircling a golden bowl representing a cornfield in stook. At this point the Brothers Colling step in and take up their positions as flanking ornaments, forming the handles. The eye is immediately led up to the Collings' crowning achievement, *viz.* the Bull 'Comet,' itself a vital piece of animal sculpture. It is interesting to note that this trophy is presented to the Royal Agricultural Society of England by the Durham County Agricultural Committee, and will be competed for annually at the Society's show for the best beast in the Shorthorn Classes. The Cup, being a Memorial one, is a perpetual trophy, and it will not be possible to be won outright. The winner each year will have the right to have his name inscribed on one of the shields provided on the plinth."

(R.A.S.E. *Journal,* Vol. 84, 1923).

40

43
A Collection of Laws which form the constitution of the Bedford Level Corporation, 1761
BY CHARLES NALSON COLE
Anthony Pemberton, Esq.

The drainage of the Fens converted a huge desolation into one of the richest agricultural areas in the country. The decisive period of reclamation took place in the 17th Century, when a company of investors under the Earl of Bedford employed a Dutch engineer named Vermuyden to ditch the Southern Fenlands as a farmer ditches marshy ground. Vermuyden worked on a gigantic scale and his ditches were rivers, the largest, the Old Bedford River, being twenty-one miles long and seventy feet wide. By the 1650's the Bedford Level was carrying crops and stock 'where never had been any before'. But as the reclaimed land dried and shrank and silt accumulated on the riverbeds, the rivers rose above the land they were supposed to drain. So hundreds of windmills were built to pump the water from the fields into the rivers. The Fenlands were not secured until the coming of steam power to drive the pumps. Thus, in the words of an inscription on a Fenland bridge, 'water was conquered by her daughter, steam.''

44
Society of Arts
PAPERS ON AGRICULTURE 1810-43
22 x 14cm.
Lawes Agricultural Trust, Rothamsted Experimental Station.

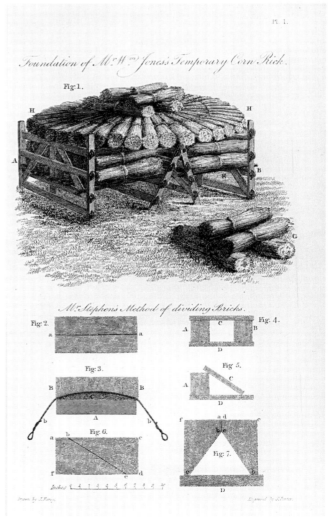

44

40
Sir Christopher Sykes, 2nd Bt., (1749-1801), 1803
MARBLE BUST BY JOSEPH NOLLEKENS (1737-1823)
Life size
Sir Tatton Sykes, Bt.

At Sledmere, situated in the Yorkshire Wolds, is one of the most important agricultural estates. Sir Christopher Sykes was responsible for the transformation of the parish from the open-field into enclosure; creating eight farms. As John Popham has noted: (*Country Life* January 16, and January 23, 1986)

> "That it was possible to create farms on the open wold, at a height of nearly 500 ft., was due to the then new development of the 'very important art' of pond-making, enabling reliance to be placed on an entirely artificial water source. By contrast, pre-enclosure farmsteads had tended to be confined to valley's where there were natural water supplies."

41
Elevation of 'Marramatte', c. 1778
Monochrome drawing on paper, 60 x 60cm.
Sir Tatton Sykes, Bt.

42
Elevation of 'Life Hill', c. 1778
Monochrome drawing on paper, 60 x 60cm.
Sir Tatton Sykes, Bt.

45
William Shipley, c. 1759-60
RICHARD COSWAY (1740-1821)
Oil on canvas, 72 x 59cm.
R.S.A., London

In 1753 William Shipley published his 'Proposals for raising by subscription a Fund to be distributed in Premiums for the promoting of improvements in Liberal Arts, Sciences, Manufactures, etc.' By 1755 the Constitution for the Society for the Encouragement of Arts, Manufactures and Commerce' was drawn up with Lord Folkestone as President and Shipley as Secretary. The first medals awarded by the Society, in 1758 were divided into Classes; Agriculture, Chemistry, Colonies and Trade, Manufactures and Mechanics and the Polite Arts.
James Barry, the Irish-born painter began his paintings for the Great Room in Denmark Street in 1777. In the fifth painting: 'The Distribution of Premiums in The Society of Arts' includes a portrait of Arthur Young, handing Corn to the President, Lord Romney. Barry wrote of the subject of this painting:

> "The distribution of Premiums in a Society founded for the purposes of raising up and perfecting useful and ingenious arts, forms an idea picturesque and ethical in itself, and makes a limb of my general subject, not ill-suited to the other parts."

46
Register of Premiums and Bounties of the Society of Arts, 1778
Pages 10-11
R.S.A., London.

47a
Transactions of the Society of Arts, 1793
R.S.A., London.

47b
Society of Arts. Prize Jug, 1846
15 x 15cm.
Minton
Minton Museum, Royal Doulton Ltd.

Minton Society of Arts Prize Jug, 1846, modelled in stoneware, ovoid shape, the neck stained blue with a continuous frieze of hops and foliage in white relief.
Marks: Moulded ribbon incised 'Society of Arts Prize Jug, 1846,' M & Co. Moulded diamond shape registration mark. This jug was produced in many colours, sizes and bodies after winning a prize in the Society of Arts competition.
It was Sir Henry Cole, a leader of the design reform movement, who persuaded Herbert Minton to submit jugs of Minton design for competition. Minton also produced a tea service to Cole's own design. This too won a prize and was greatly admired by The Prince Consort.
The Society of Arts competitions and their prize-giving system were 'intended to promote the public taste'. They led the way to discussions with Prince Albert and his executive committee (of which Cole was a key member) and, ultimately, to the Great Exhibition of 1851.

48
Silver Premium: Ceres
R.S.A., London

Ceres, the Roman goddess of agriculture, Demeter her Greek counterpart. Demeter was one of the twelve major Olympic gods. Her name means 'Mother Earth'. The Romans identified her with the Italian grain-goddess Ceres and she was also identified in ancient times with the Egyptian Isis.

49

49
Ceres with Cornucopia, lamb and vegetables, 1790-1820
Enamel colours
Stoke-on-Trent City Museum and Art Gallery

Figure of Ceres in Earthenware decorated with enamel colours. Made in Staffordshire between 1790-1820.

47b

50

Charts on the entry and dispersal of Spanish and French Merino sheep from 1784

H. B. Carter, Esq.

The first undoubted examples of the Spanish Merino in England were a gift from a French scientist in 1785 to Sir Joseph Banks PRS—one ram and one ewe—from which at his villa, Spring Grove near Hounslow, he developed his own experimental flock. Here he proved that the Spanish Merino on English grass could be a source of finer wool than any indigenous British breed could grow. From this and other evidence from France and Germany HM King George III was induced by Banks to establish, on a larger scale, a breeding flock of Spanish Merinos on his Marsh Gate farm at Kew with stock bought from France (January 1788) and smuggled from Spain itself (1788-92). But in October 1791 these were overshadowed and replaced by a gift of 4 rams and 36 ewes from the Count and Countess de Campo di Alange, owners of the famous Negretti flock, one of the finest known to the wool trade of Europe. For 25 years these were bred and managed by Sir Joseph Banks for the King at Windsor, Richmond and Kew as the first stud of pure Merinos in the British Commonwealth.

By 1810, when the Regency began, there were few farming areas in the United Kingdom to which the Spanish Merino had not spread either as pure stock or as crosses with some other British breed. A Merino Society was established in 1811 with Sir Joseph Banks as its first and only President until his death in 1820. At its peak, 1811-20, the Society had more than 400 members spread through 40 countries but mainly in Hampshire and the Home Counties. As a pure breed it probably never exceeded 25,000 and as a crossbred perhaps about 100,000 derived from any breeds but mostly from the Southdown and the Ryeland. By the end of the 19th Century it had disappeared as imported fine wool first from Germany and then from Australia rendered any economic argument for its breeding in Great Britain obsolete.

54

51

Volume XVII of the Annals of Agriculture, p. 529 illustrating Arthur Young's imported Spanish ram 'Don' (Ram No. 3 in His Majesty's Spanish Merino flock in the Little Park, Windsor) aged four years, with horns left uncut in the English manner, 1791.

H. B. Carter, Esq.

52

The Agricultural Magazine for 1806, Volume IV illustrating Lord Somerville's imported Spanish ram (Ram No. 20 in His Lordship's Spanish Merino flock at Fitzhead, nr. Taunton) aged three years with horn cut short in the Spannish manner, 1803.

H. B. Carter, Esq.

53

George III (1738-1820), 1761
National Portrait Gallery
CHARLES SPOONER
Mezzotint 35.5 x 25.5cm.

Under the name of his Shepherd, Ralph Robinson, George III, occasionally wrote on agriculture in the Board of Agriculture's publication *The Annals of Agriculture.* His interest in agriculture led to his nickname of "Farmer George".

54

Arthur Young (1741-1820), 1811
CHARLES JAGGER
28 x 21cm.
R.A.S.E.

Ironically Arthur Young, first Secretary to the Board of Agriculture, always lost money at farming. Intrigued by the idea of experimentation, Young was reputed to have conducted 3,000 experiments by the time of his death in 1820.

Young was fired with enthusiasm for farming methods. He recommended that every farmer, after having safely got in his hay should "take his nag for a summer tour, to view some farmers in well cultivated counties, and to introduce himself to the conversation of intelligent brethren, from whom he will be sure to learn something.

In 1783 Young started a journal, *The Annals of Agriculture.* He travelled 20,000 miles on his blind, white horse, and subsequently wrote a "Domesday Book" of the land.

En route Young spread his advice to adopt "turnip husbandry", teaching how cattle could be fed on turnips in winter quarters, and how straw could be made into yard manure for the "mending of soils."

In 1793 William Pitt established the Board of Agriculture. As secretary, Young pressed the Board to encourage more potato growing.

As a result of Young's various endeavours, Britain increased its arable land by 10,000 square miles and production per acre was doubled. George III, 'Farmer George' said to Arthur Young:

"Mr. Young, I am more obliged to you than to any man on my Dominions."

55

"The Plough" 4 June 1801
MEZZOTINT VALENTINE GREEN
75 x 54cm.
M.E.R.L.

Bears inscription: "Ye Generous Britons, Venerate the Plough" (Thomson's Seasons, Spring)
To the Right Honourable Lord Carrington, the Vice Presidents and the Rest of the Members of the Board of Agriculture.

56
Official Stamp of the Board of Agriculture
R.A.S.E.

In 1793 a Board of Agriculture and Internal Improvement was set up by Pitt's Government. Not a government department in the formal sense, being founded by Royal Charter and financed by an annual exchequer grant. Sir John Sinclair, an M.P. and Scottish landowner was the prime mover. King George III became the patron of the Board, which consisted of sixteen ex-officers and 30 ordinary members, a treasurer and secretary (Arthur Young). C. S. Orwin records that "the first task undertaken by the Board was the preparation and publication of a series of county surveys, describing the State of agriculture and the progress of inclosure and improvement in each. By 1806 a complete and authoritative issue had been made, a series of great value to the historian of the period.
In 1822, after many difficulties, including withdrawal of the Treasury Grant, the Board was dissolved.
Following the dissolution of the Board, the administration of agricultural and landed interests, so far as the State was concerned, was diffused amongst a number of commissions—the Tithe Commission, 1836, the Copyhold Commission, 1841, the Inclosure Commission, 1845—all of which merged subsequently in the Land Commission, a separate department under the jurisdiction of the Home Secretary. The outbreak of cattle plague which swept through the country in 1865 led to the formation of the Cattle Plague Department, under the Privy Council. It became the Veterinary Department in 1870, to deal with a variety of scheduled diseases of animals. A movement for the co-ordination of all these and other activities, such as Agricultural Statistics, Woods and Forests, etc., came to a head in 1879, when a Department of Commerce and Agriculture was proposed. It was not until 1888, however, that a Bill to establish a Board of Agriculture was introduced, which was passed into law during the following year. In 1903 the Board became the Board of Agriculture and Fisheries, and the responsibilities of the Board of Trade for freshwater and sea fisheries were transferred to it. In 1909 the appointment of a Parliamentary Secretary to the Board was authorized, and in 1919 the Board was raised to the status of a Ministry."

57

57
Sir Humphry Davy: President of The Royal Society 1820-7
c. 1820
SIR THOMAS LAWRENCE (1769-1830)
Oil on canvas
142.3 x 111.8cm.
By kind permission of the President and Council of the Royal
Society of London.

. . . continues overleaf

57 continued

From 1800-1812 under the auspices of the Board of Agriculture, Sir Humphry Davy delivered annually a course of lectures on agriculture. Published in 1813 under the title *Elements of Agricultural Chemistry,* Davy defined the science:

> "Agricultural Science has for its objects all those changes in the arrangements of matter connected with the growth and nourishment of plants, the comparative values of their produce as food; the constitution of soils; the manner in which lands are enriched by Manure, or rendered fertile by the different processes of cultivation."

and believed that:

> "Discoveries made in the cultivation of the Earth, are not merely for the time and country in which they are developed, but they may be considered as extending to future ages, and as ultimately tending to benefit the whole human race; as affording subsistence for generations yet to come; as multiplying life, and not only multiplying life but likewise providing for its enjoyment."

Humphry Davy carried out his most significant work in pure chemistry during the time of his appointment to the Royal Institution.

In 1820 Davy succeeded Sir Joseph Banks as President of The Royal Society of London. The Royal Society was awarded a Royal Charter in July 1662. Among the founders were Robert Boyle and Sir Christopher Wren. Their intention to form a group to promote the new 'Physico-Mathematicall Learning'. It was believed that the new experimental philosophy could explain many natural phenomena. Francis Bacon's 'The New Atlantis' gave much support to the Study of nature.

Charles II in his Charter referred to the Fellows as those " . . . whose studies are to be applied to further promoting by the authority of experiments, the science of natural things and of useful arts to the glory of God, the creator, and the advantage of the human race."

Still an independent body, The Royal Society has a long history of impecunity. An early attempt to establish the Society on a sound financial basis failed, principally because Charles II required money for his royal purposes and failed to bestow financial favour on the Society.

58
Sir Humphry Davy, Bart
Elements of Agricultural Chemistry
The Royal Institution, London

The course of lectures for the Board of Agriculture.

59
Sir Humphry Davy, Bart
Observations on the Processes of Tanning, 1803
The Royal Institution, London

" . . . and on the constituent parts of certain astringent vegetables." This volume from the Journals of the Royal Institution also contains on page 319 observations on the 'Burning of lands'.

60
Hortus Gramineus Woburnensis
Volume by GEORGE SINCLAIR 1816
The Royal Institution, London

"An account of the results of experiments on the produce and nutritive of qualities of different grasses, and other plants, used as the food of the more valuable domestic animals: instituted by John, Duke of Bedford.
Illustrated with dried specimens of the plants upon which these experiments have been made . . ."
George Sinclair was Gardener to the Duke of Bedford.

61
Bust of Coke of Norfolk 1752-1842
SIR FRANCIS CHANTREY (1781-1841)
MARBLE
Viscount Coke, DL and Trustees of the Holkham Estate

Sir Francis Chantrey, the English Sculptor was born near Sheffield and is celebrated for his portrait busts and monuments. He studied intermittently, in 1802, at the Royal Academy, but worked mostly in Sheffield. He became an A.R.A. in 1816, R.A. in 1817 and was knighted in 1837. His large fortune went to the Royal Academy for the purchase of 'works of Fine Art of the highest merit . . . executed in England'.

62
Portrait of T. W. Coke, Esq & Clerk Hilliard, Esq with a North Devon Ox bred and fed at Holkham considered the most perfect animal of its kind.
W. H. DAVIS
Lithograph, 71 x 86cm.
Unit of Agricultural Economics, Oxford

Coke of Norfolk studied cattle and introduced into Norfolk a breed of Shorthorns, but on being advised to try North Devons he at once began a trial (he advised always a trial of three years), between the fattening of two Devons and a Shorthorn. When killed the Devons weighed 140 stone and the Shorthorn only 110 stone though it had eaten more than the Devons.

In the first years of his farming Coke spent more than £100,000 and between 1776 and 1842 no less than £536,992 on improvements, his object being "at whatever loss or exertion to himself to bring about a permanent improvement in the condition of the soil and in the knowledge of agriculture. When he first took over Holkham he inspected the 43,000 acre estate he found a wild sheep walk "with one blade of grass, and two rabbits fighting for that", the rent roll was £2,000 which he eventually raised to £20,000.

Clerk Hilliard, who stands behind the ox was a noted agriculturalist from Thorpelands, Northampton; he was author of "Practical Farming and Grazing" published in 1836 and a noted breeder of North Devon Cattle.

62

63

63
Head of a Ram
J. Boultbee (1747-1812)
Oil on canvas, 73 x 76.5cm.
Viscount Coke, DL. and Trustees of the Holkham Estate

64

64
Coke and his Southdown Sheep, c. 1807
T. WEAVER (1774-1843)
Oil on canvas, 2m. x 1m. 20cm.
Viscount Coke, DL and Trustees of the Holkham Estate

Thomas William Coke, first Earl of Leicester of Holkham was
one of the great figures of the agricultural revolution. His great
Uncle, the first Thomas Coke (1697-1759) built Holkham Hall,
recast the farms, consolidated the family lands and enclosed
them with hedges. Thomas William Coke, 'Coke of Norfolk',
replaced most of the buildings by Kent with buildings by Samuel
Wyatt, including The Great Barn, 1790, inaugurated the most
detailed records of the crops of his tenants, granted long leases
to the best of his tenants and took in hand the lesser farms.
Coke of Norfolk, in 1778, turned his annual sheep-shearings
into what may be seen as the forerunner of the agricultural show,
where farmers could meet and exchange ideas against the
background of Coke's exemplary methods. Thomas William
Coke made farming fashionable.
Forty-three 'Holkham Clippings' were held and people travelled
from all over the world to attend them.

65

65
Sheep-shearing in a Great Barn, early 19th Century
ARTIST UNKNOWN
Oil on canvas, 71 x 89cm.
Viscount Coke, DL and Trustees of the Holkham Estate

Coke of Norfolk said that his sheep-shearings were started for the improvement of the breed of sheep. Prizes were given and rams were hired out (as depicted in Thomas Weaver's painting of the Ram letting . . ., at Dishley, 'Bakewell's estate: Tate Gallery'. By 1808 he felt that he had done all in his power to remove the Norfolk sheep which had once made Norfolk rich but which he described as 'a vile degenerate breed'. In 1792-3 he introduced South Downs which he came to recommend unreservedly. He turned over to these sheep entirely and in 1816 there were 2,004 on the Park Farm.

This painting is believed not to be of a Holkham Shearing but possibly of one which took place in the Duke of Sussex's estate.

66   Leicester Monument   66

66

Leicester Monument
Print and photographs of frieze panels
Viscount Coke, DL and Trustees of the Holkham Estate

Erected in 1847 in Holkham Park to the memory of Thomas Coke. The four corners of the plinth carry an ox, a group of sheep, a plough and a seed drill. At the top of the monument there is a wheatsheaf. One of the innovations with which Coke is credited is commemorated on the monument; the creation of the long lease of 20 years for tenanted farms. Lord Ernle noted in '*English Farming, Past and Present*' that "for 16 years complete freedom of action was accorded both in regard to rotation, management of land and sale of produce; only in the last four years had the Norfolk four-course rotation to be restored. Moreover, after this lapse of 16 years, renewal for another 20, on fresh terms for the last 16, would always be granted."

67

The Rib of Beef
Tin or plaster model of rib of beef in glass case, wooden frame, 34 x 30cm.
Viscount Coke, DL and Trustees of the Holkham Estate

68

Narrative of proceeding regarding the erection of the Leicester monument
Book published by Bacon & Co., Mercury Office, Norwich
Viscount Coke, DL and Trustees of the Holkham Estate

69

Bound Volume of Plans of the Leicester monument
Viscount Coke, DL and Trustees of the Holkham Estate

70

Document: Letter from Arthur Young at Holkham, 1803
24.5 x 20.5cm.
Unit of Agricultural Economics, Oxford

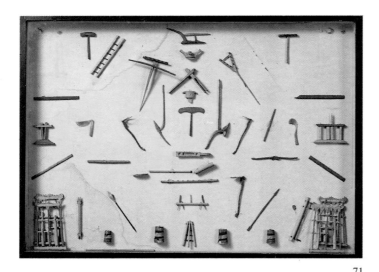

71

71

Models of Tools and Weapons
Viscount Coke, DL and Trustees of the Holkham Estate

Presented by a worker on the Holkham Estate. A conjunction of tools and weapons which brings to mind Isaiah 2:4.

> "They shall beat their swords into plowshares, and their spears into pruning-hooks: nation shall not lift up sword against nation, neither shall they learn war anymore."

72

Painting on Glass: "Agriculture Weeping over the Monument of His Grace the Late Duke of Bedford", c. 1802
37 x 27cm.
Hon. Guy Strutt

His Grace the Duke of Bedford, born August 11th, 1765, Died March 2nd 1802. When Francis Russell, Fifth Duke of Bedford died at the age of 36 his fame was so great that £3,000 was raised for a Statue to be put up in Russell Square, London. The Prince of Wales led the contributions giving 100 guineas. The statue, by Richard Westmacott, showed the Duke with one hand on a plough and the other holding Ears of Corn.

The Russell family have a long connection with agriculture. Francis, third Earl of Bedford, was instrumental in the making of the Great Bedford Level, which permitted the draining of 120,000 acres of the worst land in Cambridgeshire.

When the Fifth Duke succeeded to the title at the age of five, farming in Bedforshire was primitive. Two-thirds of the county was in common field and one-third of arable land was left fallow. The land badly needed draining to improve yields.

He established a model farm at Woburn and agricultural experiments in arable farming were conducted under the supervision of a superintendent. A botanical garden was established and a laboratory opened in order to combine field trials and scientific research.

Undoubtedly the most memorable achievement of the Fifth Duke was the establishment of the 'Woburn Sheepshearing'. When shearing time came round he opened Woburn to all who were interested to attend a week of talks and demonstrations. Competitions were held, prizes awarded to livestock, wool was sold. It was for these events that Francis Russell became known as 'The Farming Duke'.

The sheepshearings were maintained under the Sixth Duke, one of which, the 1811 event, was recorded by George Garrard, in the painting which still hangs at Woburn.

His descendant, the Ninth Duke, continued the tradition of agricultural responsibility, donating substantial funds to assist Lawes and Voelker in their early experiments (c.f. Rothamsted Experimental Station).

67

AGRICULTURE.

Weeping over the Monument of his Grace the late Duke of Bedford.

73
Woburn Sheepshearing
GEORGE GARRARD
Hand-tinted engraving, 73 x 96.6cm.
By kind permission of the Marquess of Tavistock and the
Trustees of the Bedford Estates, Woburn Abbey.
Original painting by Garrard not in the exhibition

"A DESCRIPTION OF THE PICTURE OF THE WOBURN SHEEP-SHEARING.
To the Editor of the Agricultural Magazine.
[*Agr. Mag. vol. VIII. n.s. (No. XLIV) February, 1811*, pp. 87-90]

SIR,

The art of Agriculture and the Fine Arts, having become united in perhaps the most elegant performance of the kind that has ever appeared to the public eye, in Mr. Garrard's beautiful painting of the Woburn Sheep-shearing; and Mr. Garrard having just completed a copper-plate of it, the prints of which are now ready for delivery, I presume it will be gratifying to most of your readers to see a description of this master-piece as represented by Mr. Garrard in his Prospectus, which is as follows.
                                                                                          A CONSTANT READER

In attempting a subject of this kind, comprehending upwards of two hundred figures, and near one hundred domestic animals of various kinds, it is needless to point out to those acquainted with the art, the extreme difficulty of arranging such a multiplicity of objects, with due attention to those principles by which alone a good picture can be designed. To give a just expression to every part of the work, the Artist has to mark the various periods of life, from delighted infancy to joyous age limping on crutches to behold the festive scene.—He has to attempt the air of the most exalted; to touch the native simplicity of the rustic, and to labour through all the intermediate characters in society.—He has to range over all the classes of domestic animals, to select examples, and is expected to dispose of them among his groups and figures so as to illustrate the subject; and in addition to which, his buildings, ground, and sky, must unite to give place and situation to the whole. To combine so many ideas with any tolerable degree of success, he must call to his aid, a large circle of the Sciences; and after all his efforts, he must implore the liberal eye of the public.
The subject is represented in the Woburn Park Farm-yard; point of sight from upper window in the farm-house; the great barns and ox stalls on the right; the exhibition-room on the left; and the range of stables and chaffmill in front; taking nearly the whole area of the farm yard.
The picture is divided into five parts or columns, beginning on the right, with the portraits of the great leaders of agricultural enquiry.
—*Arthur Young,* Esq. with a note book in his hand, is seen in conversation with *Sir John Sinclair* (President of the Board of Agriculture), *Sir Joseph Banks,* K.B. and *T. W. Coke,* Esq. M.P. Sir Joseph is resting on a table, on which are placed pieces of cloth, bags of samples, &c. Mr. Hill and Mr. Overman of Norfolk, behind Mr. Coke; *Mr. Davey,* Professor of Chymistry, behind Sir Joseph; and Colonel Beaumont and Mr. Praed, on the left. Lord William and Lord John Russell, the Duke of Bedford's sons (painted 1804) crossing the temporary sheepfold; two sheep-shearers in the fore-ground, are employed in presence of the gentleman, to decide, as may be supposed, some question respecting the fleece.
The group is extended on the right to the extremity of the picture by Mr. Waters and Mr. G. Baker, who is partly out of the piece. Sir George Osborne, Mr. Pickford, and Sir John Sebright, form a group behind Sir Joseph, and are relieved by a group of sheep and cattle with farmers handling and inspecting them. The celebrated Durham ox justly called the wonderful ox, is distinctly exhibited in front of the ox-stalls, under the door of which stands the Duke of Bedfords' beautiful Highland bull. The chaffmill and piggery, and the group of trees on the left relieve this compartment of the picture. Mr. Leicester, the implement maker, is conversing with

Mr. Salmon, resident surveyor of Woburn Park. In the distance the fat pigs are brought out, and the farming implements for inspection. The fat Devon heifer, so much admired by the late Duke of Bedford, and which obtained a prize at Smithfield, 1802, is shewn opposite to the Durham ox; and the portraits of *Mr. W. Parsons* and other distinguished breeders are given. The portraits of the late Mr. Reynelle, of Ireland; *Mr. Oakley,* the wool stapler; Mr. Moore of Apsley; the Rev. Mr. Hutton, and several other gentlemen will be found in this compartment. *Mr. Whitbread* speaking to Mr. Adam, by the trees on the left, completes the description of this part of the subject.

The second part is composed of a group of sheep in the fore-ground of different kinds, inclosed in a temporary fence for shearing, some farmers handling them; above which is seen the Oakley Herefordshire bull, allowed to be the handsomest that has been produced; *Mr. Westcar,* Mr. Crook, Mr. Lechmere, Mr. Wakefield, *Mr. Isted,* inspecting this animal. The Woburn ox-feeder stands at the head of the bull talking to Mr. Westcar's herdsman, who fed all the beautiful oxen that have been sent from Creslow, and which have obtained so many prizes. Above which is a group of different kinds of neat stock, yokes of oxen and groups of figures and horses relieved by the buildings; amongst which are the portraits of Lord Ossory, Mr. Plat, the late Mr. Holland the architect, &c.

To pay proper attention to the woollen staple of the country, the third column or centre of the picture is composed of his Grace the Duke of Bedford, mounted on his favourite Irish mare, receiving a specimen of broad cloth from *Mr. Tollet,* manufactured from wool of the Merino breed of sheep of his own growth. *Lord Somerville,* Mr. G. C. Gray, Mr. Curwen, compose the principal group of the picture, which is relieved by a numerous group of Noblemen and Gentlemen in conversation, and inspecting a pair of Scotch oxen. Mr. Astley, *Mr. Western,* Lord William Russell, Mr. Sitwell, *Lord Sheffield* and Mr. Farey, the Surveyor, Sir Charles Bunbury, Lord Carrington, *Lord Charles Somerset,* Lord Talbot, Mr. Marshall the Agriculturalist, Duke of Manchester, Lord Bridgewater, Mr. Hugh Hoare, Sir Thomas Carr, Alderman Curtis, Mr. R. Lee, &c. Carriages and horses in the background, relieved by the stables and clock house; and to the right of the principal group Lord Egremont conversing with Major Battine and Sir Harry Fetherstone, relieved by a group composed of a Suffolk horse, inspected by farmers The late Godfrey Thornton, J. Higgins and Lee Antony Esqrs. complete this column of the picture.

The fourth column, beginning at the fore-ground, is composed of a shepherd exhibiting a new Leicester tup, inspected by farmers, Mr. Runciman, Mr. Buckley, Mr. Stone, *Mr. Walton,* and Mr. Wilson, the Duke's bailiff. Just over this group are the portraits of Lord Winchelsea, Mr. W. W. Wynne, and also the portraits of his Royal Highness the Duke of Clarence and *Mr. Ellman.* The exhibition rooms in which the sheep are usually shewn (the front room of which is decorated with two large pictures of the South-down and new Leicester sheep painted by Mr. Garrard), forms a background to these two compartments of the picture: under the shade of which Mr. Northey on horseback is conversing with some gentlemen: crowds of persons are passing in and out of the exhibition room, where Mr. Smith of Wales may be seen above the rest claiming considerable attention. A small group to the left, *Mr. Wilbraham,* Lord Darnley, Mr. Stanley, and Gentleman from Russia, &c.

In the fifth and last column of the picture, is given a portrait of Holland, the chief shepherd, resting on his crook; his watchful dog is stretched reposing under the sheepfold; young Holland is leading out a South-down tup for inspection; the Marquis of Tavistock (painted in 1804), Lord Ludlow, and the Right Hon. Mr. Foster; on the right, *Mr. Honeyborn,* nephew and successor to the late celebrated Mr. Bakewell; Mr. Reeves, tenant to Mr. Cooke, Mr. H. Hammer, Mr. Stubbins, &c. relieved by a group in the background of horses and figures; Mr. Smith, the drainer, *Mr. T. Ellman,* Sir T, Hammer, *Dr. Cartwright,* &c.

The front corner of the picture is occupied by a small table on which are placed books and prints upon agriculture and models of cattle; an artist is seated at the table distributing models to the younger branches of the Duke's family; Lord Rio has a medallion of the late Duke under his arm, and his attention is caught by a model of a sheep that his brother Lord Edward has just received. The *artist* is occupied in presenting the model of a lamb to Lord Charles, the duke's infant son. Under the table are models of implements, port-folios and rolls of prints; in front a medallion inscribed

JOHANNES ET GEORGIANA, BEDFORDIA DEUX ET DUCISSA

M.DCCC.III''

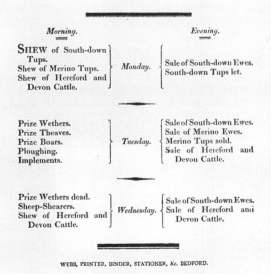

74

74
Schedule for Woburn Sheepshearing 1812
Beamish Museum.

75

LONDON MARKET.

76a

75
Self Portrait, Sketching a Bust
GEORGE GARRARD, A.R.A.
Oil on canvas, 90 x 69.8cm.
Private Collection.

76a
Butcher's Shop, 1822
JAMES POLLARD
Engraved by M. Dubourg, coloured aquatint, 22.5 x 30cm.
The Guildhall Library, City of London

Decorated with sprigs of Holly, various cuts of mutton and beef.
The notice on the carcase on the left on the print reads "Duke
of Bedford. Grass Fed", and refers to the origins of the creature.
Another notice "1st Prize" on a side of beef suggests that some
of the meat derived from a recent Show, possibly at Smithfield.

76b
Model Butcher's Shop, Early 19th Century
London Toy Model Museum

77
**Correspondence from George Garrard to 5th Duke of Bedford,
1801, including details on work carried out on various models
of livestock.**
22 x 37cm.
By kind permission of The Marquess of Tavistock and the
Trustees of the Bedford Estates, Woburn Abbey.

78
Description of the different varieties of oxen, common in the
British Isles embellished with engravings; being an
accompaniment to a Set of Models of the Improved Breeds
executed by George Garrard, upon an exact Scale from Nature
under the Patronage of the Board of Agricultures.
41.5 x 53cm.
Private Collection

Garrard's Introduction, 1800:

"It has always been the practice of polished nations to unite the
elegant with the useful, and the polite with the necessary arts, which
these serve mutually to illustrate and assist each other, and render
employment at the same time and upon the same subject, for the
man of genius and the man of labour; at once contributing to our
pleasure and necessities: producing rational amusement for the mind
and yielding healthy exercise for the body. And by interesting
different classes of people in the same pursuit, tho' in different ways,
additional energy and importance are given to the various

56

occupations in life. The Board of Agriculture having patronized several attempts at delineating the Live Stock of different countries by Painting and Engraving, and it having occured to the Author of this work, that a Picture (although it gives the most lively idea of colour, and general effect) rather exhibits a section or contour of the animal, than its real image, as ideas of thickness cannot thus be adequately converged with those of length and height, he was therefore induced to make proposals for executing Models of the Improved Breeds of British Cattle, in which exact proportion in every point, should be accurately preserved. His plan was submitted to the Board of Agriculture, and had the honor of meeting with considerable encouragement, being referred by a Committee of that Board to the Duke of Bedford, and the Earl of Egremont.

Models were in consequence prepared from the best specimens that could be procured under the inspection of those noblemen, and being examined at a Committee of the Board of Agriculture, were much approved.

With such additional encouragement, and being desirous to obtain for works of this nature, a degree of estimation hitherto unknown in this country, he petitioned the legislature, and succeeded in procuring of the patronage of an Act of Parliament to secure the Copy-Right of all new Models in Sculpture, as well as for the general benefit of the Art, as to appropriate to himself the right of disposing of casts from his own Models upon the success of this undertaking, Mr. Garrard had the honour to receive the congratulations and thanks of the Royal Academy.

These works are not intended merely as matters of curiosity, they exhibit, at once, the ideas of the best judges of the times, respecting the most improved shape in the different kinds of Live Stock-Ideas which have seldom been obtained without great expence and the practice of many years. It is presumed that, by applying to works of this kind, the difficulty of acquiring a just knowledge upon the subject may be considerably removed; and also, that distant countries, where they may be sent, will be enabled to form very perfect ideas of the high state of cultivation in which the domestic animals are produced at this day in Great Britain; and should further progress be made, these models will show what has already been done, and may be a sort of standard whereby to measure the improvements of future times.''

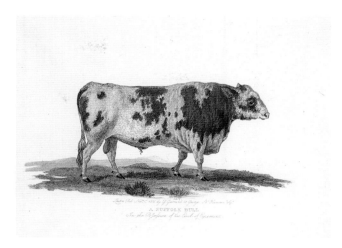

80
English Cattle: Suffolk Bull, 1805
G. GARRARD
Coloured engraving, 50 x 60cm.
Unit of Agricultural Economics, Oxford

81
English Cattle: Suffolk Ox, 1805
G. GARRARD
Coloured engraving, 50 x 60cm.
Unit of Agricultural Economics, Oxford

79
English Cattle: 1805 Buffalow Cow (Series of 28)
G. GARRARD
Coloured engraving, 50 x 60cm.
Unit of Agricultural Economics, Oxford

82
English Cattle: Improved Long Horned or New Leicester Bull,
1800
G. GARRARD
Coloured engraving, 50 x 60cm.
Unit of Agricultural Economics, Oxford

83

83
Teeswater Fat Ox, 1803
GEORGE GARRARD
60 x 45cm
The Duke of Buccleuch and Queensberry, K.T.

The visit of the Colling brothers, breeders of Teeswater cattle, to Dishley Grange, Leicestershire, home of Robert Bakewell marked a significant point in the development of Shorthorns. Following their visit in 1783, and after some time spent studying Bakewell's theory and practice of inbreeding, Charles Colling who lived at Ketton Hall bought a cow, the Stanwick Duchess, which gave rise to the family of that name and whose descendants became central figures in the great period of speculation in cattle breeding. Teeswater cattle, so called because they were bred in the Valley of the Tees were short-horned, large-framed, high yielding cattle and were also referred to as Durham, Holderness or Yorkshire cattle. The modern Shorthorn, Dairy or Beef, has its origins in the farms of the brothers Colling, one at Ketton, the other at Barmpton.

84a
Various Cattle, 1800
GEORGE GARRARD
Plaster on wire frame
Private Collection

84b
Group of Cattle including: Sussex Ox, Sussex Bull, Sussex Cow, Two Sheep, 1800
GEORGE GARRARD
Plaster on wire frame, 40 x 40 x 98cm.
The Burghley House Collection

Sussex cattle were once a purely draught breed. Yoked Sussex Oxen could be seen up to the end of the 19th Century.
Closely related to the Devon, belonging to the group of old red British breeds, the Sussex is derived from the red, medium horned cattle known to have existed in the South-East of England for at least 300 years.
The Sussex Cattle Society was formed in 1874 and the first volume of the Herd Book was published in 1879.

84a

85
Tithe-Table
60 x 90cm.
Private Collection

As this table suggests the practical interpretation of a tithe was often determined by local custom. A tithe was the tenth part of agricultural or other produce (personal income, or profits) contributed either voluntarily or as a tax for the support of the church or clergy or for charitable purposes.

The question of tithes was an important one during the time of Enclosure. In 1781 The Bishop of St. David's moved to recommit an Enclosure Bill on the ground that, like many other Enclosure Bills, it provided for the commutation of tithes. He, and many others wished to establish whether the Church stood to gain or to lose by taking land instead of tithe.

Before the Speenhamland system, before the various Poor Laws, in the early days all Church property was regarded as the patrimony of the poor and the clergy instructed to use it *non quasi suis sed quasi commendatis*. Dryden writing of the character of the Good Parson described their obligations:

"true priests, he said, and preachers of the Lord were only stewards of their sovereign Lord: Nothing was theirs but all the public store, Intrusted riches to relieve the poor."

An Act from the reign of Henry IV (15. Rich. II c.6) confirmed an earlier Act, that money from the fruits and profits of any parish church, was to be paid yearly to the poor parishioners. Following the French Revolution land-owners and tithe-owners were keenly aware of the need to dispose of surplus profits in a way which would minimise social discontent. In 1792 the French Convention tithes were abolished in one stroke. The Speenhamland system proved an admirable means by which to subdue the poor, sapping their spirit and undermining their independence. Arthur Young was among critics of the Poor Law but it endured for forty years.

85

86
The Tythe Pig
Stoke-on-Trent City Museum & Art Gallery

A humorous interpretation of the tithe: the tenth child being brought to the tithe-holder. Some 19th Century pottery is inscribed with the following verse:

"In a country village lives a vicar
Fond as all are of tythes and Liquer,
To mirth his ears are seldom shut
he'll crack a joke and laugh at smut.
But when his tythes he gathers in
True Parson then, no coin no grin
On fish on flesh on birds and beast
Alike lays hold the churlish priest
Hal's wife and sow as Gossips tell
Both at a time in pieces fell
The parson comes the Pig he claims
And the good wife with taunts inflames
But she quite arch bow'd low and smil'd
Kept back the pig and held out the child
The Priest look'd gruff the wife look'd big
Z . . . ds Sir quoth she No Child no Pig."

An earthenware figure group, decorated with enamel colours. made in Staffordshire between 1815 and 1825.

87
'The Throckmorton Coat'
PAINTER UNKNOWN. LITHOGRAPHER J. W. GILES, published c. 1835
Coloured lithograph, 72 x 48cm.
Private Collection

An extraordinary event took place on 25th June, 1811. As the result of a wager of 1,000 guineas, a coat was made from wool sheared, processed and tailored in the space of one day. Sir John Throckmorton offered the wages to John Coxeter an enterprising and prosperous cloth manufacturer of Greenham Mills, Newbury.

. . . continued overleaf

86

Coxeter commissioned an artist from Newbury, Luke Clint, to commemorate the event with a large historical oil painting. The Royal Agricultural Society of England awarded Coxeter a medal of congratulation.

> "On the day above stated at 5 o'clock in the Morning Sir John Throckmorton presented 2 South down Sheep to Mr. Coxeter of Greenham Mills near Newbury Berkshire. The Sheep were immediately shorn, the Wool sorted and spun, the Yarn spool'd, warp'd, loom'd & wove. The Cloth burr'd, mill'd, row'd, dy'd dry'd, shear'd and pressed. The Cloth having been thus made in 11 hours was put into the Hands of the Tailors at 4 o'Clock in the afternoon who completed the Coat at 20 minutes past 6. Mr. Coxeter then presented the Coat to Sir John Throckmorton who appeared with it the same Evening at the Pelican Inn Speenhamland. The Cloth was a hunting Kersey of the admired dark Wellington Colour: The Sheep were roasted whole & distributed to the Public with 120 Gallons of Strong Beer; It was supposed that upwards of 5000 people were assembled to witness this Singular and unprecedented performance, which was completed in the space of 13 hours and 20 minutes. Sir John and about 40 Gentlemen sat down to a dinner, provided by Mr. Coxeter and spent the Evening with the utmost satisfaction at the success of their undertaking."

88

Piece of the Throckmorton Coat Cloth, 1811
Collection John Gall and Rosy Allan

The paper to which the cloth is attached notes that ten tailors were employed and Sir John Throckmorton wore the coat at an agricultural meeting.

89

89

Portrait of Ebenezer Elliot (1781-1849), c. 1840
ARTIST UNKNOWN
Oil on canvas, 91 x 71cm.
Rotherham Museum

Ebenezer Elliot, 'the Anti-Corn Law Rhymer' was born on March 17th, 1781 at the New Foundry, Rotherham. The son

of an iron-founder of distinctly Radical tendencies. Influenced by the poet Robert Southey (1774-1843) who knew of Elliot's work. Elliot produced 'horror' poems suited to the task of Romantic literature. He also encountered of George Crabbe (1754-1832) and embarked on a second phase during which he wrote *The Village Patriarch, The Splendid Village* and *The Ranter.* In the last work a character named Miles Gordon, a field preacher denounces with passion the inequalities of the social system, oppressive taxes. In this volume, poetry and politics became one and indivisible.

The Bread Tax had become a vital political issue and it was the poor who suffered most. Mothers made bran dumplings for their children and scrabbled in kitchen middens for potato peelings. Men turned to pig food and horse beans.

"On a wage of 8s bread was reckoned at three half pence per mouthful!" Elliot's response came with his 'Corn Law Rhymes'.

> "Child is thy father dead?
> Father is gone!
> Why did they tax his bread?
> God's will be done!

and

> Doctor said was best—
> Food we had none;
> Father with panting breast
> Groaned to be gone;
>
> Now he is with the blest
> Mother says death is best!
> We have no place of rest—
> Yes, ye have one!"

The book appeared in 1831 and immediately attracted attention. Elliot threw himself into the political movement, forming an Anti-Corn Law Society in Sheffield in 1834, supporting one in London in 1836.

90

'The Pictorial Anti-Corn Law Almanac', 1845
28 x 40cm.
Hampshire County Museum Service

In 1804 laws were introduced to protect foreign competition by the imposition of a heavy duty on foreign corn. They were repealed in 1846. The Anti-Corn Law League was an organisation founded in 1839 by Richard Cobden and John Bright, to oppose the laws.

The 1815 law gave farmers increased protection by prohibiting the import of corn from abroad until the price at home had reached the high level of 80 shillings a quarter. This law was a reflection of the predominance of landed and agricultural interests following the end of the Napoleonic wars.

Another infamous law, passed in 1815, made it illegal for anyone who was not a squire or a squire's eldest son to kill game, and for anyone to buy and sell game. These were the Game Laws. In 1816 they were supplemented; a cottager caught with his snares at night, trapping a rabbit or hare, could be transported for seven years. Pheasant preserves could be protected with spring guns and man traps, a practice upheld by law until 1827.

91

An essay on Political economy: fluctuations of the price of corn.
J, DEBRETT (?) 1791, published by G. B. Whittaker 1828
The Royal Institution, London

"An essay on political economy; showing in what way fluctuations in the price of corn may be prevented, and the means by which all the advantages of a free trade in corn may be attained . . . ".

92

An Impartial Looker On:
Exposition of the real causes, and effective remedies of the agricultural distress.
SHERWOOD ETC. London 1822
The Royal Institution, London.

93
Count Rumford's Saucepan

A flat bottomed saucepan designed to be placed in a cooking range to ensure maximum spread of heat in contrast to previous types of cooking utensils made to be suspended over open fires. The Royal Institution, London.

94
'The Comfort's of the Rumford Stove'
GILRAY
Hand coloured engraving, 20 x 26.5cm.
The Royal Institution, London

Depicts Count Rumford, R.I., with his back to a fireplace in a domestic interior. The references is to Rumford's pioneering work on improved flues for fireplaces and cooking ranges. The mantelpiece over the fireplace includes a pressure cooker and a small saucepan or cooker.

95
Rogues in Grain, c. 1820
WOODWARD
34 x 25cm.
Unit of Agricultural Economics, Oxford

A comment on the practice of withholding corn from sale until the market price reached its apparent highest point.

96
Moloch Factory Tract, c. 1846 (post Repeal of Corn Laws)
Ink and watercolour on paper (?), 27 x 38cm.
Unit of Agricultural Economics, Oxford

The beginnings of the Industrial Revolution. A scene at the Moloch Factory. Moloch was an Old Testament deity to whom parents sacrificed their children. From the impoverished

... *continues overleaf*

95

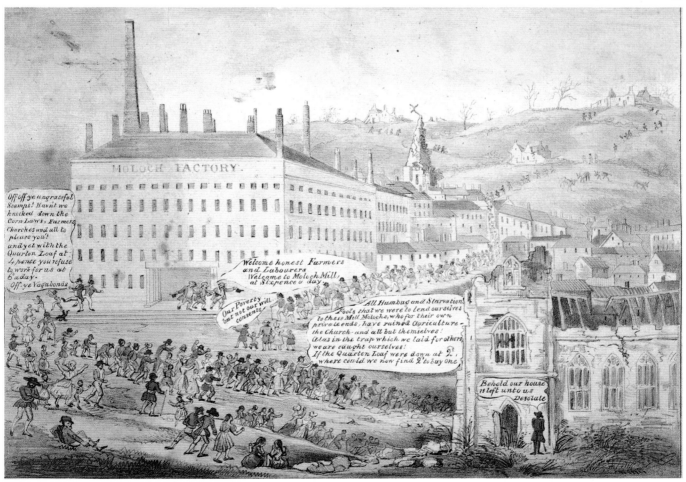

96

countryside, scattered with derelict dwellings and starving cattle comes a constant stream of men, women and children. Greeted by the Moloch Factory Owners:

"Welcome honest Farmers and Labourers, Welcome to Moloch Mill at sixpence a day." The new workers announce "Our Poverty but not our will consents."

On the far side of the steps another stream is booted out "Off, Off, ye ungrateful scamps! Haven't we knocked down the Corn Laws, Farmers, Churches, and all to please you? and yet with the Quartern Loaf at 4 pence you refuse to work for us at 6d a day—off ye vagabonds"

The new unemployed 'vagrants' leave the scene with the bitter cry "All Humbug and Starvation! Fools that we were to lend ourselves to these Mill Molochs, who for their own private ends, have ruined agriculture, the Church and all but themselves! Alas in the trap which we laid for others we are caught ourselves! If the Quartern loaf were down at 2d where could we now find 2d to buy one."

The final comment comes from a shadowy figure standing before a derelict church "Behold our house is left desolate".

There is evidence that many of the individuals who went into industry at the very beginning of the Industrial Revolution themselves depended partly on agricultural work. One Aaron Walker in 1741 made nails and mowed and sheared to help provide income as he was setting up his Foundry with his brother in Sheffield.

97

West Front of Malmesbury Abbey used for Agricultural Purposes, 1780
Engraving by W. Byrne and S. Middiman of Thomas Hearne drawing, 20 x 25cm.
Athelstan Museum, Malmesbury (North Wiltshire District Council)

A short verse accompanies the engraving:

"O it pities us to see these antique towers and hallow'd walls
Split with winter's Frost, or mouldring down,
their very Ruins ruin'd; The crushed Pavement
TIME's marble register, deep overgrown
with Hemlock or rank Fumatory,
hides together with their perishable mold
the brave man's Trophies and the good man's praise
envying the worth of buried ancestry."

98

'The Generae of Patriotism' or **'The Bloomsbury Farmer Planting Bedfordshire Wheat',** 1796
H. HUMPHREY
Hand-coloured engraving, 24 x 34cm.
Hampshire County Museum Service

This probably refers to the Duke of Bedford.

99
'Reaping', c. 1820
Hand-coloured engraving, 18 x 29cm.
Hampshire County Museum Service.

100
'Digging and Delving', 1806
Hand-coloured engraving, 28 x 40cm.
Hampshire County Museum Service.

101
'The Hero of the Chase', 1819 May
Engraving
Hampshire County Museum Service.

102
'The Farmers Toast', c. 1807-9
Hand-coloured engraving, 19 x 23.5cm.
Hampshire County Museum Service.

102

103
'Husbandmen', 1807
J. A. ATKINSON
Hand-tinted aquatint, 28 x 40cm.
Hampshire County Museum Service.

103

To sit on rocks, to muse o'er flood and fell,
To slowly trace the forest's shady scene,
Where things that own not man's dominion dwell,
And mortal foot hath ne'er, or rarely been;
To climb the trackless mountain all unseen,
With the wild flock that never needs a fold;
Alone o'er steeps and foaming falls to learn;
This is not solitude; 'tis but to hold
Converse with Nature's charms, and view her stores unroll'd.
Lord Byron, Childe Harold (1812)

104

104
'Pastoral' (Shepherd, Where is your *pipe?*), 1829
WILLIAM HEATH
Hand-coloured engraving, 40 x 56cm.
Hampshire County Museum Service

A Satirical observation on the middle-class idealisation of rural existences. The woman dressed in an 'imagined' Shepherdess's outfit encounters a 'real' Shepherd, impoverished and rough. A man far removed from the concept of the pastoral doubtless contained in the book carried by the woman.

105
'Blossom'
STEPHEN JENNER (1796-1881)
Oil on canvas, 42 x 56cm.
Jenner Museum, Berkley, Gloucestershire .

'Blossom' was the cow who infected Sarah Nelmes with
Cowpox. Dr. Edward Jenner (1749-1823) vaccinated James
Phipps against Smallpox with Cowpox taken from Sarah
Nelmes. This was the world's first vaccination and took place
in 1796. Also illustrated is Blossom's hide which is kept at St.
George's Hospital Medical School, University of London.
The patchiness of the hide occurred through loss of hair.
The horns are not original

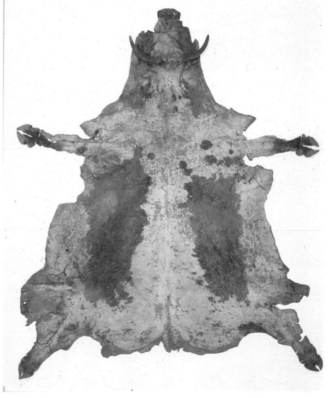

105b

106
Weather Vane: Ploughman
GEORGIAN
Beamish Museum

The weather, so important to agriculture, has very few early volumes dedicated uniquely to its analysis or prediction. A curious work, The Shepherd of Banbury's Rules, was published in 1827, written by John Claridge, Shepherd.
He writes:

> "There are a sort of half wise people who . . . can see no connection between a Cat washing her face, and the sky's being overcast with clouds, and therefore they boldly pronounce that one has no relation to the other . . . But a man of a larger compass of knowledge, who is acquainted with the Nature and Qualities of the Air, and knows what effect any Alterations in the Weight, the Dryness, or the Humidity of it has upon all Animal Bodies, easily perceives the reason why other animals are much sooner sensible of any alterations that happen in that Element than Men, and therefore to him the cawing of Ravens, the chattering of Swallows, and a Cat washing her face are not superstitious signs, but natural tokens of a Change of Weather, and as such they have been thought Worthy of Notice by Aristotle, Virgil, Pliny and all the wisest and gravest writers of Antiquity."

He recorded verses:

> "A red Evening and a grey Morning
> Sets the Pilgrim a Walking"

and

> "In the Decay of the Moon,
> A cloudy Morning bodes a fair Afternoon"

and described the pattern of winds:

> "When the Wind turns to North East, and it continues two Days without Rain, and does not turn to the South the third day, nor Rain the third day, it is likely to continue North East for eight or nine Days, all fair; and then come to the South again."

106

107

107
86 Oxen Hauling Windmill, 1797
ARTIST UNKNOWN
Watercolour
Royal Pavilion Art Gallery and Museums, Brighton (Preston Manor)

The inscription reads:

> "This mill was drawn on the 28th March 1797 from Regency Square to Ye Duke Road, Brighton, a distance of over two miles by 86 oxen which belonged to the following gentlemen:
> William Stanford Esqr. of Preston
> Mr. Hodson
> Mr. Hamshare
> Mr. Scrase   the expedition was commanded by Tos. Hodson
> Mr. Trill
> Mr. Hall

The portly figure to the left of the man in a white smock is identified with an inscription as Mr. Stanford.

108

Mahogany Meat Safe, c. 1800

76 x 38 x 44cm.

N. G. G. Wadham, Esq.

A mahogany meat safe and cool cupboard, zinc lined with ice slide below.

108

109

Collection of Bank notes: including Vignette engravings:
Halifax bank notes: Piece Hall Cloth Exchange
Godalming bank
Wivelscombe bank
Chepstow old bank etc.
Black Ox bank

Courtesy Archivist Lloyds Bank plc

The Halifax bank notes illustrate The Piece Hall Cloth Exchange in Halifax, possibly based on Burgess's engraving in Jacob's 'History of Halifax'. This magnificent building dating from 1779 was saved from demolition in 1972 by one council vote. A quadrangular, colonnaded building, it served, in the days before the mills, as a cloth trading market for the cottage industries of the surrounding Pennine hills and valleys. Each door opening onto the colonnades originally led to a small room used for trading 'pieces' of hand woven cloth. There were 315 such rooms. The plan is believed to be by John Hope of Liverpool. For further information on banking and droving c.f. entries on Smithfield market.

109

110

Collection of bank notes including vignette engravings
Midland Bank plc

110

111
Gilded Carved Pig, c. 1840
Great Grimsby Borough Council

The pig probably dates from the first half of the 19th Century, and was one of the emblems used to decorate the shop front of Fletcher's pork butchers shop at 152 Victoria Street. The shop was popularly known as the 'Monkey, Pig and Pie' Shop.

112

Map: the road from Gloucester to Coventry: vignette of Shepherd and Shepherdess

JOHN OGILVY

35 x 46cm.

Private Collection

113

'New Map of the Manour of Rock', 1743

83 x 93cm.

C. J. Bosanquet, Esq.

There were two great enclosure movements; the first were the Tudor enclosures. Prior to this the general system of land management was Open Field Farming. The village of Laxton in Nottingham is the last surviving open field village and a superb map, made by Mark Pierce in 1635 (now in the Bodleian Library, Oxford) records the system and beautifully illustrates the occupations of the land.

The first enclosure movement was connected with sheep as C. S. Orwin has written in *A History of English Farming*:

"By the time of Henry VII, there had begun an enclosure of wastes, grass commons and woodlands on a considerable scale, to facilitate the extension of the Lords' sheep farming; and finally, in a number of places, they and their larger tenants began to make enclosures of arable strips in the big open fields for the same purpose. Contemporary legislation and literature bear witness to the hardships which this exploitation of the wool market was apt to bring to the smaller tenants of the manors . . . others occupying no more than a few strips, or having nothing except the right to turn out stock on a grass common and dependent upon opportunities to sell their labour for the rest of their means of living, found these opportunities getting less and less as more and more ploughland went down to grass." This was a system that affected the great Midland plain in particular; from Berkshire and Gloucestershire to Staffordshire and Nottinghamshire; and Warwickshire, Northamptonshire and Leicestershire were especially affected by Tudor enclosure."

The second great enclosure movement took place between 1760 and 1815 when over 1,800 Acts were passed by Parliament for the enclosure of Open arable fields and meadows. Land was transformed, not only the green fields but also 'waste land', to hedge and ditch enclosure. Arthur Young was amongst those who participated in the crusade against 'waste land'. To Young 'communal village' was an anachronism which perpetuated into the age of enlightenment the methods by which Piers Ploughman had toiled on the manors of John of Gaunt.

Young also pointed out an undesirable effect of enclosures:

"By nineteen out of twenty Enclosure Bills the poor are injured and most grossly."

The break-up of the old system made the move away from subsistence farming possible. The enclosures helped England by aiding greater production of corn and as a result greater wealth, to help survive the economic struggle against Napoleon.

114

Estate Map, Rock, 1870

40 x 48cm.

C. J. Bosanquet, Esq.

115

Drainage Map, Rock, 1845

93 x 120cm.

C. J. Bosanquet, Esq.

The map shows field drains on the Rock Estate, Northumberland in 1845.

116

A Map of the Lordship of Newton-Willows, 1717

67 x 77.5cm.

The Duke of Buccleuch and Queensberry, K.T.

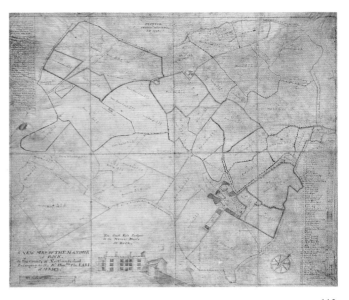

113

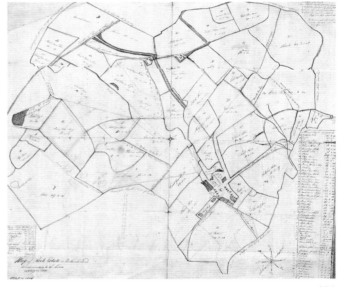

114

117

Map: Batsford Estate, 1748

80.01 x 67.31cm.

Batsford Estates (1983) Co. Ltd.

"Survey of the Upper part of the parish of Battesford belonging to Thomas Edwards Freeman, Esq., surveyed by Henry Gillett."

118

Map: Parish and Manor of Battesford, 1764

81.28 x 215.9cm.

Batsford Estates (1983) Co. Ltd.

"Survey of the Parish and Manor of Battesford in the County of Glocester, coppy'd from a survey of Henry Gillett by Saml. Driver."

119a

Map: Parish of Moreton-in-Marsh, 1821

Ink and watercolour on goatskin(?), 74.3 x 89.54cm.

Batsford Estates (1983) Co. Ltd.

"A map of the Parish of Moreton-in-Marsh in the County of Gloucester."

119b
Estate barn, c.1790
Photograph
M. Hartley

A photograph of a barn at Whernside Manor (formerly West House) in Dentdale. Classed as an estate barn, differing in both plan and detail from the usual dales barn which accommodated only cows and hay. Large doors on both gable ends and front of the barn admitted carriages, a smaller door led into a handsome stable. The cowshed was on the left and behind a very large hay mow.

Above the stable and carriage or coach house are small rooms for harnesses and stores.

The barn was built by Edmund Sill towards the end of the 18th Century. He also built a mansion, Whernside Manor, nearby on the profits from plantations in Jamaica. It is said that slaves helped build the barn but no documentary evidence has yet been found.

The Sill family were not the only family in the Yorkshire dales to own a plantation in the West Indies. Strictly, as a result of Lord Mansfield's ruling in the case of the slave 'Somerset', every slave by the mere fact of landing on English soil became free. Prior to this slaves brought to England were treated as slaves.

120

120

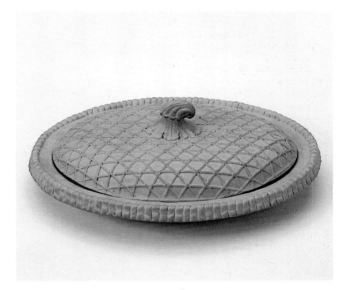

121

120
Cauliflower Series: Plate, Tea jar, Teapot and lid, Coffee pot and lid, c. 1760
City Museum and Art Gallery, Stoke-on-Trent

Earthenware Staffordshire pottery made between 1760 and 1770. Plate moulded with cauliflower curd at edge and leaves at centre, green glaze on leaves, clear glaze on curd. Tea jar moulded in the form of a cauliflower, leaves at base covered in green glaze, curd at top covered in clear glaze. Teapot and lid, as for Tea jar, and also Coffee pot and lid.

121
Pie Crust Ware, c. 1800-06
Impressed TURNER
City Museum and Art Gallery, Stoke-on-Trent

Dish and lid, pie-crust ware, cane-ware body; interior has clear glaze, exterior unglazed. Made by Turner and Co., Lane End, Staffordshire between 1800-1806. Made at a time when flour was in short supply and that which was available was at a prohibitive price: these 'pie' crusts would give the appearance of a pastry top to what was simply a casserole.

122 & 123

124

125

122 and 123
Shepherdess and Shepherd, c. 1790-1800
City Museum and Art Gallery, Stoke-on-Trent

Earthenware Shepherd and Shepherdess decorated with green glaze and high temperature colours. Made in Staffordshire 1790-1800.

124
Goat, kid and lamb, c. 1800-20
City Museum and Art Gallery, Stoke-on-Trent

Figure group of goat, kid and lamb. Earthenware decorated underglaze with high temperature colours. Made between 1800-1820. Origin uncertain, somewhere in Britain.

125
Figure of Cowherd, cow and dog
City Museum and Art Gallery, Stoke-on-Trent

Earthenware figure of cowherd with cow and dog, decorated with high temperature underglaze colours. Made between 1800 and 1820. Origin uncertain, somewhere in Britain.

126

126
Two Cauliflowers on Plate, c. 1780-1800
City Museum and Art Gallery, Stoke-on-Trent

Small (6.5cm. long) plate with two cauliflowers made in earthenware. Make unknown, likely to be of Staffordshire origin. Made between 1780-1800.

127

127
Figure of boy with eggs and a rabbit
City Museum and Art Gallery, Stoke-on-Trent

Figure of boy with rabbit and eggs. Earthenware decorated with enamel colours. Made in Staffordshire between 1815 and 1825.

128
Tankard
City Museum and Art Gallery, Stoke-on-Trent

Earthenware tankard, printed decoration overglaze in black, filled in with enamel colours: "God Speed the Plough". Made by Dixon, Austin and Co., Garrison Pottery, Sunderland, 1820-26.

128

129   131   130

129
Cow creamer with Milkmaid
City Museum and Art Gallery, Stoke-on-Trent

Cow cream jug and lid in earthenware. Milkmaid and milk pail. Decorated in high temperature colours, base green glaze. Impressed mark: Taylor & Co.
Made at the Tyne Pottery, Newcastle-upon-Tyne.

130
Cow Creamer
City Museum and Art Gallery, Stoke-on-Trent.

Earthenware cow cream jug and lid, decorated with red and black dots in enamel colours, green base in enamels. Made in Britain 1800-1830, exact location unknown.

132   397   133

131
Cow Creamer
City Museum and Art Gallery, Stoke-on-Trent

Cow cream jug. Earthenware, decorated underglaze with high temperature colours. Made between 1800-1830 somewhere in Britain.

132
Cow Creamer with Milkmaid
City Museum and Art Gallery, Stoke-on-Trent

Earthenware cow cream jug with milkmaid. Decorated underglaze with black, yellow, green. Made somewhere in Britain between 1800-1830.

133
Cow Creamer with Calf
City Museum and Art Gallery, Stoke-on-Trent

Earthenware cow cream jug and lid with calf. Decorated with high temperature colours. Made somewhere in Britain 1800-1830.

134
Figures of Spring, Summer, Winter
City Museum and Art Gallery, Stoke-on-Trent

Earthenware group of seasons decorated with enamel colours. Attributed to James Neale, Hanley, Staffordshire. Made between 1780-1800.

134

135

138
Hay Makers: Apple Gatherers:
GEORGE SMITH of Chichester
Engravings 1794 (orig. pub John Boydell 1760's)
both 43.5 x 55.5cm.
Pallant House, Chichester

The 'Hay Makers' and 'Apple Gatherers', along with 'Rural Cot' and 'The Merry Villagers', made a set of four paintings by George Smith illustrating The Four Seasons, a subject given greater currency by the popularity of Thomson's poem, 'The Seasons'.

George Smith's early 'genre' paintings of peasants at work owe much to 17th Century Dutch landscape painting. Along with artists like Gainsborough and Lambert, the Smiths both encouraged and serviced a growing taste for rustic scenes, and set the seeds for the Morland, Wheatley tradition which was continued into the 19th Century by artists such as Collins, Shayer and Witherington. Some of George Smith's cottage scenes also strongly influenced the rustic style of architecture, which became popular in the late 18th Century. The Hamlet at Versailles (created 1783-1785) has a number of 'Smith-like' cottages; and Lady Craven's rural cottage built at Fulham around 1780 (now destroyed) also showed a debt to his work.

135
The Lost Sheep
City Museum and Art Gallery, Stoke-on-Trent

The Lost Sheep, an earthenware figure decorated with enamel colours. Made in Staffordshire 1790-1820.

139
Sixteen London Cries, c. 1640
ARTIST UNKNOWN: published 1735 from early 17th Century (c. 1640) plates and sold by W. Herbert at Golden Globe in London Bridge.
Line engraving, 41 x 31cm.
Guildhall Library, City of London

136
Premium Painting: Landscape Pastoral, exhibited 1761
GEORGE SMITH of Chichester
138.5 x 174.8cm.
Cheltenham Art Gallery and Museums

In 1760, eight years before the formation of The Royal Academy, The Society for the Encouragement of the Arts, Manufactures and Commerce held their first exhibition. George Smith of Chichester won the Premium for the best original landscape, a prize of £50—the second prize of £25 went to his brother John. The following year George Smith again won the £50 Premium for this painting, which shows a classical pastoral landscape with what is apparently Chichester cathedral in the far distance. Such works certainly encouraged people to search out Claudian views in the British landscape and had a profound influence on contemporary perceptions of nature. For three years the Smith brothers so dominated the prizes for landscape at The Society for the Encouragement of the Arts that thereafter, according to the rules, they declined to enter.

137
Still Life with Joint of Beef, on a pewter dish 1750
GEORGE SMITH of Chichester
Oil on canvas
70 x 82cm.
Chichester City Council

139

140

141

140

Smithfield Market, 1810
THOMAS ROWLANDSON
Watercolour, 28 x 44cm.
Guildhall Library, City of London

In 1174 William Fitzstephen, a clerk to Thomas à Becket, wrote of 'Smithfield' Market:

> "A smooth field where every Friday there is a celebrated rendezvous of fine horses to be sold, and in another quarter are placed vendibles of the peasant, swine with their deep flanks, and cows and oxen of immense bulk.''

The lanes and roads leading to the market acquired suitable names: Cowcross, Cow Lane, Cock Lane, Chick Lane. By 1394 there were 95 commercial inns in the Smithfield area outside the walls.

By 1725 Londoners were consuming 60,000 cattle, 70,000 sheep and 239,000 pigs. Animals were driven enormous distances. The story of the drovers centres around long and often dangerous journeys from Wales, Scotland, and the West Country.

Drovers carried news as they made their progress to or from London. They were also responsible for the large sums of money from the sale of their charges and also for the creatures on their outward journey. Money had to be carried back through remote and lonely places haunted by thieves of many kinds.

The solution was to devise a safe means of transferring money, and the history of banking is linked with that of droving.

141

Bartholomew Fair, c. 1813
THOMAS ROWLANDSON AND JOHN NIXON
Etching, coloured, 24 x 35cm.
Guildhall Library, City of London

From the reign of Henry II (1133-89) Bartholomew Fair was held for three days during the month of August. Originally a festivity which grew up out of the growing cloth trade in Europe. European merchants would travel to Bartholomew Fair to purchase their supplies of cloth. To the cloth trader various other goods were sold and bear and bull-baiting took place.

The Fair continued and by the late 18th Century side shows had replaced the traders of cloth. Street entertainers and sellers of trifles proliferated.

In 1855 the Fair was closed down. Victorian society was disapproving of the rowdiness and violence fostered by one of the oldest public holidays.

Fresh Gathered Peas Young Hostings LONDON Pois rames Pois Nouveaux ecorés
Plate 7

144

142

Cries of London No. 5: Water Cresses . . ., 1795
THOMAS ROWLANDSON, engraved by H. Merke
Etching with aquatint, coloured, 26.5 x 21cm.
Guildhall Library, City of London

144

Cries of London No. 7: Fresh Gathered Peas . . ., 1795
FRANCIS WHEATLEY, engraved by P. BONATO
25.5 x 19.5cm.
Guildhall Library, City of London

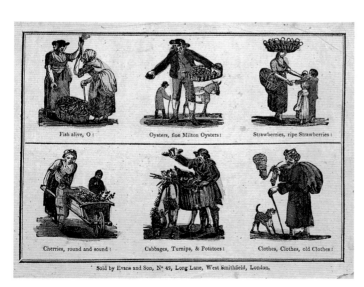

SALE OF A WIFE IN SMITHFIELD MARKET.

143

Street Sellers: Fish, Oysters, Strawberries, Cherries, Cabbages, Clothes, c. 1820
ARTIST UNKNOWN, sold by Evans and Sons
Coloured wood engraving, 15 x 20cm.
Guildhall Library, City of London

145

Sale of a Wife in Smithfield Market, 1797
MATTHIAS FINUCANE, published by Laurie and Whittle, 53 Fleet Street
Line engraving, 20 x 25cm.
Guildhall Library, City of London

A cruel, but popular subject of many prints of the period.

mithfield-Market. (Death of) This Print is Pub.ᵈ in Commemoration of Smithfield-Market, & Dedicated to the Rt.Hon
he Lord Mayor. & Corporation of the City of London. with my best wishes to the inhabitance of Copen-
agen-fields & Islington. — N.B. The nighest Police court Clarkenwell !!!"   J.L.marks Long Lane Smithfield.

146
Death of Smithfield Market, c. 1855
JOHN LEWIS MARKS, publisher
Coloured lithograph, 17.5 x 29cm.
Guildhall Library, City of London

On Monday 11th June, 1855, the last market at Smithfield was
held. Public indignation about the live cattle market had reached
fever-pitch. Charles Dickens wrote many times about the
unbelievable squalor and horror of the place.

Herds of cattle were often ambushed by gangs of thieves who
would cosh the drovers and use the stampeding animals as cover
for their pick-pocketing. This image gives an impression of the
life of the market. A Master Drover, wearing the arm badge
issued by the City Corporation, raises his goad aloft. A
gentleman fends off a bull with his umbrella not aware that his
pocket is being picked. The bull tosses a policeman in the air
and tramples men and women from the Royal Society for the
Prevention of Cruelty to Animals underfoot. In the background
a stretcher carried by policemen bears a body, and a boy is
overcome by stampeding sheep and pigs. Two bulls fight,
ignoring the drover's goad.

At 3.15 p.m. the great bell in the market square signalled the
close of trading. A new market, the Caledonian Cattle market
was opened by Prince Albert on 13th June, 1855.

147

147
The Village Butcher, c. 1791
JOHN CRANCH of Bath (1751-1821)
Oil on panel, 13.8 x 15.6cm.
Royal Albert Memorial Museum, Exeter

148
The Village Baker, c. 1791
JOHN CRANCH of Bath (1751-1821)
Oil on panel, 13.8 x 15.6cm.
Royal Albert Memorial Museum, Exeter

149
Dunster Castle and Yarn Market, c. 1740
NICHOLAS POCOCK (1741-1821)
Watercolour on paper, 49.8 x 71.6cm.
Royal Albert Memorial Museum, Exeter

In the foreground a packhorse and a waggon with bales(?) of
wool. Trading of cloth is carried on in the building on the right.

148

150a
Two a Penny White Heart Cabbages, late 1750's
PAUL SANDBY
Watercolour on paper, 22.5 x 14.6cm.
Nottingham Castle Museum and Art Gallery

150b
Castle Street, Salisbury, looking South, 1829
W. H. BARTLETT
Etching, 15 x 20cm.
The Salisbury and South Wiltshire Museum

151a
"Selling Peas"
GEORGE MORLAND (1762-1804)
Oil on canvas, 69.5 x 90cm.
Private Collection

This picture was engraved by E. Bell and published by T. Ladd
in 1801, together with a companion piece 'Selling Cherries'.
Morland was a master of the rustic genre and at his best he was
unsurpassed. Such was the popularity of his work that the
forging of works by 'Morland' became an acknowledged scandal
by the 19th Century. Along with William Shayer Senior and
Thomas Sidney Cooper, Morland's reputation has suffered
from a staggering number of copies, imitations and fakes.
It is now hard to appreciate that Morland's images of rural life
could sometimes appear disturbing to some of his
contemporaries, who were concerned about the possibility of
the revolution in France occurring in this country. To them
Morland's peasants could often appear to be idle and dissenting.
Prints of Morland's work frequently show the peasants more
contented and happy than they actually appear in the original
painting.

149

151b
Cattle Market, Norwich, 1827
R. F. RICKARDS
Oil on canvas, 89 x 128cm.
J. S. Blomfield, Esq. Collection of 19th Century Country and
Sporting Paintings
Of Market Day, Richard Jefferies wrote in Hodge and his
Masters:

> "In the crush are many ladies who would find their business
> facilitated by coming on a different day. But market-day is a tradition
> with all Classes; even the gentry appear in greater numbers. If you
> go forth into the market-place you will find it thronged with farmers.
> If you go into the Corn Hall or Exchange, where the corn dealers
> have their stands, and where business in cereals and seeds is
> transacted; if you walk across to the auction yard for cattle, or to
> the horse depository, where an auction of horses is proceeding;
> everywhere you have to push your way through groups of
> agriculturalists."

151b

152

154

152
The Farmyard with Cock, 1809
J. M. W. TURNER
29.5 x 43.7cm.
The Royal Academy of Arts, London

Between 1806 and 1819 Turner defended himself against the
charge that his pictures were "of nothing, and very like", by
publishing a series of landscape engravings under the title Liber
Studiorum, which treated the different types of landscape
including this of a farmyard.

153
"The Cottagers", n.d.
GEORGE MORLAND
Oil on canvas, 123 x 145cm.
Private Collection

154
Farmhouse, Ashton, Devon
JOHN WHITE ABBOTT (1763-1851)
Pen, ink and watercolour on paper, 18.1 x 23.1cm.
Royal Albert Memorial Museum, Exeter

The Shepherd of Banbury recorded in 1827 some collected
versus for every month of the year, quoted then as they continue
to be quoted now.

> "Janiver Freeze the Pot by the Fire
> If the Grass grow in Janiveer
> It grows the worse for all the Year.
> The Welchman had rather See his Dam on the Bier
> Than to see a fair Februeer.
> March wind and May Sun
> Make clothes white and Maids Dun.
> When April blows his Horn
> It's good both for Hay and Corn.
> A cold May and a windy
> Makes a full barn and a tindy.
> A Swarm of Bees in May
> Is worth a Load of Hay.
> But a Swarm in July
> Is worth a Fly."

155
Prospect of Worcester from the East, c. 1750
Attributed to JOHN HARRIS, Fl. 1720-1755
Oil on canvas, 94 x 153cm.
Worcester City Museum and Art Gallery

September: a distant panoramic view of Worcester taken from
the grounds of The Red House, with a farmer, reapers and a
sportsman shooting partridge.

The birds rise up from the Corn to be fired at by the man with
a gun, as three reapers cut and stash the crop. The garden gate
is ajar, perhaps left open by the landowner who talks to one
of the reapers. A man and women with their dog pass by, the
woman looking into the garden. This is a panoramic view,
painted as though from the interior of The Red House itself.

Also in the foreground two farm labourers climb onto a hayrick,
one drinking from a vessel, the other reaching out for it. Below
them a sow with litter forages, and a cock and hen pick at the
ground.

The enclosed fields are clearly depicted, several with a haystack
in the corner.

Beyond the City of Worcester which shows the Cathedral, the
Churches of St. Andrew and, to the right, St. Nicholas, the river
Severn flows, an important commercial artery along which boats
may be seen moving.

To the left of the painting is a small, white windmill; perhaps
that destined to mill the grain being harvested.

156
'The Farm Yard', c. 1790
Oil on canvas, 55.5 x 85.5cm.
Private Collection

The farmyard is taken as a way of displaying many of the activities of agriculture. In the foreground cattle, and a milk-maid on her three-legged stool milking the cows. A goat waits nearby and a man, possibly the cowherd accompanied by his dog, leans on a staff. A horse in harness, which will pull the red and blue wagon, is led to the farm pond, to drink by his handler; on the far side of the pond a boy (the farmer's son?) feeds a family of ducks. A woman draws water from a well, another walks towards the farmhouse, a pail in her hand with which she has just filled a trough at which sows and their piglets feed, geese lean out towards the pail and a hen, cock and chicks peck at scraps. A man wheels a barrow of fodder towards the cart. A turkey, hens and chicks peck the ground, behind them a red harrow lies on the ground. A man with a hay rake and harvest barrel surveys the scene. A stray pig moves towards the trough. A plough rests on the ground near the barn, and a seed drill casts long shadows. A man works in a barn, a broken wheel rests against the wall. A huge white goose is pinned to one gable end. Doves rest on the thatched roof close to their cote on the main gable end of the farmhouse, some fly overhead. Smoke comes from the huge chimney. A ladder leans against the roof. A large game cock under a wooden cage is surrounded by drinking birds; children play nearby. A woman spins wool with a spinning wheel and talks to a man. A dog, in front of its kennel looks up to a figure leaning out of a window. Beyond the open gate and wicket fence six men take hay up a ladder and onto the rick. A woman stands at the foot of the ladder and looks towards the farmhouse. A haywain drawn by four horses approaches the rick. Three figures in the field rake the mown hay into stooks. Beyond a detailed landscape; five houses, a windmill, church, water on which ships sail. In total twenty-six people make up the population of the farm. The implements have the appearance of those seen in pattern books. Why is the goose pinned to the wall? It is possible that this painting has its origins in earlier Flemish paintings of farmsteads and that this was an element borrowed directly from Flanders.

157

157
Tail piece vignettes for The History of British Birds, 1797-1804
THOMAS BEWICK 1753-1828
Engraved on box wood
Iain Bain.

158
The Farmyard, c. 1800
Engraving laid on canvas
Collection of John Gall and Rosy Allan

An engraved version of the subject. The farmhouse very close to that of the oil painting, though the word Dairy is shown painted onto a lintel. This may well refer to the tax of windows of dwellings, a dairy being exempt from the tax, this was a wily way of avoiding the payment of tax on the farmhouse. The birds pinned to the wall of the threshing barn are close to the Bewick version, although the barn itself is closer to that of the oil in situation within the yard. There is no white goose pinned to the wall of the farmhouse. Two thatched ricks, also present in the Bewick but not in the oil, are included. A pig with a curious device over its ears follows the woman with a bucket who has just fed the other pigs. A device possibly intended to stop the pig getting through fences and hedges to feed! Sheep are sheared.

159
Harvest Celebration: The Harvest Home, c. 1800
Engraving laid on canvas
Collection of John Gall and Rosy Allan

A similar farmyard where the harvest home celebrations take place. A pennant flies from the new rick, men and women dance beneath a decorative harvest sheaf. A huge pie is brought to the table; a basket overflows with apples and much cider is consumed. A farmer stands, hand outstretched with contentment at a harvest brought safely in. Cf. p. 2.

160
The Howick Red Ox, 1788
J. BAILEY
Coloured line engraving, 55 x 64cm.
Unit of Agricultural Economics, Oxford

An ox of the Teeswater breed.

"The Howick red ox belonging to Sr. Henry Grey Bart. Bred, and fed, at Howick, in the County of Northumberland. Weight: Two forequarters, 82st. 2lb; Hind do., 70st. 7lb; Tallow, 16st. 7lb; Hide, 9st. 2lb. NB 14lb to the stone. Age: Seven years when killed at Newcastle, 28 March 1787 by Mr. Geo. Pearson. Dimensions: Height at the crop, 6′ 0″; Do. loins, 5′ 10″; Do. breast from ground, 1′ 11½″; Breadth at hips, 2′ 10″; Do. at shoulders, 2′ 9″; Length from head to rump, 9′ 4″."

Drawn and engraved by John Bailey. Published 1st February, 1788.

161
The Howick Mottled Ox, 1787
J. BAILEY
Coloured line engraving, 55 x 64cm.
Unit of Agricultural Economics, Oxford

An ox of the Teeswater breed.

> "The Howick motled (sic) ox, belonging to Sr. Henry Grey Bart. Bred and fed at Howick, in the county of Northumberland. Weight: Two forequarters, 80st. 7½lb; Hind do., 72st. 0½lb.; Tallow, 16st.; Hide, 9st. 11lb. NB 14lb to the stone. Age. Seven years when killed at Alnwick 21 March 1787 by Mes Bolton and Embleton. Dimensions: Height at the crops, 5′ 10″; Do. loins, 5′ 9¼″; Do. Breast from ground, 1′ 7″; Breadth at hips, 2′ 11″; Do. at shoulders, 2′ 7″; Length from head to rump 9′ 8″, Girt before shoulders, 9′ 11″; Do. behind do., 9′ 8″; Do. at the belly, 10′ 10″; Do. the loins, 9′ 10″."

Published 1st February 1788. Drawn and engraved by J. Bailey in 1787. John Bailey was born in 1750 at Bowes and died at Chillingham in 1819. He was also the author of "Essay on the construction of the Plough"(1795).

162
"Keeping" Cattle in a Forest, early 19th Century
SCHOOL OF MORLAND
Oil on canvas, 51.5 x 69cm.
J. S. Blomfield Esq. Collection of 19th Century Country and
Sporting Paintings.

163
The Wild Bull, Chillingham, 1789
THOMAS BEWICK
Wood engraving, 19 x 24cm.
Lawes Agricultural Trust. Rothamsted Experimental Station.

The most remarkable of the race of Wild white Cattle, wrote
David Low, were those kept at the ancient park of Chillingham,
the property of the Earl of Tankerville. These appear to have
remained to nearest in character to the original races. The herd
at present amounts to about eighty in number, consisting of
twenty-five bulls, forty cows, and fifteen steers . . . The eye-
lashes and tips of the horns are black, the muzzle is brown, the
inside and a portion of the external part of the ears are reddish
brown, and all the rest of the animal is white. The bulls have
merely the rudiments of manes, consisting of ridge of coarse
hair upon the neck. The bulls fight for supremacy, and the
vanquished submit to the law of superior strength. They are
very shy and wild, and start off on the approach of danger and
when they threaten an attack they make circles around the
object, approaching nearer each time.

164a
An Alderney Bull, c. 1828
JAMES WARD, R.A. (1769-1859)
Oil on canvas, 33 x 44cm.
Private Collection

164b
An Alderney Cow, c. 1828
JAMES WARD, R.A. (1769-1859)
Oil on canvas, 43 x 35cm.
Private Collection

These paintings by James Ward are of Guernsey cattle. Between
1789 and 1802 laws were set up in Guernsey to protect the breed
against adulteration. Guernsey cattle were imported to Britain
during the 18th Century. The English Guernsey Cattle Society
was founded in 1884. The first recorded importation from
Guernsey was in 1819. Ward's painting of the Bull, exhibited
at the Royal Academy in 1828, was of one of the first bulls of
the breed to come to England.

164c
Bulls Fighting, 1788
Painted by GEORGE STUBBS engraved by GEORGE TOWNLEY
STUBBS
Engraving, 60 x 46cm.
Lawes Agricultural Trust. Rothamsted Experimental Station

Inscribed "To Robert Bakewell, Esq. this plate of bulls fighting
is most respectfully inscribed by his most obedt. Sevt. Benjn.
Beale Evans."

165

165
Study of a Cow
THOMAS GAINSBOROUGH, R.A.
Black and white chalk on brown paper, 14 x 18cm. verso & recto
Jersey Museums Service

As early as 1763 importations of cattle from France to the Island
of Jersey were prohibited to protect the purity of the breed.
Prior to the 18th Century Jerseys were exported to England
where they were known as 'French' or 'Alderney' cattle. In
about 1821 Philip Dauncey began the English development of
a Jersey herd, through systematic breeding.

166
The Blackwell Ox, 1780
GEORGE CUIT engraved by J. BAILEY
Coloured line engraving, 50 x 60cm.
Collection of John Gall and Rosy Allan

> "The Blackwell ox (rising 6 years old) bred and fed by Christr. Hill.
> Esq. of Blackwell in the county of Durham. Killed at Darlington
> 17 Dec. 1779 by Mr. Geo: Coates who sold him for £109.11.6
> Weight: Two forequarters 75st. 7lb; Hind do., 76st. 3lbs; Tallow,
> 11st; Total, 162st. 10lb. NB: 14lb to the stone."
> Dimensions: Height at the crop, 6' 0"; Shoulder 5' 9¼"; Loins
> 5' 8"; From breast to ground 2' 1"; Length from horns to rump,
> 9' 5½"; Breadth over the Shoulders, 2' 10¼"; From hip to hip,
> 2' 10½"; Gilt before the shoulder, 9' 7½"; behind do., 10' 6"—
> At the loins, 9' 6¾"."

Geo: Cuit pinxt. Bailey Sculp. Published 27 March 1780. George
Cuit (or Cuitt) (Sen.) was a landscape painter in oils and
watercolours was born in Moulton, Yorkshire in 1743, and died
in Richmond in 1818. He studied in Rome for six years.

167

167
A Calf
JAMES WARD (1769-1859)
Watercolour on paper, 12 x 15cm.
Miss Elizabeth Creak

168

168
"Rosetta", 1830
ENGLISH SCHOOL
Oil on canvas, 61 x 76.5cm.
Iona Antiques

The painting includes a scroll inscribed "Rosetta, bred by Mr. Wright, Humbleton, 1830". The owner did not want the artist's name included in the painting.

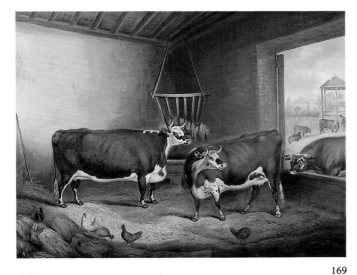

169

169
Two Heifers in a Byre, 1829
T. WEAVER
Oil on canvas, 72 x 91cm.
Iona Antiques

172

170

170
Cattle in Landscape, 1801
ROBERT HILLS
Etching, 25.5 x 33.3cm.
Goldmark Gallery, Rutland

Hills was a student at the Royal Academy School in 1788, who 'found a wiser master in the force of his own inclination, which led him to the study of animal life in the forest, the farmyard and the pasture.' Between 1798 and 1815 he issued etchings of animals of many kinds: 108 of sheep and goats, 200 of oxen, 100 of cattle, 36 of pigs. With Nattes and Shelley, Hills was a founder of the Water-Colour Society and became its first secretary.

171a
Cows and Calves, 1801
ROBERT HILLS
Etching, 10 x 22.8cm.
Goldmark Gallery, Rutland

171b
"Juno" who won the Bakewell Premium and Sweepstakes, c. 1820
J. F. HERRING, SNR.
Oil on canvas, 54 x 74cm.
Reresby Sitwell, Esq.

The painting is inscribed "Juno a Calf 9 months old the Property of and bred by Sr. G. Sitwell Bart which won the Premium and Sweepstakes at Bakewell 1820".

172
The Craven Heifer, early 19th Century
Watercolour on paper, 43 x 60cm.
The Duchess of Devonshire

A watercolour copy of "The Craven Heifer", the famous Shorthorn, standing against a landscape background containing a Gothic ruin. The original painting possibly by either E. Fryer (fl. 1817) or T. Fryer (fl. 1816) both watercolourists. An engraved version carries the inscription.

> "The Craven Heifer. To the most noble William Spencer Duke of Devonshire, this engraving of the Craven Heifer, bred and fed by the Revd. William Carr, of Bolton Abbey, near Skipton in Craven, Yorkshire, is respectfully dedicated by his Graces most obedient humble servant John Watkinson. This wonderful animal was four years old in March 1811, and is still in a growing and improving state. She weighs 30 score 17 pounds per quarter, that is 308st. 4lb, 8 pound to the stone, or 176st. 4lb., 14lb to the stone.
> Dimensions: Length from nose to the rump, 11' 2"; Height at the shoulder, 5' 2"; Breadth over the back in three different places, 3' 3"; Girt of the middle of the body, 10' 2"; Girt over the loin, 9' 11"; Girt of the foreleg below the knee, 7"."

173

Garrick, Son of Shakespear and Broken Horned Beauty
Attributed to JOHN BOULTBEE (1747-1812)
Oil on canvas, 75 x 88cm.
Unit of Agricultural Economics, Oxford.

Robert Fowler of Little Rollwright in Oxfordshire carried on the work of Bakewell at Dishley. With his superb herd of Longhorn cattle he may even be said to have surpassed Bakewell.

The Sire of Garrick 'Shakespear' (174) is the subject of a painting by J. Boultbee at Rothamsted Experimental Station, previously given to H. B. Chalon, cleaning revealed the time band.

Shakespear was calved in 1778, and was Fowler's most famous animal. He was let to Thomas Princep for two seasons at 80 guineas a season. The connection with Bakewell comes from the Sire of Shakespear, 'D' a bull hired from Bakewell to Fowler.

When Garrick was sold at the Rollnight dispersal of 1791 he fetched 205 guineas and was five years old. 'Brindled Beauty' a cow by Shakespear out of 'Long Horn Beauty' fetched 260 guineas.

174

Shakespear
Attributed to JOHN BOULTBEE (1747-1812)
Oil on canvas, 75 x 88cm.
Unit of Agricultural Economics, Oxford

174b

The 5th Lord Berwick's Hereford: Walford 1859
W. H. DAVIS
Oil on canvas, 50.5 x 65cm.
The National Trust

Walford was Lord Berwick's best bull.

174c

The 5th Lord Berwick's Hereford: Cherry
W. H. DAVIS
Oil on canvas, 50.5 x 65cm.
The National Trust

Cherry was the first of Lord Berwick's Herefords.

175

Brindled Beauty
Attributed to JOHN BOULTBEE (1747-1812)
Oil on canvas, 73 x 88cm.
Unit of Agricultural Economics, Oxford

Brindled Beauty made 260 guineas at the dispersal sale of the Rollsight head of longhorns. She was a daughter and sister to Shakespear and was sold to Knowles and Co.

176

Old Nell
Attributed to JOHN BOULTBEE (1747-1812)
Oil on canvas, 75 x 88cm.
Unit of Agricultural Economics, Oxford

'Old Nell', calved c. 1765-70. Substantial space is given over to the Longhorned breed by David Lowe who wrote that:

> "The long-horned breed as it existed before the artificial improvements to which it has been subjected, varied in size with the natural and acquired fertility of the districts in which it had become indigenous, being larger in the richer plains, and smaller in the mountains. The prevailing colour of the animals was black and brown, and they had more or less of white on the body, a streak of that colour always extending along the spine. They had thick dark skins, and abundant hair. Their horns were long and bending downwards; a peculiarity, however, which seemed to give place to the influence of external agents, since, at the Eastern and Southern limits of the breed in England, their horns frequently turned upward, in the manner of other cattle inhabiting these districts. Their bodies were long, their sides flat, and their shoulders heavy as compared with their hind quarters. They were hardy, capable of subsisting without shelter, and on indifferent food, but they were slow to arrive at maturity. Their flush was of a dark colour, and the fat of a yellow tinge. They were of docile tempers and steady in the Yoke, through sluggish in their motions."

177

Long Horn Beauty
Attributed to JOHN BOULTBEE (1747-1812)
Unit of Agricultural Economics, Oxford

This painting, and those of 'Old Nell', 'Garrick', 'Shakespear' and 'Brindled Beauty' were acquired by C. S. Orwin, first Director of the Institute of Agricultural Economics. The paintings came to Orwin in an interesting way. C. D. B. Williams wrote to R. E. Stone at Oxford in 1979, with some fascinating details: and Miss J. Knight in 1987.

> "The five paintings were inherited by Richard Fowler, Robert Fowler's son and sold by him by auction when he gave up farming in 1800.
> . . . My grandfather bought the paintings from Mr. George Price. They hung at Rollright until shortly before my family disposed of the village when my mother sold them to your director.
> Regarding the unnamed bull, we cannot be sure but we think he may well be 'Garrick' by Shakespear out of Broken Horn Beauty. He was five years old at the time of Robert Fowler's dispersal sale in 1791 and was sold for £215.5.0. to a Mr. Stone of Quarndon, Leicestershire. Of the rest, Brindled Beauty a daugher of Old Long Horn Beauty by Shakespear, supposed to be in calf by Garrick, sold to Mr. Russell of Cubington, Warwickshire for Messrs. Knowles & Co. for £273.
> Long Horn Beauty. I think this may in fact be Old Long Horn Beauty, who, like Old Nell was the daughter of one of the original Canley cows and the Bakewell bull Twopenny.
> Old Nell. Also a daughter of one of the original Canley cows and the bull Twopenny.
> In eight years breeding she produced progeny which together with herself were sold for more than a thousand guineas, which at that time had never been beaten by any cow in the Kingdom.
> Shakespear. This bull was used extensively by Robert Fowler and sired many notable cattle but was probably dead at the time of the disposal sale."

178 and 179

Longhorn Bull: Not named
Attributed to JOHN BOULTBEE
Oil on canvas, 66 x 83cm. and 73 and 89cm.
Unit of Agricultural Economics, Oxford

180

Particulars of the Breeding Stock. Late the property of Mr. Robert Fowler, of Little Rollright, in the County of Oxford, deceased.
R.A.S.E.

At the sale of little Rollright, the first pedigree sale in the world, held on March 29, 30th and 31st, 1791 many well known cattle were sold and dispersed, for example:

> "Beauty: By Shakespear, of Old Long Horn's daughter in calf by Garrick.
> Long Horn'd Beauty: By her own brother, a son of Long Horn's, of Old Beauty.
> Brindled short tail: By Shakespear, of a daughter of Old Short Tails, in-calf by Garrick."

174

176

173

177

175

178

181

181

The Bull Patriot, 1809, signed
Thomas Weaver
Oil on canvas, 118 x 143cm.
Unit of Agricultural Economics, Oxford

The Shorthorned bull is shown, typically of Weaver, with a seated herdsman and dog. Patriot was bred by George Coates of Great Driffield, Yorkshire, the founder of the first Herd Book in the world in 1822. Patriot was subsequently bought by "John Holt, James Conington, Thos. Marris and John Richardson Esqrs."

A coloured mezzotint (1810) was dedicated to the "Right Honble. Charles Lord Yarborough, Baron Yarborough of Yarborough in the county of Lincoln, President of the Agricultural Society for the division of Lindsey, in the said county" by Thomas Weaver, and was engraved by William Ward, A.R.A., the elder brother of James Ward/born 1766, died 1826.

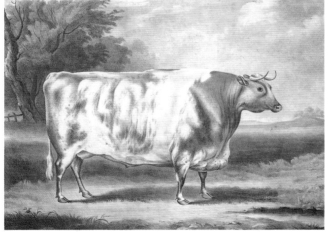

182

182

The Rutland Prize Ox, 1834
W. H. Davis painter and also lithographer
Printer C. Hullmandel.
Coloured lithograph, 60 x 74cm.
Unit of Agricultural Economics, Oxford

This print from the collection at Oxford was included in one of Augustus Walker's exhibitions at his gallery in Bond Street in the 1930's.

The Rutland Prize Ox was a Durham ox (popular amongst French breeders during the 19th Century). The lithograph is inscribed:

"The Rutland Prize Ox, 1834, the property of Mr. Robt. Smith, Burley on the Hill. This ox, of he Durham breed, obtained the first prize of 15 sovereigns at the Rutland Agricultural Society's Shew, at Oakham, also at the Smithfield Club Show the first prize of 20 sovereigns, in class 1. Printed by C. Hullmandel. Painted from life and drawn on stone by W. H. Davis animal painter to His Majesty, Church St. Chelsea."

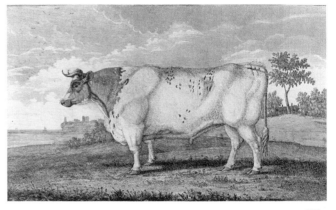

183a

183a

The Whitley Large Ox, 1789
Thomas Bewick: Published and sold by Beilby and Bewick April 10, 1789
Etching with some line engraving and aquatint, 37 x 45cm.
Unit of Agricultural Economics, Oxford

Thomas Bewick was born in Cherryburn (where there is now a memorial museum) and died in Gateshead in 1820. Here Bewick depicts a Teeswater ox against a landscape background which includes Tynemouth Priory.

"The Whitley large ox, belonging to Mr. Edward Hall of Whitley in Northumberland; Weight: Four quarters, 149st. 8, Tallow, 19st. 5, Hide, 10st. 7, Head, tongue, feet and heart, 7st. 13. Total: 187st. 5. (N.B. 14lb to the stone). Age: Rising seven years when killed at Newcastle by Mr. Thos. Horsley, weighed at the publick weigh house March 21st, 1789. Dimensions: Height at the crop; 5′ 9″; Do. at the loins, 5′ 11½″; Breast from the ground, 1′ 6″; Breadth at hips, 3′ 0½″; Do. at the shoulders, 2′ 6″; Length from head to rump, 9′ 8½″; Girt at shoulders, 10′ 3″; Do. at the belly, 10′ 9½″; Do. at the loins, 10′ 4½″."

183b

"Vaccination", A Favourite Young Cow, 18th June, 1810
M. Dubourg, Engraver, Edward Orme, Publisher
Aquatint part printed in colours, 50.5 x 42cm.
Private collection

183c

Longhorn Cow: Not named
Attributed to John Boultbee
Oil, 73 x 89cm.
Unit of Agricultural Economics, Oxford

184

The Colling Shorthorn Heifer, Seven years old, 1811
Thomas Weaver, engraved by W. Ward
Coloured engraved proof, 51 x 60.5cm.
Private Collection

185
Portrait of a Bull, c. 1817
JOHN GLOVER (1767-1849)
Oil on canvas, 255.3 x 365.7cm.
Bowes Museum, Barnard Castle, Co. Durham.

John Glover of Appleby, President of the Society of Painters in watercolours, emigrated to Australia in 1830. This painting has an inscription verso which reads Bt. "by J. Bowes in 1840 for £3.10s at Sir Simon Clarke's Sale''; and a manuscript label: Mr. Peel, 17 Golden Square, London, by Hoades, Feby 27th, J. Ral.
A similar work by Glover was sold in London in 1988 which came from Captain Lloyd at Gyrn Castle.

186a
Coates Herd Book, 1822
"The General Shorthorned Herd Book: Containing The Pedigrees of Shorthorned bulls, and co of the Improved Durham Breed''
From the earliest Account to the year 1822
by George Coates of Carlton, near Pontefract
Otley: Printed by W. Walker at the Wharfdale Stanhope Press, Top of the Market Place 1822
R.A.S.E.

The world's first herd book. Divided into two sections *Bulls* and *Cows and their Produce.* A typical entry for a bull:
   "(594) Sir Dimple,
   Calved in 1810, bred by Mr. C. Colling;
   got by Comet, d. (Daisy) by a Grandson of Favourite''
or:
   "(486) Nutmeg
   Got by Juniper, d. by Chilton, g.d. by Trunnell, gr. g.d. by
   Favourite, gr. g.d. by The White Bull''
and for a cow:

BRIGHTEYES
Calved in 1807

Bred by Mr. Gibson, got by Mr. C. Colling's Alexander, d. (Red Acamb,) by Traveller, g.d. by a Son of Bolingbroke.

Produce in		Names &c. of produce	By what Bull	By whom Bred	Present Owners, & c.
1810, red	B.C.		Petrarch	Mr. Gibson	
1811, roan	C.C.	Young Brighteyes	do.	do.	
1812, red & white	B.C.		Sir Oliver	do.	

B.C. means Bull Calf and C.C., Cow Calf.

186b
The Devonshire Ox, 1801
JAMES WARD (1769-1859)
Oil on canvas, 60 x 75cm.
Unit of Agricultural Economics, Oxford

Best known for his monumental canvas, Gordale Scar, Yorkshire, James Ward was a brother-in-law to George Morland. He worked throughout England and he was a frequent exhibitor at the Royal Academy, showing 287 paintings there. Ward also painted a fat Devon heifer bred by Francis Quartly of Molland, North Devon.

187

188

187
Plough Boy, 1795 September (? see below)
W. WILLIAMS, signed on reverse
Oil on canvas, 50.5 x 38cm.
Unit of Agricultural Economics, Oxford

A common name for a cart horse "Plough Boy" was a true bred Suffolk cart horse. At the time of painting he was four years old and the property of Mr. Chinnery of Great Welnetton, Suffolk.

Rothamsted Experimental Station has a mezzotint of another "Plough Boy" dated c. 1800 from a painting by Fs. Sartorius, engraved by W. Pyott. If bears the inscription "Plough Boy, a true bred Suffolk cart horse five years and; the property of Mr. Steele of Sutton, in Surrey".

Boalch writes that this could be the Plough Boy which was foaled in 1795 and travelled in Suffolk [Shire Horse Studbook, 1, 1880]. The date on the Williams painting may refer to the month and year of birth of 'Plough Boy' and they may, despite differences between the works, be one and the same animal.

188
J. Cotes, MP for Salop., 1810
T. WEAVER: Engraved by W. WARD pub. March 17th 1810 by T. WEAVER
Mezzotint, 73 x 87cm.
Unit of Agricultural Economics, Oxford

Mounted on a cob, John Coles is painted in the park of Old Woodcote House. Two men adjust the share of a wooden spring plough, to which a pair of Welsh horses are about to be harnessed.

The print is dedicated to the members of the Shiffnal Agricultural Society.

190b

189
Gloucester Old Spot Pigs, early mid 19th Century
STEPHEN JENNER (1796-1881)
Oil on canvas, 18 x 22.5cm.
A Member of Council, R.A.S.E.

190a
Sow and Pigs, c. 1797
GEORGE MORLAND (1762/3-1804)
Oil on canvas, 30.5 x 38cm.
Private Collection

190b
Two Pigs in a Sty late 18th Century
GEORGE MORLAND
Oil on panel, 18 x 2.5cms.
A Member of Council R.A.S.E.

Although it is extremely difficult to be specific about the identification of breeds of pig at this early date these animals

189

may belong to the breed of Oxford Dairy pig which was fed on the by-products of milk which was used in the production of butter for the London market. Several breeds were fed in this way, including the Gloucester Old-Sport who was nourished on whey from Double Gloucester cheese and apples from the cider orchards.

191
The Cottager's Wealth, 1793
GEORGE MORLAND
Oil on canvas, 37 x 47.5 cm.
Private Collection.

192
"Slut", 1803
T. GOOCH engraved by T. HILL
Colour, aquatint, 21.5 x 29cm.
Lawes Agricultural Trust. Rothamsted Experimental Station
> "Slut, a strayed forest sow, was trained to point and stand at game as staunch as any dog; this curious animal was late in the possession of F. W. Sykes, Esq., to whom this plate is inscribed, by his most obedient humble servant, T. Gooch."

193
The Yorkshire Hog, 1809
Engraved R. POLLARD
Colour, aquatint, 42 x 52cm.
Lawes Society Trust, Rothamsted, Experimental Station

> "The Yorkshire hog . . . this specimen of an improved breed of this useful animal was bred by Benjn. Rowley of Red House near Doncaster and fed by Josh Hudson on the estate of Col. Beaumont of Bretton Hall and . . . this stupendous creature for height and length far exceeds any of this species yet seen measuring 9' 10" long, 8' round the body, stands 12½ hands high, 4½ years old and weighs 1,344 lbs or 160 stone, 8lbs to the stone or 96 st. 14lbs to the stone, and would feed to a much greater weight were he not raised up so often to exhibit his stature. He has been viewed by the Agricultural Society and the best judges with astonishment and excited public curiosity so much that the proprietor for admittion money to see him in 3 years has received near 3,000 pounds."

195
This Celebrated Ewe, bred by Mr. Wilcox of Moor Hall, Warwickshire, c. 1800
Line engraving printed in colours, 46.5 x 60.5cm.
Private Collection

196
Worcester Ewe, 1821
Painted by J. BARINGER, Engraver C. TURNER, published by MR. MARSHALL
Mezzotint, proof, 48 x 58cm.
Private Collection

197

197
Mr Freestone and his Sheep, 1824
THOMAS WEAVER.
Oil on canvas, 71 x 92cm.
Iona Antiques.

Inscribed: "2 shear, 3 shear, 4 shear, 6 shear bred by Mr. Freestone."

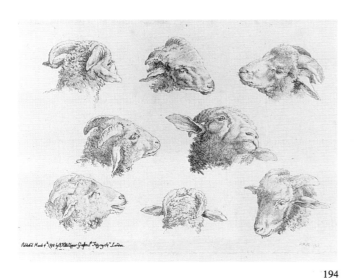

194

194
Heads of Sheep
ROBERT HILLS
Etching, 15.5 x 21cm.
Goldmark Gallery, Rutland

198

198
Five Leicester Sheep.
W. H. DAVIS (1803-1865)
Oil on canvas, 67 x 80cm.
Unit of Agricultural Economics, Oxford

93

199

Sheep Salving, 1828

JAMES WARD: S. in monogram J.W. RA 1828. James Ward (1769-1859)

Oil on canvas, 84.1 x 119.6cm.

Birmingham Museums and Art Gallery

The picture was formerly entitled *Sheep Shearing* until it was pointed out by Mr. John West in 1985 that the subject was sheep salving, a widespread farming method to prevent sheep scab and parasites until compulsory dipping was introduced in 1905. The salve was a mixture of Stockholm Tar and butter applied to the sheep's skin with a short stick. In the foreground, one man grips a sheep's head between his knees and parts the fleece for the salver. In the sheepfold, another salver is using a forked stick to hold his sheep still while he parts the fleece with one hand and applies the salve with the other.

(lit: C. R. Grundy, *A Catalogue of the Pictures and Drawings in the Collection of Frederick John Nettlefold,* Vol. IV, p.102 repr.).

(prov: H. E. Crawley; F. J. Nettlefold, his bequest to Birmingham 1947).

200

Various Breeds of Goat, 1815

Hand-coloured Engraving, 35 x 30cm.

Demelza Spargo.

Low writes that in the British Islands, the number of Goats "has been continually diminishing, with the extension of sheep, and the progress of agriculture".

He suggested that "Families who keep a single cow would find a goat or two always useful, as supplying milk when that of the other was wanting, and experience shows that the humbler cottagers would derive a profit from having one or two of these animals which could be maintained on food which the cow would reject. Persons even in large towns could, by means of the Goat, readily supply themselves with milk far superior to that which they can now obtain. Goats are frequently taken to sea for the purpose of supplying milk on ship-board, and they are better fitted for this purpose than any other animal."

200

201

Farm Labourer carrying a flail, late 18th Century?
ARTIST UNKNOWN
Oil on canvas, 31 x 26cm.
Unit of Agricultural Economics, Oxford

In *The Farmers Kalendar* by 'An Experienced Farmer',
published in 1778 the activities of the month of September
describe the harvest and in particular warns the farmer about
his threshing team:

> "*Fifthly,* comes the threfhing, in which I will venture to pronounce,
> that a gentleman who gives not the moft circumfpect attention the
> very *minutiae* of his bufinfs, will be cheated to the amount, perhaps,
> of five of fix, or even ten *per* cent. of his whole crop. It is a fact
> known in many parts of *England,* that many workmen fcarce ever
> threfh in the fame cloaths they do their other bufinefs; they have
> coats with pockets in the lining, that will hold each half a peck: but
> befides this piece of knavery, there are likewife the methods of filling
> bags, and burying them in the ftraw, or in any convenient place near
> the barn, and bringing them away in the night, or other convenient
> time. *Sixthly,* it is meafured; I need but mention this article.
> *Seventhly,* it is carried to the granery, from thence loaded into the
> waggon, and drove to market, or the perfon's that has bought it;
> and the gentleman may depend on it, that unlefs he fees it meafured,
> facked, and loaded, according to his bargain, his heap may fuffer
> a frefh deduction; for it is a very eafy matter to throw up a fack
> too much, and no difficult one to drop it at a labourer's houfe, or
> convert it into money.
> Let not the reader imagine, that I have ftrained facts or probability,
> to make room for thefe deductions; nor have I wantonly attacked
> a fet of people with imputations of difhonefty, not to be found
> amongft them."

202

Girl Carrying Wheatsheaf, 1826
Signed JOHN LINNELL
Oil on panel, 19 x 14.5 cm.
Julian Simon Fine Art

Writing of the year 1860 in *Farming Memoirs of a West County
Yeoman* S. G. Kendall described the wet weather and one of
the not so obvious effects:

"In our country districts, every second or third parish boasted its
local flour mill—and these mills as a rule partly fed our local and
agricultural population, who where dependent on our home grown
production of wheat to supply their local needs from one harvest
to another.
Moreover these country mills were necessary not only to the welfare
of agricultural labourers of those times, since after harvest the wives
and children of our workmen laboriously gleaned in the harvest
fields— after the crops were carried home—and in my earlier days
I have often threshed by our machine for each one of our women
varying quantities such as from one to three sacks of excellent
grain—of over 240 lb. per sack—free of charge which when sent
to the miller produced a good wholesome supply of bread for
themselves and their families for several weeks, helping those families
to tide over the long expensive winter until work became more
plentiful and general in the early spring.
A harvest, therefore, such as was experienced in the year 1860, was
not only a disaster to the farmer himself, but also to those loyal
work-people and their families who were so dependent on his
employment—and the gleanings they gathered in the harvest fields,
which very practically helped to supplement their scanty earnings
in those days, when the farmer—providing the harvest was
indifferent— cut down his wages bill during the winter.
Moreover the gleaner's harvest was likewise badly affected, both
in quality and quantity, since not only does the grain sprout during
a very wet harvest, but storms and drying winds alternately following
closely on each other's heels tend to open the chaff, which contains
the golden grain—and the precious increase easily sheds itself—
and is lost on the ground when under such conditions, although much
straw might have been gleaned by those industrious women and
children, yet when it was threshed after such seasons, the yield
naturally was not only damaged in quality, but also deficient in
quantity.
After a wet harvest such as was experienced in the year 1860—my
mother often assured me (and indeed I have sampled it myself) that
two knives were required to cut the bread when it came to the table—
one to tear or cut and the other to clean the used knife before another
portion could be taken from the loaf, as the dough (or sponge) made
from the flour produced from sprouted grain fails to 'rise' properly
after the already risen yeast has been mixed with the flour, neither
will it bake correctly in the oven, but runs more or less into a
glutinous sticky mass surrounded by a doubtful-looking crust—the
inside of the loaf when baked being stodgy and sticky with a sickly,
sweet unpalatable flavour."

205b

204
Morning, 1810.
Sir Augustus Wall Callcott, R.A. (1779-1844)
Oil on canvas, 99.5 x 133.5cm.
Royal Academy of Arts, London

205a
A Gypsy Encampment, c. 1840
John James Chalon
Oil on canvas, 95 x 125cm.
The Royal Academy of Arts, London

205b
Rustic Landscape with Sheep
John Linnell (1792-1882)
Oil on canvas, 26 x 35.6cm.
Royal Albert Memorial Museum, Exeter

205b
Farm Labourer on a Road
James Ward.
Oil on canvas, 60 x 45cm.
Private Collection

In Volume I of the Annuals of Agriculture by Arthur Young,
1786 some figures were recorded from the period 1769-1770:

"To a boy keeping the swine, 112 days at 4d. To a man mowing
weeds, 7 days at 8d."

In a fascinating essay, which deals with the recent loss of
America, Young put forward his ideal plan for improving
English agriculture.

"I wish I was a king, said a farmer's boy: Why, what could you
do if you was a king? I would swing upon the gate and eat bacon
all day long. So also may I wish I was king: If I did, it would be
for the pleasure of executing such a plan as this for personal
amusement."

203
Lakeland Packhorse, "The Bell Mare", 1757.
R. T.
Oil on canvas, 66 x 99.5cm.

Sporting tumbler bells and red ribbons the "Bell Mare" seems
to be stepping out, bearing her pack of wool, before her
companion has finished his drink. More than a hundred years
later William Morris would use the image of a packhorse in an
evocation of a Golden, rural age' in the prologue to "The
Wanderers".

"Forget six counties overhung with smoke,
Forget the snorting steam and piston stroke,
Forget the spreading of the hideous town,
Think rather of the packhorse on the down,
And dream of London, small and white and clean,
The Clear Thames bordered by its gardens green."

203

206

Man with a Scythe, mid-19th Century
ARTIST UNKNOWN.
Paper on panel, 24 x 25cm.
The National Trust, Knightshayes

Following the end of the Napoleonic Wars the great era of
agricultural prosperity came to an end. The country went back
onto the Gold Standard and prices fell. Many farmers went
bankrupt. Labourer's wages were reduced to starvation level,
many could not find work.

The depression remained acute for twenty years. The land
became impoverished. In 1830-1 sheep-rot killed two million
sheep. Starvation stared the agricultural workers, men, women
and children, in the face.

"Distress bred discontent", writes Lord Ernle in *"English Farming
Past and Present"* and discontent disturbances fostered by political
agitation. Luddites smashed machinery and agricultural labourers
destroyed threshing machines, they burned down farm houses,
haystacks and wrecked the shops of butchers and bakers. 1830-1
was the time of Captain Swing and his followers, when agrarian
fires blazed from Dorsetshire to Lincolnshire."

206

207

207

Cornfield with Figures in Sunlight
PETER DE WINT (1784-1849)
Oil on canvas, 58.1 x 106.4cm.
Southampton City Art Gallery

Purchased by Southampton in the late 1930s this painting by
de Wint has not previously been exhibited outside the City Art
Gallery.

208

A Lane, East Bergholt, n.d.
Attributed to JOHN DUNTHORNE, JUNIOR (1798-1832).
Oil on canvas, 38 x 30cm.

and

209

Landscape, probably Dedham Vale, n.d.
Attributed to JOHN DUNTHORNE, JUNIOR (1798-1832)
Oil on canvas, 22.7 x 33.6cm.
Colchester and Essex Museum

210

210

Harvest Scene, Hackney, 1814
WILLIAM WALKER, engraved by W. J. Bennett
Coloured aquatint, 38 x 62cm.
Guildhall Library, City of London

211
The Oxen and Plough, c. 1800
D. CLOWES
Oil on canvas, 60 x 95cm.
Iona Antiques

Oxen yoked to a wheel plough is an ancient image. The normal team was eight oxen and the implement was extremely cumbersome; often up to twelve oxen had to be harnessed, two abreast. By the Middle Ages horses were beginning to be used and in the twelfth century a mixed team of one yoke of oxen and a horse in front was recommended. A report exists that at Bocking in Essex an acre a day could be ploughed if four oxen and two horses were used. Mixed teams were still used up to the early 19th Century.

212 (i) (ii) (iii)
Landscape with Cattle and Figures
JAMES LEAKEY (1775-1865)
Oil on canvas, 53.5 x 77cm.
Royal Albert Memorial Museum, Exeter

James Leakey, an Exeter artist, specialized in painting picturesque rural scenes, although he was also a portrait and figure painter. His idyllic landscapes bridged the gap between 18th and 19th Century attitudes to the countryside and show a debt to the Smiths, Gainsborough, Morland and Shayer.

212 (iii)

212 (ii)

212 (i)

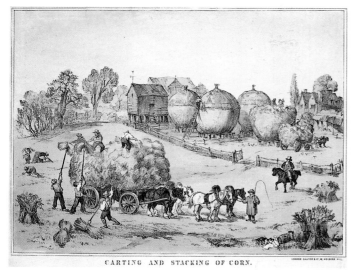

CARTING AND STACKING OF CORN.

213

214

213
Carting and Stacking Corn, c. 1860
ARTIST UNKNOWN
Coloured lithograph, 41 x 56.5cm.
Hampshire County Museum Service

214
Agricultural Scenes: Farm Wagons
W. H. PYNE (1769-1843)
Goldmark Gallery, Rutland.

The watercolourist and writer William Henry Pyne had begun in 1803 to publish *Microcosm, or a picturesque delineation of the arts, agriculture, and manufactures of Great Britain. In a series of above six hundred groups of small figures for the embellishment of landscape* ... It was intended as instruction for art students rather than historical record. The original etchings by Pyne were of sufficient interest for a second edition to be published in 1845, with a text by C. Gray, drawing from social, industrial, and political experiences at a time when economy was still predominantly agricultural. It was divided into two parts: early trades and industries, and English rural life.

215

215
The Watering Cart, January 1805
WILLIAM HENRY PYNE
Coloured aquatint, 41.5 x 56cm.
Hampshire County Museum Service

Plate 39 from Pyne's ''The Costume of Great Britain'' which was also written by him. The work was printed 1804-5 and published 1819-20 by William Miller.

216(i)

216(ii)

216(i)
Still Life, 1829
BENJAMIN BLAKE
Oil on panel, 26 x 20cm.
The Salisbury and South Wiltshire Museum

Benjamin Blake's first exhibited paintings were of landscapes, but he soon specialized in still life painting of dead game and vegetables. These show a strong debt to Dutch 17th Century paintings. He exhibited at the Royal Academy, the British Institution and the Society of British Artists, becoming a member of the latter in 1824.

216 (ii)
Still Life, 1828
BENJAMIN BLAKE
Oil on panel, 25 x 20cm.
The Salisbury and South Wiltshire Museum

217a
The Painter's Home, Ambleside, 1803
JULIUS CAESAR IBBETSON (1759-1817)
Oil on oak panel, 30 x 42cm.
Ferens Art Gallery, Hull City Museums and Art Galleries

217c
"Haymakers" and "Reapers", c. 1790
GEORGE STUBBS (1724-1806)
Mixed method engravings, 60 x 90cm. each
Private Collection

Engravings after the oil paintings of the same name.

217b
View from Golding Constable's House, East Bergholt, c.1800
JOHN CONSTABLE (1776-1837)
Oil on canvas, 33 x 75cm.
Master, Fellows and Scholars of Downing College, Cambridge

This view painted about 1800, is taken from an upstairs window at the house of Constable's parents, in East Bergholt. His father's windmill can be seen in the distance at the centre of the composition. In front of the wall on the left, a herdsman and two cattle have been painted, causing the omission of a charming flower garden.

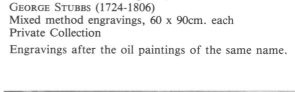

217c

The Industrial Phase

c. *1820-1880*

Both the agrarian and the industrial revolution reach back to the Tudor period. It was then that England ceased to be a self-contained agricultural community and began to develop her industrial resources, with assistance from foreign exiles such as the Flemish weavers who helped establish the supremacy of the woollen trade and the Dutch engineers who directed the first land reclamation schemes in the Fens.

Up to the end of the 18th Century the most important industrial raw material had been wood—all early machines were made of wood and it was essential—in the form of charcoal—as the foundation of the metal industries which used it to smelt ore. It was again in the Tudor period that coal began to replace wood as fuel.

By the end of the 19th Century the steam engine had become a universal motor destined to transform the whole economy both in the industrial and agricultural sectors and the farmers became part of a vital economic partnership with industry. While Luddites smashed industrial machinery their agrarian equivalents turned against the steam powered threshing machines which had robbed them of their winter work.

New materials emerged from factories from around the 1840's; mass produced fittings, galvanised iron, Portland cement. The production of agricultural machinery was totally revolutionized and new machines began to appear.

Patrick Bell, a student of Divinity at St. Andrew's with an interest in mechanics whilst walking in his father's garden (or so the story goes) noticed a pair of garden shears sticking in a hedge had the idea that mechanical scissors rather than scythes might be made the basis of a reaper. By 1828 he had produced a reaper which worked on that principle.

> "A five foot cut left the stubble three to four inches high, free from loose straw, and the cut corn was deposited on the side of the machine in a regular manner. Without raking the corn could be collected into compact and well-formed sheaves. Six to eight people, gathering, binding and setting constituted the team of workers. One horse propelled the machine from behind. The estimated cost of the reaper was £30."

Bell did not take out a patent, a deliberate decision in order that "the machine might go out into the world free of any avoidable expense". Sadly this meant that local variations of his machine were substandard and his reaper was eclipsed by the American McCormick reaper, which would first be seen in England in the Great Exhibition of 1851.

Mechanical reapers and threshers, such as those shown in 1851 became far more widely used, but mechanisation was a gradual process. The great names connected with Agricultural Engineering were James Howard of Bedford, Robert Ransome and John Fowler, all instrumental in the development of the plough.

Apart from the Great Exhibition another occasion which occurred annually presented an opportunity for new machinery and methods to be inspected: the show of the Royal Agricultural Society of England. The Society was formed at the suggestion of Earl Spencer, to complete the group of societies that for long had been doing much useful work among farmers. The Society held its first meeting in May 1839. In May 1840 the English Agricultural Society received its Royal Charter incorporating its aim: "the object of perfecting the System of English Agriculture by the union of practice with science . . . "

The 1850's have been seen as 'the golden age of English agriculture', the mid-Victorians called their business *High Farming;* there was prosperity and pride in the countryside.

Towards the end of the 1870's the situation changed. An economic depression related to Europe and America coincided with a series of bad seasons on the land. "Three years of bad weather culminated in 1879 in a sunless summer and abnormal rainfall." Yields of corn were reduced in many areas by 50%. Disease devastated livestock. The importation of foodstuffs increased dramatically and bad seasons no longer provided high prices for the more fortunate farmer.

In 1886 the Royal Commission on Depression of Trade was presented with a figure of £42,800,000 which represented the amount by which the yearly income of landlords, tenants and labourers had diminished.

Between 1881 and 1911 the agricultural population declined from 1,190,000 to 972,000; a figure which included skilled rural craftsmen, blacksmiths, saddlers, wheelwrights etc.

The acute depression, which had followed the greatest era of English agriculture persisted until the outbreak of the First World War in 1914.

218

218
Portrait of Justus Freiherr von Liebig (1803-1873) 1874
TRAUTSCHOLD
Oil on canvas, 75 x 62cm.
Property of J. R. Stourton, Esq.

Liebig's theory of plant nutrition, said Sir E. J. Russell, "came like a thunderbolt on the world of science". When Liebig published his theory in 1840 it was widely believed that plants drew their carbon and other nutrients entirely from the humus in the soil. Liebig said that a crop rose or fell exactly in proportion to the amount of mineral substances given to it in manure. His "law of the minimum" stated that the shortage or absence of only one essential constituent from the soil would make that soil barren.

There were many flaws in Liebig's conclusions and John Lawes at Rothamsted set out to challenge Liebig, who had patented what he believed to be the 'ideal' manure. It contained potassium compounds and phosphates but no nitrogen compounds and it was made insoluble by fusion with lime and calcium phosphate so that it should not be quickly washed out by drainage water.

Lawes started trials with Liebig's patent manure and in 1846 got 20¼ bushels of wheat to the acre with it. By adding one cwt. of sulphate and nitrate of ammonia the yield was increased to 29¼ bushels, while 14 tons of farmyard manure added to the unmanured plot only raised the yield there to 27¼ bushels. The "nitrogen controversy" between Lawes and Liebig continued til the latter's death.

Both Henry Gilbert and Augustus Voelcker attended Liebig's lectures at the University of Giessen and owed much to his enthusiasm.

Liebig is also well known for the extract of beef that he invented: staying with a scientific friend called Muspratt, in Liverpool, he devised a meat extract for Muspratt's ailing daughter. The girl recovered and at his death Liebig bequeathed this portrait to his friend Muspratt. When many years later Miss Muspratt died she in turn bequeathed it to the Liebig Meat Extract Company which incorporated 'Fray Bentos', 'Oxo', etc.

219 *detail*

219
Sir John Bennet Lawes (1814-1900)
H. HERKOMER
Oil on canvas, 167 x 110cm.
Lawes Agricultural Trust, Rothamsted Experimental Station

John Bennett Lawes was a leading exponent of links between agriculture and chemistry. He made Rothamsted famous as the first farm research station and the fields there have been talked, and written about, more than any in the world.

When Lawes took over the farm at Rothamsted the Napoleonic Wars had impoverished the nation generally. Lawes, like many other landowners had to get bigger returns.

In 1839 he used burnt bones and mineral phosphate decomposed by sulphuric and other acids, in pot and small plot experiments he had good results on turnips! In 1841 he used 20 tons of superphosphate on his land. It was all mixed in a thatched barn in an iron trough. The mixture was stirred until it set sufficiently to be taken out and heaped.

There was a small pond nearby and the barn door left ajar so that the men could rush out and wash themselves if they got splashed.

These investigations into the affects of dressing turnip crops with bones dissolved in sulphuric acid led to the patent no 9353 of 1842 and the first factory, in 1843, for the manufacture of mineral superphosphate manures that were to become so important in agricultural industry. In that year, Lawes began a regular series of crop manure and rotation experiments at Rothamsted, and a similar series of experiments on animal feeding and biochemistry was begun in 1847.

Lawes' work between 1843 and 1880, combined with experiments conducted by the Duke of Bedford at Woburn and the Duke of Leicester at Holkham, where the soil was a thin, shallow sand-loam, showed that wheat needed abundant nitrogen, though it was agreed that mineral manures must be available to ensure the full action of the nitrogen.

A continuous sequence of papers and reports on his various experiments, over 130 in number, were published by him with his colleague Dr. (later) Sir Henry Gilbert, in the proceedings of the Royal Society, the Chemical Society, the Royal Agricultural Society and others. Sir John was active in the latter society for 52 years, becoming its vice-president in 1878. Among his other good services to agricultural was a practical and philanthropic concern for the welfare of the farming community in the village of Harpenden near Rothamsted.

The Rothamsted Experimental Station, now the oldest in the world, continues agricultural investigations over all areas excepting animal research. The station also contains one of the finest collections in existence of agricultural books, and of prints and paintings of British farm livestock from 1780 to 1910.

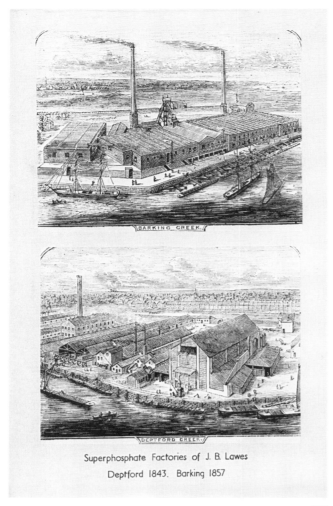

Superphosphate Factories of J. B. Lawes
Deptford 1843. Barking 1857

220

222

220
Drawings of Lawes Superphospate Factory at Deptford 1843 and Barking 1857
39 x 26cm.
Lawes Agricultural Trust Rothamsted Experimental Station.

221
Sir Henry Gilbert (1817-1901)
ARTISTS UNKNOWN
Oil on canvas, 137 x 110cm.
Lawes Agricultural Trust Rothamsted Experimental Station.

Joseph Henry Gilbert went to Rothamsted in June, 1843. J. B. Lawes took Gilbert on to carry out experiments on theories which he had already begun to disprove, including Liebig's theory that plants received all their necessary nitrogen from the air. Gilbert spent almost all of the rest of his life controverting Liebig's "Mineral Hypothesis".
Gilbert was born in Hull on August 1st, 1817. He lost his left eye at the age of 15 in a gun accident in which his right eye was also damaged. When he was 23 he went to Giessen, where he took a farming course under Liebig. He worked as a chemist to a calico printer in Manchester then at the age of 26 began his work at Rothamsted.
The unbroken succession of wheat on Broadbalk Field at Rothamsted was due to Gilbert. Lawes wished it to be ploughed up, but Gilbert prevailed over him.
His work often took him abroad, and he liked to take great columns of figures with him. For his lectures at the Chicago Exhibition of 1893 he wanted such enormous tablets to display that theatrical canvas had to be purchased. They were sent to America wrapped around a long pole.

222
Sutton's Seed Cabinet (c.1900).
182 x 91cm.
The Duke of Buccleuch and Queensbury, K.T.

A decorative display of the grasses recommended by Martin H. Sutton in his essay "Permanent Pastures: their formation and development".

223
Sutton's Farmers Year-Book. Centenary edition 1906.
27.5 x 21.5cm.
Suttons Seeds.

Lists of seeds for the year 1906 including prices including:
> "Sutton's Standard Mixtures of Grass and Clover Seeds".
> For Permanent Pasture, 25/- per acre and The New Yellow Turnip, Sutton's Mikado 2s 6d per pound.

224
Volumes: Permanent Pastures: Their Formation and Improvement
by MARTIN H. SUTTON, 1867.
18 x 22cm.
Sutton's Seeds.

Laying down land to permanent pasture and the improvement of old grasslands was reprinted from an article by Martin H. Sutton in Vol XXII, Part II of the Journal of The Royal Agricultural Society of England.
An expanded edition with colour plates by Martin J. Sutton was published and received enthusiastic reviews. *The Daily Telegraph* described Sutton's aims:
> "Mr Martin J. Sutton, in a very comprehensive work on pastures, advances a strong plea for more general sowings down of land to grass . . . instead of depending almost entirely on wheat and other grains for returns, farmers ought to breed, rear, and fatten at least three times as much stock, so that their incomes may be derived from meat, milk, and dairy goods. To do this effectually, either a great deal more land must be sown permanently to grass or . . . alternate grass layers must be allowed prolonged tenure."

225

Botanical Descriptions, Analyses and Illustrations of the Principal Grasses and Clovers used in Permanent Pastures and Alternate Husbandry.
MARTIN J. SUTTON, 1888
16.5 x 25cm.
Sutton's Seeds.

Extract of section from "Permanent Pastures", published in 1888 with a note from Dr J. A. Voelcker (1822-1884), which begins:

> "The analyses in the following pages represent the chemical composition of the several grasses and clovers opposite which they appear. Each variety was grown separately and was perfectly pure; the same being taken, in every instance, as nearly as possible at the time when it would have been cut for hay."

226

Box of Grasses related to work of Dr. J. A. Voelcker at Rothamsted:
Inscription:
Analysis of Natural Grasses by Dr. J. Augustus Voelcker extracted from Mr. M. J. Sutton's work on "Permanent and Temporary Pastures"
Lawes Agricultural Trust, Rothamsted Experimental Station

226

227
J. A. Voelcker (1822-1824)
19th Century Photograph.
Lawes Agricultural Trust, Rothamsted Experimental Station.

Dr. Augustus Voelcker (1822-1884) was born in Frankfurt and attended The University of Giessen. There he attended lectures given by the renowned Justus von Liebig, on agricultural chemistry. In 1847, he obtained a post in Edinburgh as assistant to James Finlay Weir Johnson, chemist to the Agricultural Chemistry Association of Scotland, where for the first time Voelcker came into contact with farmers and their problems. After two years of study he was appointed Professor of Chemistry at The Royal Agricultural College of Cirencester. His scientific laboratory work was always combined with practical field tests. In 1855 he was appointed consulting chemist to the Royal Bath and West of England Agricultural Society, and two years later to The Royal Agricultural Society of England.

Voelcker's chief interest was in manure, some of his first tests were to find what changes farmyard manure underwent when stored in different ways. Subsequently he studied the drainings from manure heaps and then the investigation of the changes liquid manure underwent once in contact with various soils. He was able to investigate the absorptive powers of different soils, and proved that soils absorb ammonia. Through this he discovered that the most valuable soluble constituents of manures are rendered less soluble, though not quite insoluble, when applied to the soil.

227

228

"Society of Agriculture" (1809)
Painted and engraved by Pugin and Rowlandson.
Aquatint engraving, 37 x 44cm.
M.E.R.L.

229

English Society of Agriculture, First meeting at Oxford 1839
Designed by W. A. DELAMOTTE
Lithographer: T. PICKEN.
Coloured lithograph, 30.5 x 21cm.
R.A.S.E.

230 detail

230

**Country Meeting of the Royal Agricultural Society at Bristol,
June 30th, 1842.**
RICHARD ANSDELL
Oil on canvas, 5.19 x 2.5m.
also: Key to painting: 73 x 32cm.

Behind a foreground of agricultural implements more than 130
members of the society are portrayed.

231

John Charles, 3rd Earl Spencer (1782-1865)
RICHARD ANSDELL (1843)
Oil on canvas.
Private Collection

John Charles Spencer, Viscount Althorp and Third Earl
Spencer, First President of the Royal Agricultural Society of
England. The painting shows the 3rd Earl Spencer with Mr.
J. Elliot (Steward at Althorp) and Mr. Hall (Steward at
Wiseton). the herdsman, John Wagstaff, holds Lord Spencer's
famous bull Wiston. There is a landscape background.

106

Original Charter of 1840 incorporating the English Agricultural Society as the Royal Agricultural Society of England.
R.A.S.E.

Extract of the first and eighth parts of the Royal Charter:

"Victoria, by the Grace of God, of the United Kingdom of Great Britain and Ireland, Queen, Defender of the Faith, to all to whom these presents shall come, greeting.

1. Whereas our right trusty and right entirely beloved cousin and counsellor, Charles Duke of Richmond, Knight of the most noble Order of the Garter, our right trusty and right entirely beloved cousin, George Henry Duke of Grafton, Knight of the most noble Order of the Garter, our right trusty and right entirely beloved cousin, John Henry Duke of Rutland, Knight of the most noble Order of the Garter, our right trusty and right entirely beloved cousin, George Granville Duke of Sutherland, our right trusty and entirely beloved cousin, Arthur Blundell Sandys Trumbal Marquis of Downshire, Knight of the most illustrious Order of Saint Patrick, our right trusty and right well beloved cousin and counsellor, John Charles Earl Spencer, our trusty and well beloved Robert Henry Clive, Esquire, Sir Francis Lawley, Baronet, and Sir Thomas Dyke Acland, Baronet, our right trusty and well beloved counsellor, Sir James Robert George Graham, Baronet, and our trusty and well beloved Henry Handley, and Joseph Neeld Esquires, and others of our loving subjects, have formed themselves into a Society for the general advancement of English Agriculture, and for the purpose of prosecuting the following national Objects, namely:—First, to embody such information contained in agricultural publications, and in other scientific works, as has been proved by practical experience to be useful to the cultivators of the soil; second, to correspond with Agriculture, Horticultural, and other Scientific Societies, both at home and abroad, and to select from such correspondence all information which, according to the opinion of the Society, may be likely to lead to practical benefit in the cultivation of the soil; third, to pay to any occupier of land, or other person who shall undertake, at the request of the Society, to ascertain by any experiment how far such information leads to useful results in practice, a remuneration for any loss that he may incur by so doing; fourth, to encourage men of science in their attention to the improvement of agricultural implements, the construction of farm buildings and cottages, the application of chemistry to the general purposes of Agriculture, the destruction of insects injurious to vegetable life, and the eradication of weeds; fifth, to promote the discovery of new varieties of grain and other vegetables useful to man or for the food of domestic animals; sixth, to collect information with regard to the management of woods, plantations and fences, and on every other subject connected with rural improvement; seventh, to take measures for the improvement of the education of those who depend upon the cultivation of the soil for their support; eighth, to take measures for improving the veterinary art, as applied to cattle, sheep, and pigs; ninth, at the Meetings of the Society in the country, by the distribution of prizes, and by other means, to encourage the best mode of farm cultivation and the breed of live stock; tenth, to promote the comfort and welfare of labourers, and to encourage the improved management of their cottages and gardens; And have subscribed and expended divers large sums of money in the prosecution of these their national and patriotic objects, being regulated in their purpose by the strictest exclusion from their councils of every question of discussion having a political tendency, or which shall refer to any matter to be brought forward, or at any time pending, in either of our Houses of Parliament: And having such objects, and being regulated by such essential principle, they have humbly besought us to grant unto them, and such other persons as shall be approved and elected in manner hereinafter mentioned, our Royal Charter of Incorporation for the several purposes aforesaid.

8. We further will and declare it is our Royal pleasure that the said Charles Duke of Richmond shall be the first president of the said Royal Agricultural Society of England, and that he, with the said George Henry Duke of Grafton, John Henry Duke of Rutland, George Granville Duke of Sutherland, Arthur Blundell Sandys Trumbal Marquis of Downshire, John Charles Earl Spencer, Robert Henry Clive, Sir Francis Lawley, Sir Thomas Dyke Acland, Sir James Robert George Graham, Henry Handley, and Joseph Neeld, shall be members of the first council, any three or more of whom shall hereby be invested with full power, being first duly summoned to attend, to appoint, on or within ten days preceding or following the twenty-fifth day of the present month of March, such persons to be trustees, vice-presidents, council, governors, members, honorary members, corresponding members, and foreign members, as they shall respectively think fit."

235

233
Photograph of Joseph Arch (1826-1919)
20 x 40cm.
Agricultural & Allied Workers' Trade Group of the T.G.W.U.

Thirty-eight years after six men from Tolpuddle were found guilty 'of administering and being bound by secret oaths' under an Act passed in 1797 which had been designed to deal specifically with the Naval Mutiny of that year, and sentenced to seven years' transportation, Joseph Arch was visited by two or three men at his home in Barford, Warwickshire.

The "Tolpuddle Martyrs" had, with the assistance of two members of The Grand National Consolidated Trades Union, formed the Tolpuddle Lodge of the Friendly Society of Agricultural Labourers. It was with a view to founding a National Agricultural Labourers' Union that Joseph Arch received his visitors. On May 29th, 1872 Joseph Arch was elected Chairman of the Union. The entrance fee to the union was 6d and contributions at 2d a week. The immediate aim of the union was declared to be 16s a week for a nine-and-a-half-hour working day.

In 1880 he successfully fought an electoral campaign as a Liberal. He stood again in 1885 and was again successful. He was further elected in 1892 and 1895.

234
Plaster casts of the hands of Joseph Arch.
18 x 9cm.
M.E.R.L.

235
Banner of the National Union of Agricultural Workers
by TUTHILL of Chesham.
Agricultural & Allied Workers Trade Group of the T.G.W.U

The banner of the Warwickshire County Section of the N.U.A.W. with portrait of Joseph Arch.

The National Union was concerned not only with wages. It had a comprehensive policy of political and social reform, one of its greatest triumphs was the granting of the parliamentary franchise to agricultural workers by Gladstone's administration in 1884.

It was in the following year that Arch entered Parliament as member for North-West Norfolk.

236
"The Hope of the Future", 1872.
J. E. MATTHEW VINCENT
70 x 85cm.

Print: Chronical Steam Printing Works, Leamington, Warwickshire.
One of two prints for The Agricultural Labourers Movement: Picture of English Rural Life.

237
"Past and Present", 1872.
J. E. MATTHEW VINCENT
70 x 85cm.

Print: Chronical Steam Printing Works, Leamington, Warwickshire.
One of two prints for The Agricultural Labourers Movement: Picture of English Rural Life.
Transport & General Workers' Union, Agricultural and Allied Workers' Trade Group, Region 5.

238
Record of the first meeting of the Lincolnshire Farmers Union
25 x 20cm.
Lincolnshire & South Humberside County Branch of the N.F.U.

On 31st August, 1904 nine gentlemen agreed to start a farmers union. The first meeting was held on Friday 2nd September, 1904.

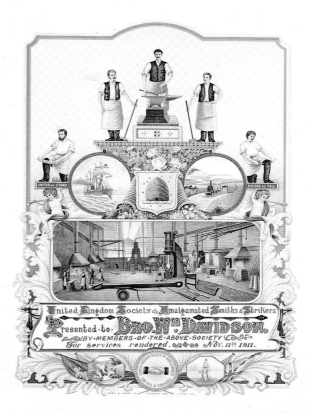

236

239
UK Society of Amalgamated Smiths and Strikers, 1911
Stone lithograph, 45 x 40cm.
Beamish Museum.

A certificate presented on November 11th, 1911 to Bro. Wm. Davidson.

240
Great Exhibition 1851, 1851
Coloured lithograph, 48 x 67cm.
M.E.R.L.

241
A Word in Season
SAMUEL SMITH 1851
The Royal Institution, London.

A word in season; or, how the corn-grower may yet grow rich, and his labourer happy. Addressed to the stout British farmer. Ninth edition, re-arranged and revised; with full directions for carrying out the plan of growing wheat.

237

242
Model of Webb's Sheep.
41.5 x 16 x 26 62cm.
R.A.S.E.

A model of a four-year-old Southdown Ewe. Bred by Jonas Webb, Esq., and presented by him to Jonathan Thorne, as a perfect specimen of the breed. Property of Samuel Thorne, Thornedale, Washington Hollow, Duchess County, New York. Kept with the model at the Royal Agricultural Society of England's London offices is a handwritten note on Jonas Webb's transactions; it reads:

"Jonas Webb Babraham.
In 1844 Sold 15 rams to Monsieur Gerard (?) Paris.
   1845 Five ewes died, frozen down.
   1847 Sold to Portugal.
   1848
   1849 Emperor of Russia 2 rams.
      [Margin in note: 1850 Thos. Bates Sh. Sale]
   1853 Jonathan Thorne New York 6t. 2nd prize Ram at Lewes for 130 gs and 20 ewes and one "Special Ewe" for Mr. Rotch
"The Model" presented is of a four-year-old ewe. They made it in USA to scale and sent it to J.W.
   1855 Duke of Richmond hired No 116 for the season at 170 gs.
      & Pearce of "Kinser Hill" (?) took one at 131 gs. Won 1st Paris that year. Emperor gave candelabrum.
   1858 Emperor of France bought three lambs.
      Samuel Thorne, USA again, 6 yearling ewes.
   1859 Samuel Thorne USA bought rams 180 gs.
      Australia, bought 9 rams 'Bradley, Sydney' (+36 ewes and rams went to Aust. later).
   1860 Samuel Thorne 1st Paris yearling Canterbury.
      R.A.S.E. 1st Canterbury 250 gs.
Samuel was a son of Jonathan Thorne and it was Samuel who took out the 'Duchess' Shorthorns from Lord Ducie's sale in *1853* (the year the model ewe went out). These passed through Morris and Becar to Jas. D. Sheldon who sold to Walcott and Campbell, New York Mills, who had the great sale in 1873 when 15 'Duchess Herd' got £367 g...18 each."

Twenty years after Bakewell's experiments which had resulted in the Dishley Leicester, John Ellman of Glynde, Sussex, embarked on a programme which would have international influence on the sheep industry.
His new material was the local heath breed of the Downs: fine-boned, leggy, with light forequarters and a speckled face. He transformed this animal into the compact, blocky creature known as the Southdown. John Ellman's work was continued by Jonas Webb of Babraham in Cambridgeshire, and the fame of the breed sped rapidly. The Breed Society was formed in 1892.
A statue of Jonas Webb was erected in Cambridge with funds subscribed by 'farmers and friends in many lands'.

243

The Breeds of the Domestic Animals of the British Isles.
Described by DAVID LOW, ESQ., F.R.S.E.
Professor of Agriculture in the University of Edinburgh. 1842.
Vol 1 The Horse and the Ox.
and illustrated with plates from drawings by Mr. W. Nicholson.
Reduced from a series of portraits from life, executed for the
Agricultural Museum of the University of Edinburgh, by Mr.
V. Shields R.S.A.
Vol II The Sheep, The Goat and the Hog.
30 x 42cm.
R.A.S.E.

David Low (1783-1859) was the son of Alexander Low of The
Laws, Berwickshire. Educated at Perth Academy and Edinburgh
University, he worked with his father in Berwickshire and
established a reputation as a surveyor and valuer. In 1817, he
published his *Observations on the Present State of Landed
Property* which was an analysis of the agricultural economy in
the post-Napoleonic Wars depression. In 1825, he settled in
Edinburgh, joined the Highland and Agricultural Society and
was elected a Director the following year. He started the
Quarterly Journal of Agricultural in 1826 and was its first editor
from 1828 to 1832. He was also one of its most prominent
contributors in this period.
David Low was appointed second Professor of Agriculture in
The University of Edinburgh in 1831. The animal paintings and
the Agricultural Museum were the result of Low's own ideas
and effort. On taking up office, he produced the plan for the
Agricultural Museums and submitted it to the government.
From 1833, he received an annual grant of £300 from the
Treasury. Further funds came through the Board of Trustees
and more from the Professor's own private resources.
The project of the paintings of animal breeds must have been
one of his first loves. He himself commissioned the Scottish
Academician, William Shiels, to travel round the British Isles
painting all the old native breeds of domesticated animals and
also the newly established breeds and crosses of the best-known
animal breeders of the day and immediately preceding
generations. The results of this work were published in 1842
in his fine folio volumes, *The Breeds of the Domestic Animals
of the British Islands,* which costs 16 guineas. On its publication,
the French Government commissioned a translation. Low retired
from the Chair of Agriculture in 1854.
The Royal Museum of Scotland is responsible for saving the
original paintings for Laws book. The museum now owns 35
paintings (many of which are still in an unrestored state).
Without their intelligent action the paintings would have been
destroyed.

244

The Old English Black Horse
WILLIAM SHIELS, R.S.A.
Oil on canvas, 130 x 170cm.
The Royal Museum of Scotland

"Stallion, by Old Blacklegs, from a Mare of the Dishley blood,
bred by Mr. Broomes at Ormiston, Derby."
Low notes that "the race of Horses of a black colour has existed
in Europe from a remote age" and was "widely spread through
Holland, Belgium, Central Germany, Switzerland and the Baltic
States." It is also widely spread in England.
"But" writes Low "the older Black Horse of the Fens and
Midland counties differs in several respects from the modern
cultivated race. Few now exist in their original state of
rudeness . . . they have coarse heads, large ears, and thick lips,
largely garnished with hairs. They have coarse shoulders, stout
hairy limbs, broad hoofs, and short upright posterns. They are
strong, of a soft temperament, and eminently deficient in action,
spirit and bottom."
. . . Robert Bakewell, of Dishley, in the county of Leicester

THE OLD ENGLISH BLACK HORSE.

244

began to apply those principles of breeding to the improvement
of the Draught Horse, which he had adopted with unrivalled
skill and success in the case of the other domestic animals. He
acted upon the conviction that the properties of the parents,
with the respect to both form and temperament, can be
transmitted to the progeny and rendered permanent by
continued reproduction. He went himself to Holland, and
importing several mares, crossed them with native stallions; and
pursuing a course of careful selection, he formed at length a
stock which he regarded as possessed of the properties required.
He does not appear to have attemped any mixture of the blood
of horses of high breeding, but to have confined himself to the
kinds suited for slow labour . . . Leicester and the adjoining
counties of Derby and Stafford, became distinguished for the
breeding of this class of horse."

245

Breed of the Zetland and Orkney Islands
WILLIAM SHIELS, R.S.A.
Oil on canvas, 150 x 120cm.
The Royal Museum of Scotland

"Ram, 3 years old, of the Ancient breed, from the Isle of Enhallow-
Ewe, 3 years old, from the Island of Rousay; bred by William Traill,
Esqr. of Woodwick. The lamb a cross with the pure Cheviot."

Low writes:

"The sheep of this race inhabit a group of Islands and Islets which
lie to the North of the Pentland Firth . . . they have manifestly a
common origin with the Sheep of Norway and other parts of
Northern Europe".
He continues "The Sheep over a great part of the islands are pastured
in common, and the general treatment of them is rude in a
remarkable degree. The animals are often left to their own resources
in the bleak and desolate islands in which they are imprisoned . . .
when sheep are wanted from the pastures, they are run down by
dogs; and hence these poor creatures acquire a great terror for the
dog as in other countries they do for the wolf or other beast of prey.
The dogs termed *Had* or Sheep Dogs, are taught to select a particular
sheep and run him down; and curious old laws existed regarding
the property and control of these animals. Under the whole of this
barbarous system, the mortality is excessive; all the profit to be
derived from a proper management of a flock of sheep is lost; and
all the means are foregone of improving the breed, by the selection
of male and female parents."
The Merino sheep was crossed with the native sheep but the
progeny were unable to withstand the rigour of the climate. The
crossing of the breed with the Climate was more successful.

246

Cheviot Ewe and Lamb

WILLIAM SHIELS, R.S.A.

Oil on canvas, 138 x 101cm.

The Royal Museum of Scotland

Bred by Mr. Thomson of Attonburn, County of Roxburgh. Low accords many pages to the Cheviot breed including an account of the Etterick shepherd James Hogg of a dreadful snow storm and subsequent flooding which occurred on the 24th and 25th of January 1794 . . . 'When the flood after the storm subsided, there were found at the Beds of Esk and the shores adjacent one thousand, eight hundred and forty sheep, nine black cattle, three horses, two men, one woman, forty-five dogs and eighty hares, besides a number of other animals.''

The Cheviot breed is derived from a district of trap, situated in the north of Northumberland. An extremely hardy breed, devoid of horns.

Low concludes:

> "The Cheviot breed, naturalised in counties so wild and tempestuous, and spreading over so large a tract of country, must be seen to be of the highest economical importance . . . it has become the interest of the breeders to direct attention to the improvement of the form of the animals, holding the quality of the wool to be a secondary consideration. Nevertheless to this extent attention to the wool is proper: a fine and close fleece indicate constitutional hardiness in the individuals, and should therefore be carefully attended to as a character in the breeding parents.''

247

Berkshire Pig

WILLIAM SHIELS, R.S.A.

The Royal Museum of Scotland

The paintings in Low's book are the work of William Shiels (1785-1857). Shiels was a Berwickshire man who became a founder member of the Royal Scottish Academy in 1826. His first painting exhibited in Edinburgh was a neo-classical scene *Ulysses Meeting His Father Laertes*, but this does not seem to have been typical of Shiels' work. He painted some portraits and many countryside genre scenes and some house interiors. In 1833, he began work on the animal breed paintings and travelled round the British Isles to paint his subjects from life. For this, Shiels was employed by Professor Low personally rather than by any official body such as the University or the Highland Society. (In the late 1830s, William Nicholson, another academician began to draw the paintings for the lithographs for Professor Low's book).

The example used for Shiels' painting was bred by Mr. Loud of Mack Stockmill, Warwickshire. Low notes that the painting represents the 'old and characteristic form of the race' and that the great improver of the breed was Richard Astley, Esq, of Adstone Hall, "from the direct descendants of whose stock the present specimen has been derived."

248

The Celebrated Spottiswoode Ox, c.1803

ALEXANDER NASMYTH

Oil on canvas

The Royal Museum of Scotland

The Spottiswoode Ox was painted in the opening years of the 19th Century and records the achievements of that early phase of animal breeding for which graphic evidence is comparatively rare in Scotland. It belongs to the same generation of improved cattle and breed type as the shorthorn Durham Ox, and, originating in the Borders and Berwickshire, lives very much in the Teeswater and North of England shorthorn ambit.

249

A Wether of the New Leicester Breed, c. 1838

WILLIAM SHIELS, R.S.A.

Oil on canvas, 140 x 121.5cm.

A wether, or one-year shearling of the long wool breed favoured by Bakewell and Coke.

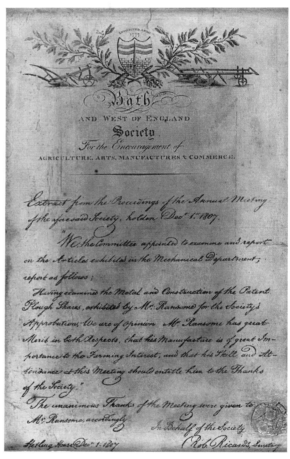

250

250

Certificate awarded to Ransomes by The Bath and West Agricultural Society, c.1807

48 x 34cm.

Ransomes, Sims and Jeffries plc

Mechanisation appeared late in the agrarian revolution; a few firms such as Ransomes of Ipswich came into being early on. Robert Ransome founder of the firm was born in 1753 at Wells, Norfolk. In 1789 with a capital of £200 and one workman he moved his foundry to Ipswich which had good access to markets and raw materials. It was here that he made a tremendous technological breakthrough—the "chilling" process which produce a cast-iron ploughshare with a hard under-surface and a relatively soft upper surface which would retain its sharpness through use. Particularly of use where the soil was light and dry, the widespread use of this share did much to ensure that the cast share superseded the laboriously manufactured wrought-iron share.

251
Decorative display of medals awarded to Ransomes: in form of a Star, glazed with wooden surround.
190cm. diameter
Ransomes, Sims and Jeffries plc

252
Map of Foundry Estate, c. 1813
57 x 47cm.
Ransomes, Sims and Jeffries plc

Between 1809 and 1815 business doubled at Ransomes. Partly because of the boom which occurred during the Napoleonic Wars and partly because of East Anglia's dominant position in arable farming.

251

253

253
Recreation at Ransomes Foundry, early 19th Century
Water colour on paper
Ransomes, Sims and Jefferies plc

Ransomes were also involved in production of items for the early railways. Robert Ransomes method of "chilling" was applied to iron crossings. Between 1847 and 1867 around 12,000 miles of railway were constructed using Ransomes materials.
In 1841 the business transferred to the new Orwell Works. A dinner was held to mark the occasion and the motto "Success to Plough and Rail" was adopted.
By 1849 the workforce was over 1,000.

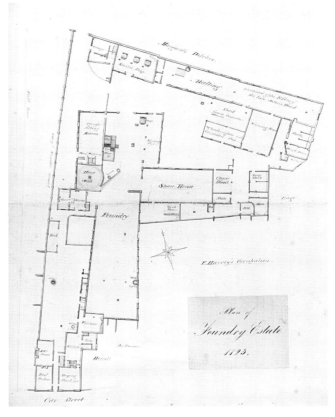

252

255

255
"Russian Scene" with Ransomes Plough, 19th Century
Thomas Smythe
Watercolour on paper, 84 x 112cm.
Ransomes, Sims and Jeffries plc

Arable farming expanded in eastern Europe with the abolition of serfdom. Ransomes extended their exports to eastern Europe selling many steam ploughing engines and threshers from their merchant warehouse in Odessa. Much publicity material remains from this period, and is included in the exhibition.

256
Threshing Scene, 19th century
Thomas Smythe
Watercolour on paper, 80 x 112cm.
Ransomes, Sims and Jeffries plc

From the 1850s Ransomes threshing machines became progressively more efficient and capable of finishing as well as threshing the grain.

254

254
Ransomes Foundry Worker, early 19th Century
Oil on canvas, 23 x 20cm.
Ransomes Sims and Jeffries plc

256

257

257
Match Ploughing Scene, 19th Century
Thomas Smythe
Watercolour on paper, 78 x 111cm.
Ransomes, Sims and Jeffries plc

Throughout the 1850s and 60s Ransomes expanded its agricultural engineering and concentrated less on other areas of production. This was a direct reversal of the policy pursued between 1815 and 1835 when the railway boom took priority. As a result, in 1869, all railway material manufacturing was transferred to a new firm Ransomes and Rapier.

This allowed for the expansion of the agricultural machinery sector; steam engines and threshers.

Steam power dominated this period of Ransomes history and for Ransomes their achievements with threshing machines advanced rapidly through the 50s and 60s.

258

The Earth Stopper
Patchwork and watercolour, 25 x 38cm.
Museum of English Naive Art, Bath

A cutting, verso, reads:
> "The Business of an Earth Stopper, the Night previous to a Day's
> Sport is to stop up the Fox's Earth whilst he is out Feeding.
> The above gently Swain is supposed to be on his way home, when
> by a sudden turn of the lane he is brought plump upon what he
> conceives to be nothing more or less than the D***l, but which in
> fact is a simple Sweep and his Donkey."

261

259

Nell, The Rat Hunter, 1852
J. WHITEHEAD
Oil on canvas, 50 x 67cm.
Museum of English Naive Art, Bath

Rats provided many threats to those who lived in rural areas
(in addition to the viruses carried by them in urban areas). A
good rat-catching dog was a valued member of the farming
household. This painting by J. Whitehead commemorates
"Nell" the rat-hunter of Failsworth, aged three years and nine
months.
The cause of her premature death is not recorded. This is a
comparatively sophisticated tribute with a background almost
Claudian in its composition.

261

Terrier and Rat in Cage
R. D. WIDDAS (1826-1885)
Oil on canvas
Iona Antiques

Richard Dodd Widdas was born in Leeds in 1826; in addition
to being an animal painter, he also painted shipping scenes. He
died in Hull in 1885.

260

262

260

A Ratter in an Interior
Attributed to Merlin T. Ward
Oil on canvas
Iona Antiques

Terriers were preferred as ideal ratters, with their rough coats.
They were small, compact, quick, determined and had a good
nose.

262

Painting on glass of Billy "Champion Rat Killer", 1823
50 x 60cm.
Collection of John Gall and Rosie Allen.

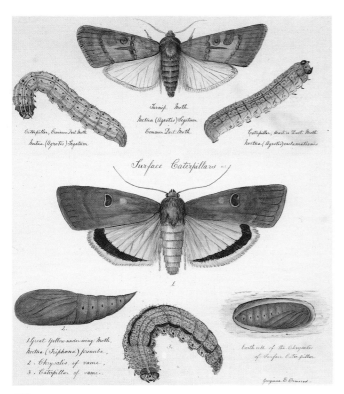

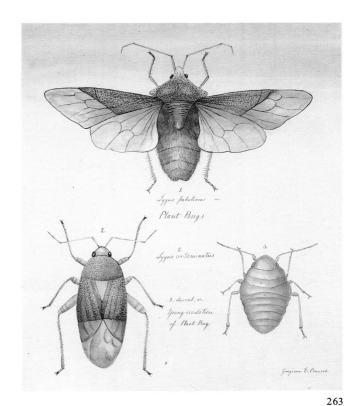

263
Insect Pests
Watercolour on paper
Georgiana Ormerod
for
Eleanor Ormerod
A.D.A.S.

Georgiana E Ormerod painted many illustrations of insects which could cause damage to crops to accompany her sister, Eleanor's, lectures on the subject in the late 19th Century. Here, reproduced, are "Plant Bugs" and the Turnip Moth and Great Yellow-under-wing moth. These may well have been used by Eleanor Ormerod when she gave her historic lecture to the Royal Agricultural Society of England.

Wild Convolvulus   Mrs Angell.

264

264
"Convolvulus and Green Wheat", 1867
HELEN CORDELIA ANGEL NÉE COLEMAN (1847-84)
Watercolour and gouache, 183 x 302cm.
Royal Albert Museum, Exeter

A troublesome weed, Convolvulus, which bears beautiful trumpet-shaped flowers, pulls down cereal stems. As late as 1958 it was noted that where the weed is abundant, prolonged drying of sheaves may be necessary in order to dry out the weed before stacking.

265

265
Hens and Cock, 1857
G. B. NEWMARCH
Oil on canvas, 51 x 61cm.
Iona Antiques

A whiteface black Spanish cock with three hens. George Newmarch was a painter who between 1828 and 1873 painting portraits of animals and military subjects. Fred Hams writes in "Old Poultry Breeds" that this breed was popular in Bristol as early as 1750.

266

266
Hens and Cockerel
JOSEPH CRAWHALL
Oil on canvas, 20.3 x 39.4cm.
The Duchess of Devonshire

267
Hen and Chicks, 1851
J. F. HERRING, SENIOR
Oil on canvas, 30 x 25cm.
Private Collection

268
Three Cockerels

and

269
Cockerel and Hens, 1855
WILLIAM J. SHAYER
Oil, 45 x 60cm.
Property of Robin Thompson, Esq

The first book in English on Poultry husbandry was "The Discourse Oeconomique" by Prudent Choyselet, translated out of the French by R.E., published in 1580. It pre-dated by one year the first English work on the subject, that written by Mascall.

Choyselet writes to a friend, injured in the civil wars of the times, and attempts to demonstrate to him how, by the investment of 500 livres, from the small amount of capital which remains to him, he may re-establish his fortune.

To choose hens:

> "You shall choose the yongest, whiche are apter to laye then the old: And the common, more then thei of kinde: or the Blacke, Redde, and Taunie, whiche are more fruitfull then the Graie or White, as *Aristotle* affirmeth in his Historie of beastes in the firste booke, the firste Chapiter. And also thei whiche have their creaste or combe double and upright, as witnesseth *Plinie* in his naturall Historie. Also *Palladius* and *Petrus Crescencis* in his booke of Housbandrie. Likewise *Carolus Stephanus* a man of our tyme, and diligente gatherer of thynges Economike, parteinyng to Householde and Housebandrie.
> Thei of a meane bignesse, are the beste, havying their breast large, their bodie well fleshed, not with long spurres like unto Cockes, for thei commonly breake their Egges. Take heede also that thei be not to fatte. Witnesse the good wife, whiche beyng in love with her Henne, fed her so well, and made her so fat, that she left laiyng, as rehearseth *Esope* in his Fables."

To choose cocks:

> "In like maner you shall buye Cockes, to sort or matche them: sixe score Cockes shall suffice for the twelve hundreth Hennes. For one Cocke maie suffice for ten Hennes. Thei maie coste you tenne Souses the peece, over and above the price of the Hennes: whiche amounteth to xlviij. Frankes. Thei of the age from a yere and a halfe, unto twoo yeres, are the beste.
> To knowe them well, you shall consider the Plumage, or Feathers. The Blacke, Red, and Taunie, are the beste. Also thei that have their Combe or Creaste upright, and double, or divided. Their eyes redde and glisteryng: Their becke, shorte and hooked: well spurred: their goyng, hautie and proude: Their voice strong and soundyng: and sutche as crowe mutch, representyng sutche a majestie, as did the Cocke of the Persians, whiche among them was reverenced, and honoured for a kyng, as reciteth *Aristophanes*. At the least, that thei shewe a certaine hardinesse, as thei which the *Carians*, people of the lesse *Asia*, bore upon their Morion or Helmet, goyng to battaill: as *Alexander de Alexandro hath written in the xx. Chapiter of his first booke.*"

270a
Pair of Game Fowl
A. R. REED
Oil on board, 22.1 x 29.7cm.
Professor and Mrs. C. Manwell

270b
"Indian Runner Duck" and "Buss Turkeys"
Hand coloured engravings
Private Collection

271
"Our Poultry"
HARRISON WEIR, F.R.H.S. Vol. I

Illustration of Black-Breasted Brown Red Prize Leghorn. The property of Mrs Lister Kay. From "Our Poultry".

272
A Sussex Farm
HENRY HERBERT LA THANGUE (1859-1929)
Oil on canvas, 76 x 60cm.
Ferens Art Gallery, Hull City Museums and Art Galleries

BLACK-BREASTED BROWN-RED PRIZE LEGHORN.
The property of Mrs. Lister Kay.

270a

273
Northamptonshire Agricultural Show at Burghley House 1875
WALTER RAY WOODS
Oil on canvas, 153 x 91.5cm.
The Burghley House Collection

273

274

The Victoria Jersey Cow

THOMAS SIDNEY COOPER, C.V.O., R.A. (1803-1902)
Oil on panel. 46 x 61.5cm.

During the summer of 1848 Her Majesty Queen Victoria commissioned Thomas Sidney Cooper to paint, at Osborne, this picture of the prize Jersey cow, which had been presented to her by the Corporation of Guernsey. She also requested that its calves should be included in the composition.

When Queen Victoria saw the painting she was delighted with the result, exclaiming "Oh Yes that is my Buffie!". This was the name she had given the cow, as its large dewlap resembled a buffalo's. The cow's official name was, however, "Victoria", because the white mark on the forehead of the animal formed a "V", This mark was common on the forehead of cattle, although particularly pronounced on 'Buffie'. Cooper observed that if the mark was seen upside down the letter 'A' could be recognised. He cleverly made it a feature of his painting so that it represented the initials of both "Victoria" and "Albert".

275

Princess Helena

F. W. KEYL (1823-71)
Watercolour, 53 x 67cm.

The Shorthorn heifer stands in an enclosure at Shaw Farm with three ducks.

276

Hereford Bullock: 1st Prize Smithfield, 1867
F. W. KEYL
Oil on canvas, 53 x 68cm.

277

Lambs in Home Park, 1868
F. W. KEYL
Oil on canvas, 30 x 45cm

278

Shorthorn Heifer, 1868
F. W. KEYL
Oil on canvas.

The above five paintings are loaned by gracious permission of Her Majesty the Queen.

279

Prize Cattle with owner and herdsman (c.1850)
UNKNOWN
Oil on canvas, 90 x 115cm.
Iona Antiques

280

Hereford Bull
H. S. QUINTIN
Oil on canvas
Iona Antiques

The Hereford was developed from local Stock, improved by the introduction of Dutch blood, by Herefordshire farmers, notably the Tomkins family in the late 18th and early 19th Centuries. They belong to the middle-horn group of breeds and are this related to Devon and Sussex Cattle. The modern appearance of the Hereford was established by the end of the 19th Century.

The Hereford Book was first published in 1846.

281

281

Three Devon cattle with a farmer, 1850
J. LODER, Bath
Oil on canvas, 58 x 75cm.
Iona Antiques

Devon cattle are a dark-cherry red, known also as 'Red Rubies', they have medium-sized horns, a blocky build with small and neat, short legs. Nigel Harvey writes in "Discovering Farm Livestock" that they were valued as draught animals and were among the earliest cattle which the Pilgrim Fathers took to the New World; indeed the first furrow cut by a plough in New England was driven by Devon oxen.

The most notable breeder of Devons was Francis Quartly of Molland He bought excellent stock during the Nepoleonic War when prices were inflated and his neighbours could not resist his offer.

282

282

White bull, 19th Century
ARTIST UNKNOWN
Oil on canvas
55 x 66cm.
Unit of Agricultural Economics, Oxford

283

White Heifer and Landscape, 1812
BRUNSCOMBE?
Oil on canvas, 63 x 75cm.
Unit of Agricultural Economics, Oxford

284

284

**Champion Aberdeen Angus Heifer and Reserve Number
Bullock at the Smithfield Club Show,** 1881, 1882
R. WHITFORD
Oil on canvas, 50 x 75cm.
Iona Antiques

The Aberdeen Angus was first developed in the early 19th
Century by Hugh Watson of Keillor, in Angus (Tayside) from
half a dozen of his father's 'best and blackest cows' of the local
breed.
Another breeder was William McCombie of Tillyfair whose
Angus cattle were incredibly successful, winning at the
Smithfield Show in 1867. He exhibited 'Black Prince', who
created such a sensation that he had to be taken to Windsor
by Royal Command, for Queen Victoria to see. The herdsman,
when asked about the steer's diet, replied: "Just heather bloom,
heather bloom".
McCombie seized the opportunity presented during the
Victorian era, of the new steamships, which made possible the
transport of fresh meat from Scotland to the London Market.

285

285

Francis Quartly, c.1850
Painter, T. MOGFORD
Engraver, F. JOUBERT
Engraving, 45 x 54cm.
Private collection

Engraved by F. Joubert after the painting by T. Mogford 1850.
Francis Quartly, of Molland, North Devon, stands against a
background of hilly, wooded landscape, his right hand resting
on a Devon cow, his left holding hat and stick, a calf in the
right foreground in front of a thatched shed.

286

Prize Bull and Prize Cabbage
Oil on board, 32.5 x 70cm.
Museum of English Naive Art, Bath

A naive painting of some ambition, including landscape with
farmhouse. Works such as this may have been produced by
coach-painters or sign-writers, itinerants who painted things
precious to those who owned a prize bull or a model farm.

287

Nine Angry Bulls
Oil on canvas, 48 x 75cm.
Museum of English Naive Art, Bath

Nine angry bulls rush towards a hare. All human life makes
a rapid exit from the furious scene, one of the most lively to
be found in English Naive painting.

288
Longhorn Cow in Wooded Landscape, 1840
E. M. Fox
Oil on canvas 61 x 75cm.
Private collection

A rather late depiction of the Longhorn. While by 1800 the
breed was probably the most popular in Britain this did not last
for long as the Longhorn began to be neglected in favour of
the Shorthorn.

289
Thorney Prize Ox, 1858
James Clark
Oil on canvas, 59 x 69cm.
M.E.R.L.

290
Shorthorn Bull, 1845
J. Loder
Oil on canvas, 66 x 80cm.
M.E.R.L.

291

291
"Duchess Gwynne and Siddington", 1874
A. M. Williams
Watercolour on paper, 18 x 37cm.
Beamish Museum

The painting shows Siddington 7th at six years and Duchess
Gwynne at 12 years.

292
Red Poll Heifer, 1841
Artist unknown
Oil on canvas, 63.5 x 76.5cm.
The Red Poll Cattle Society

The Red Poll is a breed which derives from a crossing between
the Norfolk, a hardy beef type, and the Suffolk Dun, a superb
dairy breed. This took place in the early Victorian period. An
early breeder was John Hammond.

293
Volume I: The Norfolk and Suffolk Red Poll Book, 1877
Henry Evren
The Red Poll Cattle Society

294
Silver Model of "Telemachus"
40cm.
The Burghley House Collection

Made by Robert Garrard, London, in 1872. Telemachus was
a prize bull from the Burghley Estate in Lincolnshire.

295

295
Silver Cow Cream jug, 1902
Miss Elizabeth Creak

Cow cream jugs are Dutch in origin. All early English Silver
examples were made by John Schuppe a Dutch immigrant
Silversmith who registered his first mark in 1785 in London at
Little Dean's Court, St Martins-le-Grand. He continued to work
into the 1770's and possibly later. All original cow cream jugs
have a fly on the lid. The ceramic versions all carry a slightly
later date.

297

296

296
Four improved Leicester Ewes, 1843
W. H. Davis (1783-1864)
Oil on canvas, 65 x 77cm.
Member of Council, R.A.S.E.

W. H. Davis painted mainly prize farm animals and exhibited
thirty works at the Royal Academy. He lived from c. 1834 until
1850 at 9, Church Street, Chelsea. In 1834 he was 'Animal
Painter to his Majesty' and in 1839 to 'Her Majesty'.

297
"Glory" Devon Longwool Ram, 1855
ENGLISH SCHOOL
Oil on canvas, 74 x 87cm.

Livestock: "Glory" won second prize at the Bath and West
Show at Bath, June 8th 1854. Bred by Thomas Potter of Yellow
Ford. In the background Yellow Ford, Thorverton.

298
"Matchless" Yearling Ram (Leicester) 1859
ENGLISH SCHOOL
Oil on canvas, 69 x 79.5cm.
Tiverton Museum

Livestock: "Matchless" won first price in Class 23—Yearling
Ram, Leicestershire Breed, at the Bath and West Show, at
Barnstaple, 1859. Bred by Thomas Potter of Yellow Ford. In
the background Yellow Ford, Thorverton.

299

299
Sheepdog Carrying Shepherd's Crook, c.1840.
ENGLISH SCHOOL
Oil on canvas 39 x 47.5cm.
Iona Antiques

Just as there are different kinds of Sheepdog, so there are
various crooks for different uses. Some crooks are intended to
catch around a sheep's limb, some around their necks.

300

300
Dog, 19th Century
Oil on canvas, 20 x 30in.
The Duchess of Devonshire

A 'primitive' painting of a dog, close in appearance to the Old
English Sheepdog.

301

301
Shepherd's Show Chest
170 x 35cm.
Collection of John Gall and Rosy Allan

In this a shepherd would stow his crooks. Painted and decorated
with two sheep at the front.

302

302
Shearling and Dog, c.1820
DAVID DALBY of York
Oil on canvas, 41.5 x 54cm.
Iona Antiques

A shearling is a one year old sheep which has been shorn once.
The painting is inscribed "This Shearling No. 52 in 1820 won
the premium at Bedale. The property of Mr. John Rob".

303
Shepherd's Neck Crook
Wood and metal
M.E.R.L.

304
Shepherd's Leg Crook
Wood
M.E.R.L.

305

305
**A proud owner with his Shepherd and flock of prize Costwold
Sheep,** 1861
RICHARD WHITFORD
Oil on canvas, 102 x 132cm.
Iona Antiques

An as yet unidentified owner of Cotswold Sheep dating from
1861.

306

306
Three Cotswold Ewes: First Prize Smithfield Show, 1875
RICHARD WHITFORD, 1876
Oil on canvas, 52 x 61cm.
Member of Council of R.A.S.E.

Professor David Low's entry on the Cotswold Sheep:
> "The Cotswold Breed of Sheep derives its name from a tract of low
> calcareous hills in the eastern division of the county of Gloucester,
> forming part of the great Oolite formation of England, which,
> commencing with the moorlands of Yorkshire, stretches diagonally
> across the islands, and looses itself in the British Channel, near the

Isle of Portland. The Gloucester portion of this track is of moderate elevation, comparatively infertile, yet capable of cultivation, and yielding in the natural state a short sweet herbage. It was formerly a range of bleak wastes, employed in the pasturage of Sheep, and much of it was in the state of common; but with the progress of the last century, the commons were appropriated, and cultivation was extended. It derives its name from Cote, a sheep-fold, and Would, a naked hill. It was early noted for the numbers of sheep which it maintained, and the fineness and abundance of their wool. 'In these woulds,' says the translator of CAMDEN, 'they feed in great numbers, flocks of sheep, long-necked and square of bulk and bone, by reason (as is commonly thought) of the weally and hilly situation of their pasturage, whose wool, being most fine and soft, is held in passing great account amongst all nations.'' Other writers refer to the excellence and abundance of the wool of the Cotswold Wolds. DRAYTON contrasts the rich fleece of Cotswold with the flocks of Sarum and Leominster, and gives the palm to Cotswold for its more abundant produce.''

''T'' whom Sarum's plaine gives place, though famous for its flocks:
Yet hardly doth she tythe our Cotswold's wealthy locks:
Though Lemster him exceed in finenesse of her ore,
Yet quite he puts her downe for his aboundant store.''

The faithful and laborious STOWE, in his Chronicles, states, that in the year 1464, KING EDWARD IV, ''concluded ammnesty and league with KING HENRY of Castill, and JOHN, King of Aragon, at the concluding whereof, hee granted licence for certain Coteswold Sheepe to be transported into the country of Spaine, which have there since most mightily increased and multiplied to the Spanish profit, as it is said.'' The worthy writer is not wholly satisfied that the Spaniards owned all their Sheep to England; for, adds he, ''true it is, that long ere this were Sheepe in Spaine, as may appear by a pattent of King HENRY the Second, granting to the weavers of London, that if any cloth were found to be made of Spanish wool, mixed with English wool, the maior of London should see it brent.'' ADAM SPEED who wrote in 1620, describes the wool of the Cotswold Sheep as similar to that of the Ryeland. ''In Herefordshire, especially about Lempster, and on those famous hills called Cotswold Hills, sheep are fed that produce a singular good wool, which for fineness, comes very near to that of Spain, for from it a thread may be drawn as fine as silk.'' The precise character of the Sheep which produced this wool is now unknown. They were probably similar to the large fine-woolled breeds of the adjoining counties of Wilts and Berks, a supposition which agrees with the locality of the districtd, and with ''the long necks and square of bulk and bone'' ascribed to the Cotswold Sheep by CAMDEN, and explains the distinction of DRAYTON between the wealthy locks of Coteswold, and the less abundant ore of Lemster. MARKHAM, indeed a writer of the time of Queen ELIZABETH, speaks of the Cotswold Sheep as having long wool, but this testimony cannot weigh against the direct authority of Speed in a later age; and we cannot be sure that the term long, as used by MARKHAM, is anything else than relative, as applied to the two kinds of wool.

The Sheep, however, which now possess the same country, and have inhabited it beyond the memory of the living generation, are a Long-wooled race, and thus entirely distinct from the Sheep of the ancient forests, wolds and downs, which produced the former fine wool of England. They are of the larger class of British Sheep, and all their characters denote them to be a breed of the plains and richer country. The period of their introduction is unknown, but it probably took place pretty late in the last century, with the appropriation of the commons, and the extension of tillage in a degree sufficient to supply artificial food to a larger kind of animal. A traditional belief has always existed in the country, that the modern race is not the original one of the Cotswold Wolds; but no intelligible account can be obtained from any one now living of the time or manner of its introduction. It was probably derived from the upper part of Oxfordshire, or from Warwickshire, the ancient breed of which it seems in some respects to have resembled; and the change may have been chiefly produced by crossing.''

307
Best Pen of Cotswold Ewes: First Prize Smithfield Show, 1875
RICHARD WHITFORD, 1876
Oil on canvas
51.5 x 61.5cm.
Member of Council, R.A.S.E.

308

308
Mr Garne's Cotswold Sheep, Northleach, 1866
R. WHITFORD
Oil on canvas, 81 x 112cm.
Unit of Agricultural Economics, Oxford

This painting is the subject of some discussion. Although shown as being of Mr. Garne's sheep, the inclusion of the work is a calendar published by Farmer's Weekly in 1970, aroused the interest of Mr. Frank Houlton, a grandson of William Lane of Bibury.

The shepherd carries folded over his arm a sheep's coat, used to protect the fleece of a sheep once when finely groomed for exhibition. Inscribed upside-down, on the cloth in the name Lane.

Whitford included the tower of Northleach in the background. The faces and legs of the sheep are trimmed to accentuate the massive body.

William Lane, like Garne, was a great breeder of Cotswolds. Born in 1814 he died in 1908.

309

309
The Prize Ram
ENGLISH PRIMITIVE
Oil on canvas, 26.5 x 51.5cm.
The Duchess of Devonshire

310
Windermere from Troutbeck, 1803
JULIUS CAESAR IBBETSON
Oil on canvas, 56 x 73cm.
Ferens Art Gallery, Hull City Museums and Art Galleries

311
Robert Lane, his Foreman, Shepherd and Five Prize Cotswold Rams, 1861.
G. R. WHITFORD
Oil on canvas, 90 x 116cm.
Private Collection

Robert Lane with his foreman, Mr. Day and Shepherd. Mr. Lockey with five prize rams which fetched an average of 100 guineas apiece. No. 13 fetched 120 gns. and No. 6 100 gns.

312
Valentine Barford with his Bakewell Leicester Sheep, c. 1850
Painter: H. BARRAUD Lithographers M. AND N. HANHART
Coloured lithograph, 66 x 77.5cm.
Private Collection

The painting was "Presented to Mr. Valentine Barford, by his friends as a token of respect for his upright conduct and of his great perseverance and ability in keeping up the true character and form of the pure bred Bakewell Leicester Sheep."
Valentine Barford is portrayed, book in hand, with the Sheep against a landscape background.

313
Pen of Theaves, 1858
RICHARD WHITFORD
Oil of canvas, 64 x 95cm.
M.E.R.L.

314
Border Leicester Ram 'Sir Walter' with Mr. J. Aitchison, Agent, and Mr. A. Thompson, Shepherd of the Rock Estate, 1869
Photograph, 15 x 21cm.
C. J. Bosanquet, Esq.

315
Hampshire Down Ewes, 1880
RICHARD WHITFORD
Oil on canvas, 54 x 67cm.
Iona Antiques

The Hampshire Down Sheep was developed in the early 19th Century by the use of Southdown rams on ewes of traditional Wiltshire and Berkshire breeds, notably by William Humfrey of Oak Ash, near Newbury in Berkshire. In 1839 he bought four of Webb's Southdowns at the first Royal Show and by skilful crossing founded the new breed.
This painting inscribed "First prize pen of Hampshire Down Ewes, shown at the Smithfield Club Show, Christmas 1879. The property of Frank R. Moore of Littlecote."

316
A Portrait of John Boys (1749-1824)
Oil on canvas, 32 x 52cm.
By kind permission of John and Anthony Boys, Great-Great Grandsons

John Boys was the author of the Agricultural Survey of Kent published in 1794. He came from a distinguished family and farmed at Betteshanger, near Deal. A great friend of Arthur Young and John Ellman of Glynde, Sussex, he was a founder member of Canterbury Farmers' Club which will celebrate its bicentenary in 1993. (The Club which met after the Saturday market at Canterbury in the Fleece Inn, when members would compare notes on prices and markets. The Club has been an important centre of support at times of difficulty in the East Kent region; during the great agricultural depression c. 1880-1914 and both World Wars.)
Boys was a leading agriculturalist; the first to have a threshing machine in Kent; the owner of a fine flock of Southdown Sheep, a keen experimenter and an enlightened employer.

320

317

319

317
Lakeland Landscape with Cattle, Sheep and Shepherds, 19th Century
TAYLOR LONGMIRE (1841-1914)
Oil on canvas, 50 x 68cm.
The National Trust

The animals depicted are a Dairy Shorthorn Cow, Swaledale and Cheviot Sheep. The Swaledale is, after the Herdwick, the hardiest of British breeds. The fleece has two coats, an outer coarse coat which repels the rain and a fine undercoat which keeps the animal warm. Its name derives from the river Swale in Yorkshire.

318
Two Swaledale Sheep, Windsmere and Langdale Pikes from Low Wood, 19th Century
TAYLOR LONGMIRE (1841-1914)
Oil on canvas, 41 x 57cm.
The National Trust

319
Flock of Herdwick Sheep at Windemere seen from Low Wood, 19th Century
TAYLOR LONGMIRE (1841-1914)
Oil on canvas, 65 x 45cm.
The National Trust

Nigel Harvey in "Discovering Farm Livestock" notes that these are the hardiest of all British breeds. At birth they are almost black, but turn to grey and then at maturity, white. "It is said that John Pell's coat was not 'gay' but 'grey' for it was made from home-spun Herdwick wool."

320
Swaledale Ram from Troutbeck looking south down Windemere
TAYLOR LONGMIRE (1841-1914)
Oil on canvas, 55 x 42cm.
The National Trust

321

321
Staffordshire Plaque of Ram, c.1830
24 x 33cm.
Private collection

Earthenware plaque, green and yellow glazes.

323

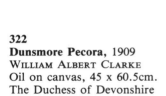

322

324

322
Dunsmore Pecora, 1909
WILLIAM ALBERT CLARKE
Oil on canvas, 45 x 60.5cm.
The Duchess of Devonshire

323
Ditchford Duchess, Ditchford Blossom, Lockinge Bay Leaf,
1909
W. A. CLARKE
Oil on canvas, 35.8 x 81.3cm.
The Duchess of Devonshire

324
Shire Horse, 1890
ALBERT CLARK
Oil on canvas
Iona Antiques

Albert Clark belonged to a family of painters who specialized
in painting horses.

325
"Cup Bearer III" a Suffolk Stallion
J. DUVAL
Oil on canvas, 45 x 54cm.
Suffolk Horse Society

Cup Bearer III was bred by C. Frost of Wherstead, Ipswich,
Suffolk in 1874.

326
Volume I Suffolk Horse Stud Book, 1880

The Suffolk Horse Society

The Suffolk Punch is the oldest British Breed of heavy horse,
and one of the oldest breeds of farm animal. Little is known
of the early history of the breed but there has been a "sorrel"
or chestnut, and distinct breed of carthorse in East Anglia since
at least 1500.

The detailed history begins with a Stallion known as Crisp's
Horse of Ufford foaled in that village in 1708. Every Suffolk
horse has a pedigree which may be traced back to Crisp's Horse.
A record of purity rivalled only by the thoroughbred horse.
Until the advent of the tractor, arable East Anglia was the home
of enormous numbers of Suffolks; agriculture in the area
revolved around the breed. As farmers mechanized after WWII,
horse numbers dwindled rapidly so that by the 1950's the Suffolk
breed came near to extinction. It was kept going by a small
handful of breeders.

Volume I of the Suffolk stud book, published in 1880, is rare.
It was the work of Herman Biddell, first secretary of the Suffolk
Horse Society. He spent two and a half years collecting a massive
amount of sales material and talking to informed individuals
such as 'Barber' Moyse of Framlingham who was born in 1789
and had a vast knowledge of the Suffolk.

The book was illustrated by Duval. Biddell said to him that to
"produce individuality of Character in the portrait of a Suffolk
horse requires no little practice."

327

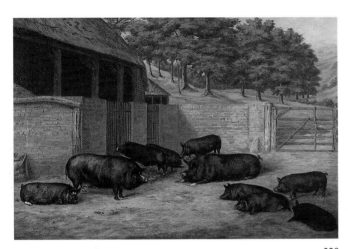

328

330

327
Gloucester Old Spots, c. 1840
ARTIST UNKNOWN
Oil on canvas, 40 x 54cm.
Iona Antiques

The Gloucester Old Spot is traditionally white with black spots and has lop ears.
These pigs were most popular among villagers, kept by smallholders and cottagers in the Severn Valley in paddocks or orchards, which is why they are sometimes called the 'Orchard Pig'.

328
Family of Pigs, c. 1880
H. J. BROOKS
Oil on canvas, 47 x 66cm.
Iona Antiques

Probably Berkshire pigs, note the white points: tail, snout and feet, and the prick ears. The Berkshire is the British breed which owes most to the imported Asian pigs.

329
Sow and Piglets in a Sty, 1854
J. HERRING, SNR.
Oil on panel, 24 x 29.5cm.
Private Collection

330
A Fat Pig; Northleach, n.d.
Attributed to JOHN MILES of Northleach
Oil on canvas, 46.5 x 56.5cm.
Iona Antiques

A fat pig bred and fed by Mr. C. Gillet, of Sherborne, near Northleach which weighed 38 score and 11 lb.

331
A White Boar, c. 1850
JOHN DALBY
Oil on canvas, 23 x 29cm.

332
Lincolnshire Curly Coat
Oil on canvas, 36 x 45cm.
Iona Antiques

The Lincolnshire Curly Coat is a breed now extinct. It was a breed used in the development of the Chester white breed from Pennsylvania; derived from crosses between the Yorkshire, Lincolnshire and Cumberland.

333

333
Three Berkshire Pigs
R. WHITFORD (1854-1887)
Oil on canvas, 55.5 x 46cm.
Private Collection

Three Berkshire Pigs believed to be bred and owned by John Treadwell of Model Farm, Upper Winchendon, Aylesbury, Bucks, who commissioned the painting from Richard Whitford. Whitford specialised in the portraiture of prize farm animals and lived in Evesham and Northleach where many of his paintings were executed. On several of his paintings, the inscription 'Animal Painter to the Queen' is written but it is not known whether or not this is a self-styled title.'

334

334
A Bacon Hog: Neapolitan Breed, 1848
R. FARMER
Oil on canvas, 31 x 41cm.
Iona Antiques

Asian pigs found their way to Italy in ancient times. During the late 18th and early 19th centuries pigs of Asian origin were imported into Britain in some quantity, either directly from China or Siam or indirectly, in the case of the Neapolitan, through Mediterranean types.
This painting inscribed on reverse: "A Bacon Hog weighing 27st. 3lbs. of Lord Western's Improved Neapolitan. Bred and Fatted by C. Steward. Killed 1848. Painted from Nature by R. Farmer, 1848."

335
Neapolitan Boar and Sow, 1834
ARTIST UNKNOWN
Oil on canvas, 54.5 x 66cm.
Iona Antiques

The Neapolitan breed was remarked on by Professor David Low as having remarkably good flesh. But he concluded, "the best Hogs of Italy are supposed to be produced in the Duchy of Parma. They are of larger size than those of Naples, while they possess even greater aptitude to fatten, and yield pork equally white and delicate."

336
Market Place, Salisbury, c. 1850
ARTIST UNKNOWN
Watercolour on paper, 22.5 x 28cm.
The Salisbury and South Wiltshire Museum

Tethered cattle and sheep in pens, cabbages, carrots and other vegetables in a square, with very few customers; a town crier can be seen in the background.

337
The Poultry Cross, Salisbury, c. 1840
ARTIST UNKNOWN
Watercolour on paper, 28 x 22.5cm.
The Salisbury and South Wiltshire Museum

338
The Onion Fair, Salisbury, 1865
WALTER TIFFIN
Pencil and watercolour on paper, 31 x 37cm.
The Salisbury and South Wiltshire Museum

337

339

339
Boston May Sheep Fair, c. 1850
GEORGE NORTHOUSE
Lithographers Day and Haghe
Coloured lithograph, 58 x 73cm.
Unit of Agricultural Economics

Inscription: "To the gentry, farmers, graziers, dealers, tradesmen, &c. of Lincolnshire, this engraving of Boston May Sheep-fair, is most humbly dedicated, by their very obedient servant, George Northouse."

338

336

340

340
'Market Day, Malmesbury', 1868
H. C. BRYANT
Oil on canvas, 64 x 78cm.
Fine Art of Oakham

A late Summer market with baskets of produce including
damsons, marrows and unmistakably Victorian posies. Henry
Charles Bryant specialised in genre landscape and market scenes
of which this is one of his finest.

341
"Market Day", 1907
W. FRANK CALDERON (1865-1943)
Oil on canvas, 91 x 102cm.
Worcester City Museum and Art Gallery

342
**Gypsy horse-'fair' in a downland setting with cattle and post
windmill**, late 19th Century.
CHARLES COLLINS
Oil on canvas, 75.5 x 51.5cm.
Welholme Galleries (Great Grimsby Borough Council)

Charles Collins exhibited a large number of agricultural scenes
at the Society of British Artists from 1867 until 1893; horse or
cattle fairs, inspired by the work of Rosa Bonheur and John
Frederick Herring Senior. Such works would normally receive
more favourable hanging at the Society of British Artists than
they would at the Royal Academy. Here an impressive distant
landscape with a windmill and gypsy waggons, acts as a fitting
backdrop to the lively foreground.

343
Assessing Samples of Wheat, 1856
GEORGE DRUMMOND
Oil on canvas, 182 x 165cm.
The Company of Merchant Adventurers of the City of York

With a fine cloth a merchant burnishes the grains of wheat. One
man holds what may be a sample case. Money, including a five
pound note, rests on the cloth. The scene may take place inside
a Corn Exchange and is a moment of great importance when the
value of the crop is decided. Nothing is known about the history
of this painting by the present owners.

342

133

344

344

The Home Farm, 1844
THOMAS SIDNEY COOPER, C.V.O., R.A. (1803-1902)
Oil on canvas, 106 x 143cm.
The Royal Museum and Art Gallery, Canterbury

Cooper's superb draughtsmanship and sophisticated compositions elevated him to a position of eminence as a landscape and cattle painter. He exhibited this picture at The British Institution in 1844 under the title 'Cattle Shed'. His initials and date of the picture are shown carved on the trunk of the gnarled oak tree.

The young calf resting in the shade is beautifully observed, and throughout the painting Cooper demonstrates a marvellous eye for detail. Gypsies can be seen in the distant landscape collecting fire wood. In life gypsies were usually hated and despised by landowners and farmers, but in painting they were accepted and admired for their 'picturesque' quality.

345

A View of Canterbury from St. Stephen's, 1819
JAMES PARDON (1794-1862)
Oil on canvas, 69 x 90cm.
Canterbury Heritage-Time-Walk Museum

This view by James Pardon 1791-1862, was taken from St. Stephen's in Canterbury and was exhibited at The Royal Academy in 1819. Recorded in the distance are the Cathedral, Abbot's mill (which was destroyed by fire in 1933) and St. Augustine's Abbey.

At this time James Pardon lived at 51 St. Peter's Street, Canterbury, where he practised as a portrait and animal painter, and his work would have been seen by the young Thomas Sidney Cooper, R.A. (later to become Britain's leading cattle painter) who lived a few doors down on the other side of the street.

346

"View of the Tyne near Ryton" *and* "View of the Tyne at Scotswold", 1863
THOMAS HAIR
Watercolour on paper, both 47 x 68cm.
Trustees of the Science Museum

These watercolours by Thomas Hair, painted in 1863, are a pair of scenes of the Tyne valley which capture the growth of industry within an agricultural community.

The landscape, industrial and marine painter Thomas Henry Hair (1810-1882) was a native of the village of Scotswood, near Newcastle. Early in his career, Hair had become absorbed with the Northumbrian industrial scene, and in particular with the collieries of the north east. These he depicted in a series of fine watercolours that formed the basis of etchings for definitive *Sketches of the Coal Mines in Northumberland and Durham, 1839,* now in Newcastle University.

In 1863 a report on the industrial resources of the Tyne, Wear and Tees rivers, including reports on the local manufactures, was read before the British Association. It was edited for publication by among others the Northumbrian inventor and industrialist Sir William George Armstrong. The potential for an expansion and development that would eclipse agricultural resources was enormous.

The view of the Tyne near Ryton, shows a harvest idyll as the corn is stooked and hay is gathered into sheaves. Beyond is the smoke of a smelting house in the valley, and evidence of pitheads and furnace workings. The companion scene, captures the view at Scotswood further along the Tyne with the growth of river staithes, the coal tug, housing estate and industry inexorably encroaching upon agricultural land. Within two decades, this area of the Tyne valley had become almost totally industrialised, with Armstrong's Elswick works a prime concern.

347

Still Life with Christmas Food, December 1839
MARY ELLEN BEST
Pencil, watercolour·and bodycolour, 30.7 x 30cm.
York City Art Gallery

Yorkshire was famous for its magnificent Christmas pies such as the one dominating this picture. The most elaborate ones contained a boned pigeon folded within a partridge, within a fowl, within a goose, within a turkey, but simpler versions were also made just using goose. They were usually prepared on the feast of St. Stephen 26 December.

This picture was painted during the last winter Mary Ellen Best was in England as a single woman. She married Johann Anton Phillip Sarg at St. Olave's Church on 15 January 1840 and went to live with him in Germany afterwards.

Purchased with the aid of a grant from the Museums and Galleries Commission, 1986. Ref. Caroline Davidson, *The World of Mary Ellen Best, 1985.*

348

Farmyard Scene, 1846
THOMAS BAKER of Leamington
Oil on Panel, 59 x 75cm.
Sir Richard Cooper, Bt.

349

Children helping with Harvest, c. 1860
ENGLISH SCHOOL
Private Collection

The changing face of the harvest during the 19th Century was vividly described by Richard Jefferies in 'Hodge and His Masters' first published in a London Newspaper *The Standard* in 1879.

"On the rising ground pause a moment and look round. Wheat and barley and oats stretch mile after mile on either hand. Here the red wheat tinges the view, there the whiter barley; but the prevailing hue is a light gold. Yonder green is the swede, or turnip, or mangold; but frequent as arethe fields of roots, the golden tint overpowers the green. A golden sun looks down upon the golden wheat—the winds are still and the heat broods over the corn. It is pleasant to get under the scanty shadow of the stunted ash. Think what wealth all that glorious beauty represents. Wealth to the rich man, wealth to the poor.

Come again in a few weeks' time and look down upon it. The swarthy reapers are at work. They bend to their labour till the tall corn overtops their heads. Every now and then they rise up, and stand breast high among the wheat. Every field is full of them, men and women, young lads and girls, busy as they may be. Yonder the reaping-machine, with its strange-looking arms revolving like the vast claws of an unearthly monster beating down the grain, goes rapidly round and round in an ever-narrowing circle till the last ears fall. A crowd has pounced upon the cut corn. Behind them—behind the reapers—everywhere abroad on the great plain rises an army, regiment behind regiment, the sheaves stacked in regular ranks down the fields. Yet a little while, and over that immense expanse not one single, solitary straw will be left standing. Then the green roots show

350

more strongly, and tint the landscape. Next comes the wagons, and after that the children searching for stray ears of wheat, for not one must be left behind. After that, in the ploughing time, while yet the sun shines warm, it is a sight to watch the teams from under the same ash tree, returning from their labour in the afternoon. Six horses here, eight horses there, twelve yonder, four far away; all in single file, slowly walking home, and needing no order or touch of whip to direct their steps to the well-known stables.

If any wish to see the work of farming in its full flush and vigour, let them visit a corn district at the harvest time. Down in the village there scarcely anyone is left at home; every man, woman, and child is out in the field. It is the day of prosperity, of continuous work for all, of high wages. It is, then, easy to understand why corn villages are populous. One cannot but feel the strongest sympathy with these men. The scene altogether seems so thoroughly, so intensely English. The spirit of it enters into the spectator, and he feels that he, too, must try his hand at the reaping, and then slake his thirst from the same cup with these bronzed workers.

Yet what a difficult problem lies underneath all this!

While the reaper yonder slashes at the straw, huge ships are on the ocean rushing through the foam to bring grain to the great cities to whom—and to all—cheap bread is so inestimable a blessing. Very likely, when he pauses in his work, and takes his luncheon, the crust he eats is made of flour ground out of grain that grew in far distant Minnesota, or some vast Western State. Perhaps at the same moment the farmer himself sits at his desk and adds up figure after figure, calculating the cost of production, the expenditure on labour, the price of manure put into the soil, the capital invested in the steam-plough, and the cost of feeding the bullocks that are already intended for the next Christmas. Against these he places the market price of that wheat he can see being reaped from his window, and the price he receives from his fattened bullock. Then a vision rises before him of green meads and broad pastures slowly supplanting the corn; the plough put away, and the scythe brought out and sharpened. If so, where then will be the crowd of men and women yonder working in the wheat?.''

350
"Salisbury Plain—Showery Day"
WILLIAM TURNER of Oxford
Watercolour on paper. 27 x 40cm.
The Duke of Devonshire and the Trustees of the Chatsworth Settlement

William Turner, 'called Turner of Oxford' to distinguish him from J. M. W. Turner, exhibited mainly watercolours, including 455 at the Old Watercolour Society.

This picture shows in the foreground a shepherd and his dog watching over his flock of sheep on open land. Other shepherds, each with a single dog can be seen in the mid and far distance tending separate groups of sheep. The eye is drawn to the horizon where the shape of Stonehenge is set effectively against the light sky. To the left the sun is filtering through the rain clouds in rays of light, providing a dramatic and atmospheric effect.

351

Sawpit at the Old Farm near Woodstock

H. J. BODDINGTON, 1811-1865

Oil on canvas, 47 x 92cm.

Private Collection

Henry John Boddington was the son of Edward 'Moonlight' Williams, and a member of a large family of painters, which included George Morland and James Ward. He adopted his wife's maiden name of 'Boddington' to avoid confusion with other members of the Williams family.

This scene shows woodcutters at work on a farm near Woodstock. A trench has been dug to place the second labourer needed for the two-man saw. Cutting planks by hand was extremely hard work and the poor man in the pit had the additional burden of being bombarded by sawdust and wood-chippings.

352

Haymaking: Covering the Hayrick, 1889

B. W. LEADER (1831-1923)

Oil on canvas, 60.9 x 78.7cm.

Private collection

Benjamin Williams Leader epitomizes everything that is good in Victorian landscape painting. He was a master at his craft and an excellent colourist. Shown set in the mid-distance are farm labourers concentrating on their work of covering a hayrick. They are cleverly contrasted against the dark tones of the dominating trees towering behind them. The artist here conveys a sense of freshness and vitality that is the hallmark of much of his work.

353

Timber Hauliers

Attributed to J. F. HERNING, SNR.

Oil on canvas, 60 x 90cm.

Private Collection

The stacks of bark to the right of the canvas were to be used in the process of tanning.

354

"Corn Harvest"

P. LESLIE

Oil on canvas, 44 x 78cm.

Peter Strawson, Esq.

355

"Hay Harvest"

P. LESLIE

Oil on canvas, 44 x 78cm.

Peter Strawson, Esq.

356

Barden Tower, 1868

ATKINSON GRIMSHAW

Watercolour and bodycolour on paper, 39 x 54.2cm.

The Duchess of Devonshire

This painting shows potato pickers at work in a field by Barden Tower, near Bolton Abbey, Yorkshire. Grimshaw produced a series of views around the Wharfe Valley in the period up to 1870.

Grimshaw is chiefly remembered for his evocative moonlight dock scenes, but he was a versatile artist with a remarkable eye for detail and an outstanding ability to convey atmosphere.

357

View on the Yare with sailing barges loaded with the harvest

JAMES STARK (1794-1859)

Oil on panel, 41.5 x 59cm.

Private Collection

Grain was often transported by water; a well-known vessel was the Norfolk Wherry.

358

Haymaking—A Summer Landscape, n.d.

JAMES STARK (1794-1859)

Oil on canvas, 58.4 x 81.3cm.

Private Collection

359

Haymaking, n.d.

F. W. WATTS (1800-1870)

Oil on canvas, 68.6 x 91.4cm.

Private Collection

360

Reaping the Harvest, 1892

GEORGE VICAT COLE (1833-1893)

Oil on canvas, 118.1 x 170.2cm.

Private Collection

361

361

Tanfield Ploughman, 19th Century

ARTIST UNKNOWN

Oil on canvas, 19 x 39cm.

Beamish Museum

351

353

354

355

352

356

362

363

362

Morning, c. 1869
Samuel Palmer (1805-81)
Watercolour and bodycolour on paper, 51 x 70cm.
The Duke of Devonshire and the Trustees of the Chatsworth
Settlement

Both 'The Bellman' and 'Morning' illustrate passages from
Milton's *'Il Penseroso'*.

> "And the Bellman's drowsy charm
> To bless the doors from Nightly harm"
> [ll. 83, 84]

and:

> "Not trick and frounct, as she was wont
> With the Attic Boy to hunt;
> But kerchieft in a comely cloud,
> While rocking winds are piping loud,
> Or usher'd with a shower still
> When the gust hath blow his fill,
> Ending on the rustling leaves,
> With minute drops from off the eaves"
> [ll. 123-130]

While there are references to a Mediterranean countryside there
are equally strong elements, particularly in The Bellman' of an
English rural setting.

363

The Bellman, c. 1881
SAMUEL PALMER (1805-81)
Watercolour and bodycolour on paper, 51 x 70cm.
The Duke of Devonshire and the Trustees of the Chatsworth
Settlement

364

Crossing the Heath, 1848
D. Cox
Oil on canvas, 58 x 83cm.
Midland Bank plc

365

Farm Labourers by a Well, 1861
GERTRUDE ROGERS
Photograph, 29 x 24cm.
Private Collection

A gold-chloride albumen print form a 10″ x 12″ collodion wet
plate negative.
Miss Gertrude Rogers of Riverhill House, Sevenoaks in Kent
took many fascinating photographs until her marriage when,
unfortunately, her husband felt that it was an unsuitable
occupation for his wife, whereupon she ceased taking
photographs.

366

The Bell Inn, Cadnam
WILLIAM SHAYER
Oil on canvas
Private Collection

367

Relief of Ploughing, c. 1898
GEORGE WASHINGTON JACK (1855-1931)
Plaster, 36 x 106cm.
The Fine Art Society, London

368

In the Harvest Field, 1893
F. E. GRÖNE (exhibited 1886-1903)
58 x 80cm.
Colchester & Essex Museum

369

Garden Allotments, 1899
SIR GEORGE CLAUSEN, R.A., R.I., R.W.S. (1852-1944)
Oil on canvas, 107 x 140cm.
The Fine Art Society, London

In 1908 the Small Holdings and Allotments Act was passed.
This was of some importance, putting on the county councils
the obligation of acquiring land suitable for small holdings.
Many who applied for such land were landless
labourers—25,000 in the seven years before WWI—only 12,461
were successful. The Society of Friends played an important
role in promoting the idea of allotments where people might
grow fresh vegetables for their own consumption.

370

Landscape, Ploughing and Dibbling Beans, 19th Century
ARTIST UNKNOWN
Oil on canvas, 43.2 x 61cm.
Nottingham Castle Museum and Art Gallery

371

371
The Heavy-Horse Dealer, 1890
HENRY PAYNE (1868-1940)
Oil on canvas, 77 x 115cm.
Member of Council, R.A.S.E.

With around a million horses used to work the land this must
have been a common sight during the late 19th and early 20th
Centuries; a working team leaving the field, the new team having
gone in, and encountering the stock of a dealer.

372

373

372
Blacksmiths Forge, Portsmouth, 1849
G. COLE AND G. V. COLE
Oil on panel, 26.5 x 44.5cm.
Peter Strawson, Esq.

A vital link in rural industry the Blacksmith's forge was a
popular subject both in painting and poetry:
   "Under the spreading chestnut tree
   The Village Smithy stands;
   The Smith, a mighty man is he,
   With large and sinewy hands;
   And the muscles of his brawny arms
   Are strong as iron bands."
                    H. W. Longfellow

373
The Smithy at Newbigging, Monikie, 1873
G. W. GEDDES
Oil on panel, 59.7 x 76.2cm.
Private collection

This painting by Geddes depicts the interior of the Blacksmith's
shop. A boy in the sunlight watches the activity in the dimly
lit shop. The light from the open door catches the Blacksmith
in the action of shoeing a horse, while his colleagues rest, lit
by the furnace. The tools of their trade provide interest in the
foreground and together with the timbered roof help to 'frame'
the composition.

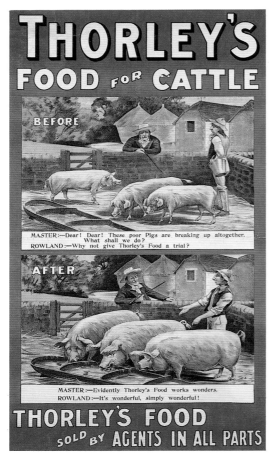

376

374
Advertisement by GAUCI for Thornley, 1883
141 x 81cm.
Beamish Museum

A. M. Gauci worked between 1848 and 1885 and painted many of the illustrations of celebrated Shorthorn cattle that appeared in Coates' Herd book.

375
Thorley's Cattle Food, c. 1880
Poster, 141 x 81cm.
Beamish Museum

376
Selection of tins etc. Corvusine, Sheep dip—Coopers in paper packet, Tippers, Osmonds Saltona, Osmonds Grease wash and tin plate advertisements: Ransom's: Swale Turner, 1900 (47 x 64cm.)
Ransome's: Plough's for all Purposes (56 x 76cm.)
Howard's Ploughs, c. 1900 (56 x 69cm.)
Beamish Museum

377
6lb. tin of Exeter Corned Beef packed in Uruguay for the Exeter Food Company shortly before WWI.
J. C. R. TREVELYAN

378
John Lawson Johnston in his Laboratory, 1895
J. LAMB
Oil on canvas, 77 x 47cm.
Hon. A. C. Lawson Johnston

Soon after the end of the Franco-Prussian War in 1871 a young Scotsman named John Lawson Johnston obtained a contract from the French Government to provide canned beef—provisions for the frontier fortresses which had surrendered so rapidly due to their inadequate food supplies. To obtain sufficient beef Lawson Johnston went to Canada and set up a factory. As the canned meat contract ran out he began experimenting with a blend of meat extract and other raw materials to form a product which he started selling in 1874 as a stimulating drink. It was called "Johnston's Fluid Beef". It was an immediate success and before long Lawson Johnston moved to a new factory in Montreal. However in 1884 this factory burned down and Lawson Johnston sold up and returned to London where he started selling the same product as "Bovril" in 1886.
(The word Bovril' derives from "bos" meaning an ox in Latin and "Vril" from "Vrilya", the "life force" in Bulwer Lytton's novel "The Coming Race".)
Then commenced a celebrated advertising and marketing campaign which was to make Bovril a national household name by the end of the Century. Earliest extant advertisements date from 1889 but in 1893 a Bovril employee, named S. H. Benson, left the company and set up as an "advertising agent" with Bovril as his first client.
In the meantime as sales of the primary product increased other products were introduced and sold along with Bovril.
Bovril posters include some of the most famous in the history of advertising—"Alas, my poor brother" in 1896 and "Bovril prevents that sinking feeling" from 1920 being the most celebrated.
In 1897 Bovril became a public company, but remained under the control of the Lawson Johnston family until 1971 when it was taken over by Sir James Goldsmith's Cavenham Foods. It is now part of the Beecham Group.

379

Bovril Salesman's Case containing entire range: includes Boer and WWI ration tins and other related items, c. 1900
33 x 46 x 32cm.
Hon. A. C. Lawson Johnston

Contents of Sample Box:-
Bovril (different bottle sizes)

Bovril chocolate	Bovril Stamnoids
Wild cherry sauce	Bovril cocoa
Bovril wine	Liebigs meat extract
Bovril beef jelly	Bovril field ration cartridges
Bovril meat juice	(used in Boer War)
Virol	Palmers Nepaul condiment
Goorkha relish	Bovril field bacon ration.
Celery salt	

380

Selection of Catalogues for Albion binders and Reapers
M.E.R.L.

In 1826 Patrick Bell, a student of Divinity at St. Andrew's with an interest in mechanics, walking in his father's garden and noticing a pair of garden shears sticking in a hedge had the idea that mechanical scissors rather than scythes might be made the basis of a reaper. By 1828 he had produced a reaper which worked. A five foot cut left a stubble 3 to 4 inches high, free from loose straw, and the cut corn was deposited on the side of the machine in a regular manner. Without raking the corn would be collected into compact and well-formed sheaves. Six to eight people, gathering, binding and setting constituted the team of workers. One horse propelled the machine from behind. The estimated cost of the reaper was £30.

Bell did not take out a patent, a deliberate decision in order that the machine might go into the world free of any avoidable expense. Sadly this meant that local variations of his reaper led to problems in efficiency, and while Bell in 1868 was honoured by the Highland and Agricultural Society 'in token of their appreciation of his pre-eminent services as the inventor of the first efficient reaping machine', his reaper was eclipsed by the American McCormick reaper, which would be first seen in England in the 1851 Great Exhibition at Crystal Palace.

382

382

Cooper's Sheep-dip Timer
10½cm. high
Private Collection

The timer runs for one minute, the length of time specified by the manufacturer, for the animal to remain immersed. It has a twist closure to protect the timer.

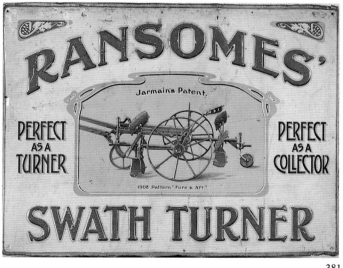

381

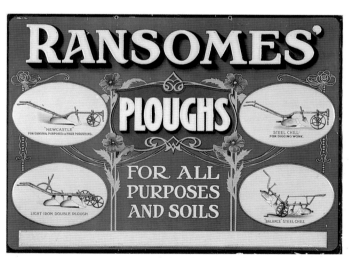

381

381

Selection of Enamelled Signs
Beamish Museum

383

383
Mug, 1802
15 x 18cm.
Collection of John Gall and Rosy Allan

Possibly from Liverpool, this piece dates from 1802. Decorated in blue and yellow colours under the glaze with motifs of wheatsheaf and farmers tools.

384
Jug
City Museum & Art Gallery, Stoke-on-Trent

Earthenware jug, printed decoration in black under the glaze, fitted in overglaze with enamel colours. Made in Staffordshire during the mid-19th Century.

385
Loving Cup
City Museum & Art Gallery, Stoke-on-Trent

Earthenware Loving Cup. Printed underglaze with "Trust in God" and "Industry Produceth Wealth". Blue lines also in underglaze. Made in Staffordshire during the mid-19th Century.

386
Hexagonal Jug
City Museum & Art Gallery, Stoke-on-Trent

Hexagonal jug in earthenware. Decoration printed underglaze in black and filled in with enamel pink and blue colours (overglaze). Name printed on the front "Richard Walton". Made in Staffordshire during the mid-19th Century.

387
Hexagonal Jug
26cm.
City Museum & Art Gallery, Stoke-on-Trent

Hexagonal earthenware jug, Printed decoration under the glaze in black: "God Speed the Plough", "Industry Produceth Wealth" and "Trust in God". Made in Staffordshire during the mid-19th Century.
Verses were a popular form of decoration on much ceramic ware. For example:

"The Farmer

O happy is the farmer and free from all care
Who rises each morning to breathe fresh air
And hears the bird's singing from every green bough.
No life like the farmers that follows the plough,
Success ere attend him and plenty and peace
May the seeds that he sows with blessings encrese
May health still around him its comforts bestow
Long life to the farmer and God speed the plough"

and so too were quotations:

"He that by the plough would thrive,
Himself must either hold or drive."

(Benjamin Franklin: Poor Richard' [1747]).
and definitions:

"Agriculture, the most useful and important
of all pursuits, teaches the nature of soils and
their proper adaptation and management for
the production of food for man and beast."

all of which are found on numerous examples of earthenware pots.

388
Jug
Lustre on rim
God Speed the Plough
23cm.
City Museum & Art Gallery, Stoke-on-Trent

Earthenware jug. Printed decoration underglaze in black, filled in overglaze with enamel colours and orange lustre: "God Speed the Plough", "Industry Produceth Wealth" and portrait of Burnet. Made in Staffordshire during the mid-19th Century.

385

384   386

388

391   392

387

389
Loving Cup With Frogs
18cm.
City Museum & Art Gallery, Stoke-on-Trent

Loving cup in earthenware. Printed decoration in black underglaze. Two frogs inside, undecorated. "God Speed the Plough" and "Industry Produceth Wealth". Possibly made in Staffordshire during the mid-19th Century.

390
Loving Cup with Frog, 1863
19cm.
City Museum & Art Gallery, Stoke-on-Trent

Earthenware Loving cup. Decoration printed in brown underglaze, in reserves of blue underglaze. Frog in base modelled and covered with black enamel. Inscription: John Brown 1863. Probably made in Staffordshire 1863.

391
Loving Cup with Frogs and Newt
14cm.
City Museum & Art Gallery, Stoke-on-Trent

Loving cup in earthenware. Printed decoration underglaze in black, Two frogs in yellow with black dots, one newt in black with yellow dots: enamel colours.
Possibly made in Staffordshire during the mid-19th Century.

392
Loving Cup
14cm.
City Museum & Art Gallery, Stoke-on-Trent

Earthenware Loving cup, printed decoration underglaze in black, overglaze filled in with pink and orange enamel colours, best gold edge-lines. Two newts, two frogs; yellow and pink enamel colours.
Possibly made in Staffordshire during the mid-19th Century.

393

394

395

393
Plate
23.3cm.
City Museum & Art Gallery, Stoke-on-Trent

Earthenware plate. Printed decoration under the glaze in blue.
Made by T. C. Brown, Westhead Moore & Co. Cavedon Place,
Hanley. Retained by Mortlock's, Oxford Street, London.
Design registered 1875. This piece dated 1888. Name of design
''Pastoral''.

394
Plate
24.7cm.
City Museum & Art Gallery, Stoke-on-Trent

Earthenware plate, printed decoration under the glaze in blue.
Floral border, scene of drovers in the centre. Unmarked.
Possibly made by Rogers of Dale Hall, Longport, Burslem,
Staffordshire 1815-30.

395
Cheese Saddle
43.5cm.
City Museum & Art Gallery, Stoke-on-Trent

Earthenware cheese saddle. Printed decoration underglaze in
blue. A version of the Willow pattern story.
Made in Staffordshire 1820-50.

144

399a

396

Oval Platter, 1936
37cm.
City Museum & Art Gallery, Stoke-on-Trent

Oval Earthenware plate. Printed decoration in black beneath the glaze. Pattern name "Rural Scenes". Made by A. J. Wilkinson, Royal Staffordshire Pottery, Burslem, Stoke-on-Trent, 1936.

397

Spill Vase (c.f. page)
27cm.
City Museum & Art Gallery, Stoke-on-Trent

Earthenware Spill Vase, cow and her calf by a stream. Enamel colours and bright gold. Made by Sampson Smith, Langton, Staffordshire in the early 20th century. Mark in raised letters on bases.

398

Potato Flask
18cm.
City Museum & Art Gallery, Stoke-on-Trent

Earthenware flask in the shape of a potato, covered in brown glaze. Made in an English country pottery during the 19th Century.

399a
Ceramic Tiles, Designed 1879
W. WISE
15.4 x 15.4cm.
Minton Museum, Royal Doulton Ltd

A number of Minton tiles from the Series of twelve 'Animals of the Farm', printed in sepia from copper-plate engravings designed by Wiliam Wise.
Marks: Moulded, Mintons China Works, Stoke-on-Trent. Moulded, Mintons Globe mark and London warehouse mark.
William Wise was inspired by *Hills' Etchings of Animals* a set of which is preserved in the Minton Archives. The Series of 'Animals of the Farm' tiles was introduced in 1879 and proved to be one of Minton's most popular tile designs.

399b
Sunderland Pottery: Creamware Mug
Sunderland Museum and Art Gallery, (Tyne and Wear Museum Service)

Creamware mug, probably made at Dawson's Low Ford Pottery, Sunderland, c.1810-1820.
Decorated with the hand-enamelled transfer-printed verse 'Industry', flanked by male and female figures and farming implements.

399c
Sunderland Pottery: Earthenware Jug, 1866
Sunderland Museum and Art Gallery (Tyne and Wear Museums Service)

Earthenware jug, inscribed 'James Pringle, 1866', decorated with transfer-printed designs including a ploughman and the verse "Success to the Farmer", a version of the "Farmer's Arms":

> "Let the wealthy and great
> Roll in splendor and state,
> I envy them not I declare it
> I eat my own lamb
> My chicken and ham
> I shear my own fleece and I wear it.
> I have fruits I have flowers
> I have lawns I have bowers
> The lark is my morning alarmer.
> So joly jolly boys now
> Here's God speed the plough
> Long life and success to the farmer."

Probably made at Scott's Southwick Pottery, Sunderland.

396

398

401

400
Coalport Ale Jug, c. 1806
JOHN ROSE
16.1cm.
Mr and Mrs J. B. Briggs

A Coalport globular ale jug in gilt and white with scroll handle; gilt decoration on the one side of barley and on the other side of hops; with an initial"M" below the lip and with scattered foliage sprays. John Rose's factory.

401
Coalport Jug, c. 1810
ANSTICE, HORTON & ROSE
18.5cm.
Mr and Mrs J. B. Briggs

A Coalport globular blue and white jug with angular handle, transfer printed in a bright blue with pagodas on river islands beneath an elaborate border and inscribed in iron-red with a four line verse beneath the lip. Anstice, Horton and Rose's factory.

402
Sunderland Pottery: Earthenware, pink lustre Jug, c. 1830-1850
Sunderland Museum and Art Gallery (Tyne and Wear Museums Service)

Earthenware pink-lustre jug, c.1830-1850, probably made at Scott's Southwick Pottery, Sunderland. Decorated with hand-enamelled transfer-prints including the "Farmer's Arms" design, which bears the legend "God Speed the Plough".

403
Sunderland Pottery: Earthenware pink lustre Frog-Mug, c. 1820
Sunderland Museum and Art Gallery (Tyne and Wear Museums Service)

Earthenware pink-lustre frog-mug, c.1820, probably made at Moore's Wear Pottery, Southwick, Sunderland. Decorated with hand-enamelled transfer-printed designs of the Wear Bridge of 1796 and a version of the "Farmer's Arms".

404
Sunderland Pottery: Creamware Jug, 1813-1819
Garrison
Sunderland Museum and Art Gallery (Tyne and Wear Museums Service)

Yellow-glazed earthenware jug, c.1810, probably made at the Sunderland 'Garrison' Pottery.
Decorated with the transfer-printed design relating to the verse "The Tythe Pig":

The Tythe Pig
In a country village lives a vicar
Fond as all are of Tythes and Liquer,
To mirth his ears are seldom shut
He'll crack a joke and laugh at smut.
But when his tythes he gathers in
True Parson then, no coin no grin
On fish on flesh on birds and beast
Alike lays hold the churlish priest
Hal's wife and sow as Gossips tell
Both at a time in pieces fell
The parson comes the Pig he claims
And the good wife with taunts inflames
But she quite arch bow'd low and smil'd
Kept back the pig and held out the child
The Priest look'd gruff the wife look'd big
z...ds Sir quoth she No Child no Pig.

405

405
Bread Plate, 1855
32cm. diameter
Minton Museum, Royal Doulton Ltd.

Minton earthenware bread plate, Shape No 427 with border of wheat moulded in high relief, naturalistically decorated in majolica glazes.
Marks: Moulded diamond shape registration mark. Impressed Shape No 427. Impressed year cypher 1855.
Leon Arnoux, who became Minton's Art Director in 1849, was responsible for many technical and design innovations with the best known being 'majolica', a range of brightly coloured low temperature glazes. Minton first exhibited these at the Great Exhibition of 1851 where they were awarded the bronze medal.

406
'Ceres' pâte-sur-pâte Slab, c.1880
L. M. SOLON
36 x 18.3cm.
Minton Museum, Royal Doulton Ltd

Minton olive green tinted Parian slab, 'Harvest', depicting a nude maiden with gossamer drapery holding a wheat sheaf and sickle with a wreath of wheat in her hair, decorated in the pâte-sur-pâte technique signed by Louis Solon.

Louis Solon, who came to Minton in 1870, was the leading exponent of pâte-sur-pâte, a technique whereby layer by layer of liquid clay was applied to a clay body forming a decoration that was part painting, part relief modelling. Solon was known to have taken 250 days to decorate some pieces in the technique, and Minton encouraged him to devote his time and energy to this style of decoration. Solon retired in 1904, but continued to work in a freelance capacity until his death in 1913.

406

407
Sèvres Style Vase in pâte-sur-pâte with medallions of cattle, c.1877
FREDERICK RHEAD
54 x 25cm.
Minton Museum, Royal Doulton Ltd

Minton celadon and olive tinted Parian vase and cover modelled after Sèvres *vase antique ferrá* with black cameos painted in white pâte-sur-pâte by Frederick Rhead.

Marks: Gold printed Mintons Globe and Crown. One cameo signed F. Rhead and the other monogrammed.

Diam: 54 x 25cm.

The time consuming technique perfected by Louis Solon involved the building up of successive layers of liquid clay on a clay body, until a part painting, part sculpture evolved. The pâte-sur-pâte work at Minton featured mainly figure work, where translucent draperies showed off the technique to great advantage.

Here, Frederick Rhead, one of Solon's apprentices, uses the pâte-sur-pâte technique to build up the images of animals on this elaborate vase. Rhead worked at Minton from c.1872-7.

407

408

410
'Hans Sloane' Botanical Plate with Cabbage leaf, turnips, parsnips etc, 1755
36cm. diameter
By gracious permission of Her Majesty Queen Elizabeth the Queen Mother

Sir Hans Sloane (1660-1753) was a renowned plant collector, physician and author. Certain of Sloane's specimen plants were included in Figures of Plants by Phillip Miller in 1756; a volume which the Chelsea Pottery drew copiously from.
The name 'Cabbage' derives from the Norman French 'Caboche' meaning head, possibly from the Latin 'Caput' of the same meaning.
There is no precise information when the species cabbage (Brassica Deracea) were brought into cultivation, although forms of cabbage have been grown in the Mediterranean for well over 2,000 years.

411
Page of designs of arrangements of agricultural implements (not in exhibition)
Wedgwood Museum

408
'Autumn' Plaque, 1877
W. WISE
55cm. diameter
Minton Museum, Royal Doulton Ltd

Minton earthenware plaque 'Autumn' depicting a girl holding a sheaf of wheat against a background of blackberry branches, one of the four 'Season' plaques painted by William Wise.
Marks: Mintons impressed. Impressed year cypher for 1877.
William Wise, designer and painter, specialised in figure painting, often using his wife or daughters as models for his work. He also designed many tile series for Minton concentrating on animals and country life. He exhibited at the Royal Academy in 1876.
Wise trained in ceramic painting at Minton's Art Pottery Studio in Kensington Gore between 1871-1875 and, from 1875-1885, was at the Minton Works in Stoke.

409
Models of Pea Pods, c.1752-7
CHELSEA
9 x 11cm.
By gracious permission of Her Majesty Queen Elizabeth the Queen Mother

From the red anchor period of the Chelsea pottery. Pea-sellers are often the subject of 18th Century prints, when carts would be brought, for example, into the City of London, from the surrounding countryside. Fresh peas were a luxury.
Peas were also dried and used in Pease Pudding.
> "Pease Pudding hot! Pease Pudding cold!
> Pease Pudding in the pod
> Nine days old."

In 1900 the garden pea **Pisum Sativum** was used in the indispensible work of Gregor Mendel, a monk in the monestry of Brno in Czechoslovakia, on which the foundations of the present-day science of **genetics** has been built, a science applied to both plant and animal life.

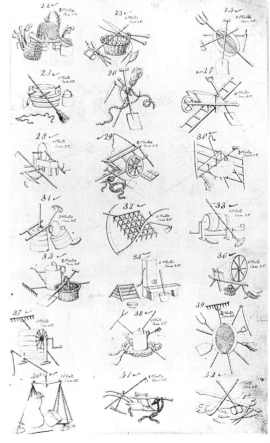

411

412
Three Plates with Agricultural Implements, 1805-7
21cm.
By courtesy of the Trustees of the Wedgwood Museum,
Barlaston, Stoke-on-Trent

Three cream coloured earthenware (Queen's Ware) plates
outline transfer printed and hand enamelled with the pattern
"Agricultural Implements".

413

413

Pair of Model Steam Ploughing Engines, c. 1895.
Weight: 2.5 cwt.
90 cm. long each.
Breamore Countryside Museum.

In 1855 Robert Scott Burn contributed a series of detailed
articles to the *Journal of Agriculture* dealing with the design
and construction of different types of portable steam engines.
In general a plough was drawn across a field by a rope or wire
between two implements: a combined engine and haulage drawn
at one end of the field and a self-propelled perpetual anchor
and pulley at the other; both of which moved slowly along the
headland in order to be always opposite the work.

414

Gloucester Long Plough (Full Size)
416 x 73 x 89cm.
M.E.R.L.

The Royal Agricultural Society's Annual Journal for 1850
contains an article on farming in Gloucester by John Bravender
who commented on this type of plough:

> "The plough in general use for common work is a very long wooden
> swing plough which is drawn with three, four, five and sometimes
> six horses at length (in a line) the most general team is four or five."

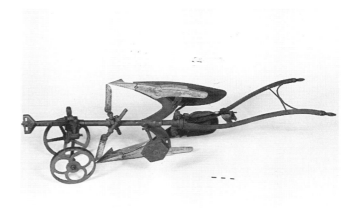

415

Breast Plough
150 x 85 x 25cm.
M.E.R.L.

The breast or push plough as opposed to the hauled plough.
Pushed into the ground by a man.

417

416

Elevator: Model
Scale 1:12
M.E.R.L.

This and all the models which follow (434-447) were used for
teaching purposes at the Department of Engineering at the
University of Reading. They are all representative of machinery
in use in the inter-war period and many survived into the 1950's.

417

Reversible or Butterfly Plough: Model.
Scale: 1:5.
76 x 18 x 24cm.
M.E.R.L.

Two sets of plough bodies, one on top of the other which may
be switched over, enable the ploughman to produce furrows
which all face the same way.

418
Seed Drill: Model.
Late 1850's.
Scale 1:6.
42 x 47 x 36cm.
M.E.R.L.

A model of a seed drill designed by Chandler and manufactered by Leaver of Bratton, Westbury, Wiltshire. This type of seed drill had a press wheel in place of a coulter (a blade or sharp-edged disc which cuts through the soil). It activated a recessed cylinder which dropped the seed into the furrow made by the press wheel.
George Fussell writes in "The Farmer's Tools" that in all essentials seed drills were of modern design by the 1860's. The *'Mark Lane Express'* remarked that there was not a vast difference in the drill of 1922 and that of fifty-years earlier.

419
Chaff Cutter: Model.
Scale: 1:6.
29 x 26 x 29cm.
M.E.R.L.

Chaff, in addition to being the husks from grain separated during threshing, is also finely cut straw and hay used to feed cattle. During the late 18th and early 19th Centuries many types of chaff cutting machine emerged. Its development was, in fact, related to that of the turnip cutter. In the 1760s the Society for the Encouragement of Arts offered a premium of £20 for a machine to slice turnips. Turnips had to be cut to feed cattle and the society had been informed that in Corinthia the turnips were always sliced by machine.

420
Drill for fertilisers: Model.
Scale: 1:4.
90 x 72 x 30cm.
M.E.R.L.

Early fertiliser drills which distributed liquid manure were made by Chandler and also by Isaac James of the Tivoli Iron Works, Cheltenham.

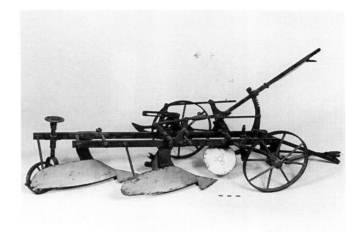

421

421
Two-Furrow Tractor Plough: Model.
Scale: 1:5.
84 x 28 x 23cm.
M.E.R.L.

Double-furrow ploughs were illustrated in c. 1650 in Walter Blith's 'English Improver'. In 1802 Lord Somerville patented an improved double-furrow plough. This was a model which improved upon the 'Vale of Taunton two-furrow swing plough', a plough which had been in use in Devon for some time. In 1792 a premium had been offered, of three guineas, by the Devon Society for the Encouragement of Agriculture and Industry to the person who, in proportion to the quantity of arable land which he owned, ploughed the greatest number of acres with a double-furrow plough.
Somerville's plough was manufactured by Robert Ransome (1753-1830), the same man who in 1755 had taken out a patent for tempering cast-iron plough-shares. A further improved share emerged in 1803, the Chilled Share, so hardened that it remained sharp when used, the friction of wear rubbing down the softer iron, so that the case-hardened edge retained its cutting properties.

422
Cultivator: Model.
Scale: 1:5.
M.E.R.L.

423
Cultivator: Model.
Scale: 1:5.
M.E.R.L.

424
Threshing Machine: Model.
Scale: 1:24.
Made by Mr. G. Froud.
M.E.R.L.

425
Traction Engine: Model.
Scale: 1:4.
Made by Mr. G. Froud.
M.E.R.L.

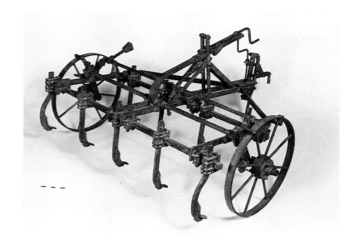
422

426
Haylift: Model.
Scale: 1:6.
158 x 63 x 42cm.
M.E.R.L.

Hay was swept onto the platform of forks which was made to pivot upwards and onto the top of a haystack. This type of haylift was in use between World War I, and II, and up to the late 1940s.

427
Cultivator: Model.
Scale: 1:5.
M.E.R.L.

428
Horse-drawn Hoe: Model.
Scale: 1:5.
56 x 18 x 28cm.
M.E.R.L.

428

429
Manure Distributor: Model.
Scale: 1:4.
116 x 44 x 41cm.
M.E.R.L.

430
Disc Harrow: Model.
Scale: 1:5.
M.E.R.L.

431
Model Harrow.
37 x 33 x 14cm.
M.E.R.L.

This is a plough harrow designed to be dragged behind a single furrow plough. A harrow is used to level the ground, stir the soil and break up clods of earth. An ancient form of harrow was made of a thorn bush weighted by a log and even as late as the early nineteenth century this form of harrow was still to be found in use.

429

432
Seed Lip.
61 x 40 x 36cm.
M.E.R.L.

A container for seed slung around the sower's shoulder, sometimes supported at the waist, from which seed was broadcast by hand. Sometimes the seed was thrown from a simple cloth bag (as depicted in Jean-François Millet's masterpiece *The Sower* c.1849-50).

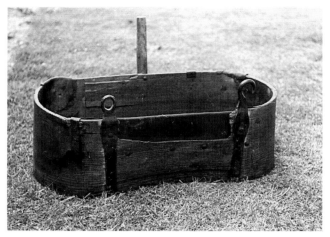

432

433
Dibble or Dibber.
82 x 11cm.
M.E.R.L.

A small hand tool used to make holes in the ground for planting or transplanting seeds or roots.

434
Scythe.
156 x 78cm.
M.E.R.L.

A manual implement for cutting grass etc. It has a long handle held with both hands and a sharpened blade that moves in a plane parallel to the ground.

435
Cradle for use with Scythe.
72 x 76 x 33cm.
M.E.R.L.

Crop falls into cradle. So that the cut crop which falls into it may be deposited on the ground in bunches.

436
Sickle
52 x 24cm.
M.E.R.L.

A sickle is used with a sawing action for cutting grass, corn, etc. It has a curved blade and short hand. This example has a serrated blade.

437
Hook
68 x 33cm.
M.E.R.L.

The hook is also used to cut hay and cereals, but unlike the sickle which is used in a sawing motion the hook uses a slashing, sweeping cut.

434

438
Bill Hook
37 x 13cm.
M.E.R.L.

The bill hook is a cutting tool with a wooden handle and curved blade terminating in a hook at its dip and is used for pruning, chopping, etc.

439
Hay Rake
and
Hay Rake of West Country design with split supports.
180 x 62cm.
195 x 73cm.
M.E.R.L.

Hand horse rakes were used in the fields for harvesting hay well into the 19th Century although in parts of the country the tedder or haymaker was gaining popularity. Many problems were encountered in the production of mechanical rakes. The Royal Agricultural Society held many trials of haymaking machines during the 19th Century. A machine made by James Lovell of Gloucestershire in 1842 was accorded much praise. His machine rather than taking the hay or grain on its rakes and throwing it over in the air, simply turned and spread it. The teeth of the rake were straight and the rakes adapted themselves to irregularities in the ground by ascending and descending on carriage wheels.

443

440
Harvesting Forks: Cereals, barley
165 x 28cm.
184 x 29cm.
M.E.R.L.

The harvesting or hay fork was used manually for spreading hay for drying, as late as the end of the 19th Century.
A tedder, or haymaking machine was designed by Robert Salmond of Woburn early in the 19th Century. Made entirely from wood it has a very long handle and two or mor long curved prongs. (later metal version = pitchfork).

441
Flail
184 x 94cm.
M.E.R.L.

An implement used for threshing grain, consisting of a wooden handle with a free-swinging metal or wooden bar attached to it.

442
Drainage Scoop
106 x 23cm.
M.E.R.L.

Before mechanisation the main tools used in land-drainage were the scythe and the sludge scoop.
A drainage scoop is similar to a spade but is made entirely from wood, and only occasionally given a metal cutting edge, and is curved rather than flat.
A worker would progress cutting back foliage and clearing ditches.
In the early 1950s, J. C. R. Cooke, F.I.C.S., reported the rate for mowing and clearing out a drain were as follows:
"Small drain—approx 3ft bed—3/- per chain
Medium " —approx 6ft bed—4/- per chain
River " —approx 30ft bed—5/- per chain."
And noted that this was a substantial improvement on rates prior to the First World War, when all men worked in bare feet.

443
Doll's Cradle in Straw Work
60cm. long
Private Collection

Doll's cradle in straw work (also known as hip work). This was the technique also used in making straw bee skeps. This cradle may be from Buckinghamshire.

444
Neighbour Skep Beehive
27 x 45cm.
M.E.R.L.

Made from straw employing the method known as 'Hip work'.

445
Nutt Beehive
79 x 42 x 72cm.
M.E.R.L.

A beautifully joined mahogany beehive with glass observation panels.

446a
Silver Gilt honey pot
13cm. high
The Burghley House Collection

Made by Paul Storr of London in 1798, this George III honey pot is in silver-gilt, and is in the form of a bee skep.

446b
Beehives in Surrey and Gloucestershire
HELEN ALLINGHAM, R.W.S. (1848-1926)
Watercolour, 52 x 36.8cm.
Private Collection

447
Smock from Kent
113 x 64cm.
M.E.R.L.

448
Yoke for carrying buckets.
90 x 20cm.
Length of chain 71cm.
M.E.R.L.

449
Pig Scraper
Made from a hoof, used to remove bristles from carcase of pig.
Wye College

450
Livestock Collar
M.E.R.L.

Carries the inscription: Sir John Blois Bart., Cockfield Hall, Suffolk.

451
Stoneware Hand Plunge Butter Churn made by Price of Bristol, 19th Century.
98 x 34cm.
M.E.R.L.

A Victorian journal recommended that
"A woman having hot clammy hands should never be a dairy-maid, for butter is very susceptible of taint, and its flavour will doubtless be spoiled by the heavy smell of sweaty hands; but naturally cool hands—made clean by washing in warm water and oatmeal, **hot soap**, and rinsed and steeped in cold water—make up butter freer of butter milk, and more solid in texture, than any implement of whatever material."

452
Rumbler Bells for Horses
39 x 48cm.
M.E.R.L.

The cast rumbler bells bear the impression R. W. which stands for the original maker, Robert Wells, of Aldbourn in Wiltshire. His foundry, in 1820, was taken over by the Whitechapel foundry, which continued the production of the bells with his impressed mark.

453a
Two Clotted Cream Pans from Devon
76 x 33cm.
M.E.R.L.

The scalded milk would be poured into these pans which were set on a slab in the cool dairy.

453b
Wooden Measures, Bushel, Peck, etc.
M.E.R.L.

454
Vacuum Flask
The Royal Institution, London

The flask was made by Mr C. Muller in February, 1902, for Mr D. Northall-Lawrie, F.I.C., M.I.Chem.E., and presented to the Royal Institution by him in 1939. It may be the second vacuum bottle made for domestic and not scientific purposes. The knitted jacket was made by Mrs D. Northall-Lawrie's mother who was not convinced of the efficiency of the flask and thought it would need protection.
"Mr C. Muller, a well known glass blower who made flasks for Professor Dewar, was living in Coburg, Germany, at the time his second child was born on 21 January, 1902', writes Mr D. Northall-Lawrie". As the baby required hot milk in the middle of the night, which meant getting up to warm it, he thought it a good idea to utilise a Dewar vacuum flask as a container for the milk.
He told me about this when over in England that Spring and, at my request, made me a similar bottle."

455
Large Stoneware Jar
52 x 32cm.
M.E.R.L.

Large stoneware jars had many uses: mainly for the storing of food by some method of preservation e.g. pickling or salting. This example manufactured by Price of Bristol.

456
Harvest Barrels
26 x 20cm.
19 x 14cm.
M.E.R.L.

A barrel in which cider or some other beverage could be taken to the harvest field. Both examples date from the 19th Century.

457
Cast Iron Wheatsheaf, 19th Century
20 x 8cm.
The Property of N. G. G. Wadham, Esq.

Sheaves of wheat were set upright in the field to dry together. These groupings constituted the stook.
One of the most popular agricultural motifs, widely found on ceramics, coats-of-arms, etc.

457

The Twentieth Century

"Back to the land
We must all lend a hand,
To the farms and the fields we must go.
There's a job to be done,
Though we can't fire a gun
We can still do our bit with the hoe"

The cataclysmic World Wars of the twentieth century precipitated, without doubt, enormous changes both in attitudes towards agriculture and its practical application.

The other major event to affect agriculture was the accession of Britain in 1973 to the European Community.

Both wars showed that Britain was not producing enough food at home and that it was essential for agriculture to be intensified if the nation was to survive. During the 1914-18 War the fact was not officially recognised until 1916 when a Ministry of Food was established, followed by the Food Production Department responsible to the Board of Agriculture in 1917.

By 1917 food supplies were critically low. It was at this late stage that the Women's Land Army came into existence, earlier attempts to create such a body had been hampered by problems of training women to work on the land. Eventually training was given to include all types of farm work. Randolph Schwabe's paintings of the period include many images of the Women's Land Army. Schwabe was the only artist commissioned by the Ministry of Information during World War I to depict work on the land; one of his projects was to record the flax harvest in 1917 at Podington, Northamptonshire. This crop was revived during the war because the material was used in the manufacture of aeroplanes.

In 1919 the Board of Agriculture was abolished and reconstituted as the Ministry of Agriculture.

Between the wars many Acts were passed and a certain number of bodies established. The 1920 Agriculture Act laid down new guaranteed prices for wheat and oats. In 1931 the Agricultural Research Council was established and various agricultural institutions became part of this body; Rothamsted, the Institute of Agricultural Engineers and other plant research and breeding stations. The Agricultural Marketing Act of the same period was designed to improve marketing, and by far it's most important result was the creation of the Milk Marketing Board.

The massive agricultural depression which had begun around 1880 was interrupted by the events of 1914 and to a certain extent the post-war period seemed to provide some basis for recovery.

However there were grave problems in all British industries, unemployment never fell below one million and in 1926 the General Strike which developed out of a crisis in the coal industry took place. In 1931 the notion of a "British Commonwealth of the Nations", an attempt to strengthen the bonds between Britain and nations of the Empire, and secure preferential tariffs amongst the various nations, met with a cool reception amongst the dominions, largely because they regarded themselves as fully independent in foreign and domestic policy.

In contrast to the years preceding World War I, some thought was given by the Imperial Defence Committee to the question of food supply during a time of war. In general the nation was far better prepared in 1939 than it had been in 1914. A Ministry of Food was formed five days after the declaration of war on 3rd September, 1939. Recruiting for the Women's Land Army began even earlier, in May of that year, and the Ministry of Agriculture assumed responsibility for it. The Women's Land Army caught the public imagination and has continued to do so many years after its disbandment in 1950. John Betjeman in 'Invasion Exercise on the Poultry Farm' gave us an unsentimental image to ponder:

"Softly croons the radiogram, loudly hoot the owls,
Judy gives the door a slam and goes to feed the fowls.
Marty rolls a Craven A around her ruby lips
And runs her yellow fingers down her corduroyed hips,
Shuts her mouth and screws her eyes and puffs her fag alight
And hears some most peculiar cries that echo through the night.
      Ting-a-ling the telephone, to-whit to-whoo the owls,
Judy, Judy, Judy girl, and have you fed the fowls?
No answer as the poultry gate is swinging there ajar.
Boom the bombers overhead, between the clouds a star. . . ."

Art came into the service of the war effort as the War Artists' Advisory Committee commissioned paintings of work on the land which could be seen by the general public and hopefully uplift sagging morale. Evelyn Dunbar's work stands out for its meticulous observation and frequent wit.

In 1940 food rationing began and in the following year Lend-Lease came into being. A system designed to provide Britain with American food, agricultural machinery and equipment it continued to the end of the war in 1945.

During the war the first artificial insemination centre was opened and the post-war years have seen an enormous expansion in this field.

In 1946 the National Agricultural Advisory Service was established; the Ministry of Agriculture taking on for the first time national advisory work. In the following year, 1947, the Agriculture Act was passed which aimed to promote and maintain a stable and efficient agricultural industry "at minimum prices consistent with proper remuneration and living conditions".

Rural electrification began on a major scale in 1953, the march of the giant pylons had begun and with it the first murmurings against the visual vandalism of the countryside. Increasing mechanisation and the use of components manufactured outside the rural community in factories led to the rapid disappearance of many rural crafts and trades which had served agriculture; wheelrights, saddlers, blacksmiths, most of the trades which had been related to the predominance of horse power. Combine harvesters soon became a familiar sight and so did vast prefabricated grain stores. In the early 1970's the once familiar sight of small bales of straw were replaced by massive cylindrical bales. The use of heavy horses all but disappeared as the motorised tractor became a common sight. Such changes throughout the century have provided artists with the job of recording sights which were about to vanish. S. R. Badmin's paintings have not been confined to the 1930's, he has continued to the present day, to look at change on the farm and to record the old with the new.

The Ministry of Food, in 1955, was amalgamated with the Ministry of Agriculture to form the Ministry of Agriculture, Food and Fisheries. Ten years later the Brambell Committee produced its report on the welfare of farm animals. A growing number of complaints were to be heard about the housing and managing systems of farm animals, and in particular about intensive systems. The report called for a degree of control.

In 1968 the Countryside Act stipulated that the Ministry of Agriculture, Food and Fisheries should advise those carrying on agricultural businesses on the conservation of the countryside. A year later the first of a series of field exercises took place at Silsoe to develop principles of compromise between farmers and conservationists.

In 1973 Britain joined the Common Market. It was pointed out at the time that there were many similarities between the Agriculture Act 1947 and the Common Agricultural Policy''. There are also marked differences, the Common Agricultural Policy provides that support for farmers comes from the price paid by the consumer. Costs to the taxpayer have arisen from the growth and disposal of surpluses. The income of a producer is supported partly by levies to maintain minimum prices for imports, partly by measures to help exports, and partly by internal market support schemes such as intervention buying''.*

During the same year the first large mammal was born after having been deep-frozen as an embryo. A bull calf called ''Frosty'' was exhibited at The Royal Show. It was also in 1973 that the Rare Breeds Survival Trust was established. Its very existence underlines the fact that animals no longer seen as commercially valuable had, possibly since the time of the livestock improvers of the late eighteenth century, been ignorantly neglected. Genetic science has shown how unique each species of animal is and how disastrous to allow the extinction of a single breed to take place.

It is hard to summarise the philosophies related to agriculture, which prevail in the late twentieth century, Many of the principles which guide those individuals who carry out research into plant and animal science derive from 18th Century beliefs in the need to increase fertility and productivity. In this century the expansion of ecological science has added new principles. We live in a hungry world and the search for an agricultural solution, capable of contributing to the eradication of this evil continues.

* 'Loaves and Fishes' (The History of Agriculture, Food & Fisheries)
HMSO 1989

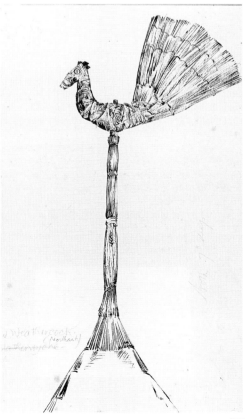

477

458

Woad Mill at Parson Drove, Cambridgeshire, c. 1900
ALFRED BALDING
Oil on canvas, 84 x 100cm.
Trustees of the Science Museum

This oil painting by Alfred Balding of Wisbech is significant as one of very few extant contemporary pictorial records of an early, longstanding and now dead industry.

The scene was captured by the artist inside the roller house of the mill. This was a circular structure with low turf walls supporting a high wide roof of timber and hurdles, thatched with reeds. The floor was about 24 feet in diameter and paved with blocks of stone.

As they were stripped from the plants, woad leaves were brought to the roller house for crushing, the first stage of processing into a commercial dye. Three crushing wheels were used, vertical edge-runner rollers of wood and metal; each was over seven feet in diameter and weighed around 15-25 cwt. Rollers were drawn by horses and revolved in a circular pan, the track filled with leaves. The horse harnesses were attached by poles to a central wooden shaft.

In the foreground women and men are kneading and rolling the crude woad into balls on sloping boards or 'forms'. This operation stained the workers' hands almost black, the colour persisting until the formation of fresh skin, and the smell inside the roller house was pungent. A tray of woad balls is carried on the head of another worker to the drying ranges in the open-sided shed. Through the doorway can be seen growing a crop of Isatis.

The mill at Parson Drove was situated near Wisbech in Cambridgeshire. Lincolnshire and parts of Cambridgeshire were the most important centres of the woad industry; the plant, *Isatis tinctoria,* flourishes in fenland and the rich soil of Wisbech and its surrounding villages was specially adapted to its intensive cultivation.

The last surviving woad mill, Parson Drove was demolished in 1914 after the outbreak of war. The artist exhibited between 1887 and 1895 but little else is known of his work. The painting was loaned for exhibition at the Science Museum in 1951, at which their model of the mill was also shown; it was bequeathed in 1965, and hung in the former Council Room for many years. Conservation work in 1984 revealed fresh details of the scene.

459

Specimens of Woad in Specimen Jars
Trustees of the Science Museum

Isatis tinctoria, a biennial herb with erect stem bearing yellow flowers. Height varies from two to five feet, flowering stem branched above.

460

Model of Woad Mill, Woad Loading Board, Hammer and Spud
Trustees of the Science Museum

There are seven principal processes in the manufacture of woad: crushing, balling, drying, a second crushing, couching, casking and carting to the means of final transport. One of the most interesting recent documents on *'Woad in the Fens'* was written and published by Norman T. Wills, of Long Sutton, Lincs.

461a

Bronze Statue: Man with a Staff, c. 1907
REGINALD FAIRFAX WELLS (1877-1951)
Bronze, 39cm.
The Fine Art Society, London

461b

Four Wemyss Pigs: 2 Pigs, 2 Piglets, c. 1900
Pottery, 2 x 40 x 20cm.
2 x 14 x 8cm.
Miss Elizabeth Creak

461c

Digging Potatoes at Sunset, 1900
SIR GEORGE CLAUSEN, R.A. (1852-1949)
Oil on canvas, 60.4 x 49.5cm.
The Duchess of Devonshire

A moment's repose for a woman who has been harvesting potatoes. A late summer sunset fills the scene with a golden glow and the freshly dug potatoes rest on the soft earth.

462

The Old Reaper, 1909
SIR GEORGE CLAUSEN (1852-1949)
Oil, 76.7 x 63.7cm.
Manchester City Art Galleries

A solitary reaper has long been a symbol for death. Longfellow wrote of "a Reaper whose name is Death, And with his sickle keen, He reaps the bearded grain at a breath, And the flowers that grow between." Clausen, in part, avoids such symbolism by his evident interest in the old man who reaps as an individual.

463

A Farmer Guiding a Harrow
SIR ALFRED MUNNINGS, P.R.A.
Oil on panel, 18.5 x 30cm.
Private Collection

461c

462

464

The Women's Land Army and Prisoners of War, c.1918
RANDOLPH SCHWABE (1885-1948)
Oil on panel, 49 x 57cm.
Trustees of the Imperial War Museum

C. S. Orwin in 'A History of English Farming' observed that
by the outbreak of the First World War in 1914, England was
dependent on imports for one-half of all its food; 75% of its
bread corn was coming from overseas. At first the Government
was not unduly worried but by 1915 the losses of shipping from
submarine warfare caused serious concern. It was not until 1917
however that a Food Production Department was built up
throughout the country with County Executive Committees
vested with powers to order the ploughing and cultivation of
fields.

The labour division provided 120,000 men mostly for seasonal
work mostly from the army but the rest were prisoners of war
and schoolboys. The women's division raised a Land Army of
16,000 full-time and 300,000 part-time workers.

The Corn Production Act of 1917 guaranteed good prices for
farmers and the corn levy was a guarantee of a fair wage for
the worker. For the first time in the history of agriculture, wages
were regulated not by supply and demand but via the
Agricultural Wages Board, an independent tribunal which would
decide, after consideration of the arguments of the interested
parties, what was necessary to give the worker a proper standard
of life.

465

**Women's Work on the Land: from "Britain's Efforts and
Ideals": ploughing, 1918**
ARCHIBALD HARTRICK
Lithograph on paper
Trustees of the Imperial War Museum

In 1916 Sir A. D. Hall, KCB, FRS, a former director of
Rothamstead wrote a book called *Agriculture after the War* in
which he stressed the need for an increased production of food
at home and the greater employment of men on the land.
He noted that £68 millions work of wheat and other grains were
imported, £57 million worth of meat and £71 millions of butter,
fruit, lard, eggs, fish etc; and stated that the British Isles was
importing about one-half of the total food consumed.

466

**Two figures of Women Students from Swanley College in
working garb**, c. 1917
Plaster, wood, leather, cloth, 34 x 15cm.
Wye College, University of London

In April 1889 Arthur Harper Bond bought Hextable House in
Kent and founded "The Horticultural College and Produce
Company". In 1890 women were admitted as students. By 1898
there were 20 male and 35 female students. By 1903 the College
had only women students and a Colonial Branch established
"to carry out the valuable indoor and outdoor training for girls
going forth to our Colonies who would be qualified to maintain
beyond the seas the best traditions of English home life." In
1945 Swanley College was amalgamated with Wye College.

466

1918-1938

467

467
Photograph "Square" Sheep by Metcalf of Barnard Castle,
c.1920
30 x 40cm.
Beamish Museum

The photograph is interesting because it clearly shows where
the fine contours of the animal, a Swaledale sheep, have been
touched out to comply with standards of conformation.

468
Sheep-shearing in Baldersdale, 20th Century
John T. Young Gilroy
Oil on canvas, 101.5 x 127cm.
The Bowes Museum, Barnard Castle, Co. Durham

469a
The Red Cow, 1933
EDWARD BAWDEN, C.B.E., R.A., b. 1903
Signed and dated bottom right 45.5 x 57.5cm.
The Fine Art Society, London

Edward Bawden studied at the Royal College of Art during the
1920's and was among those artists who were commissioned
by the W.A.A.C. during World War II.

469b
Pit: Card Game
Private Collection

A late 19th or early 20th century card game in which the players
bid for commodities; corn, wheat, oats etc.

469 b

470

473
Toilers of the Field
HARRY BECKER (1865-1928)
Etching, 15.3 x 35cm.
Colchester and Essex Museum

470
Threshing by Steam, c. 1920
T. KENNINGTON
Miss Elizabeth Creak

In 1832 William Cobbett rode through East Lothian and encountered the smoke stacks of many threshing engines. "Just at the little village of Cockburnspath we get into the county of Haddington . . . and such cornfields, and fields of turnips, such turnips in those fields, such stackyards and such a total absence of dwelling houses as never, surely, were seen in any county upon earth. You very frequently see more than a hundred stacks in one yard, each containing, on average, from fifteen to twenty quarters of wheat or of oats; all built in the neatest manner; thatched extremely well, the thatch bound down by exterior bands, spars not being used owing to the scarcity of wood. In some of these yards the threshing-machine is worked by horses, but in the greater part by steam; and where coals are at a distance by wind or water; so that in this country of the finest land that ever was seen, all the elements seem to be pressed into the amiable service of sweeping the people from the face of the earth." Even at this date, as Cobbett indicates, the steam engine was raising the problem of rural unemployment, and a few years later, in the South, labourers and small threshers would riot in protest against their loss of work in the winter, threshing corn.

471
Wooden Cow and Bull
Mrs Wilfred Shirley

Made to decorate a wedding cake.

472
Loading Sugar Beet
HARRY BECKER (1865-1928)
Pencil drawing, 10 x 20cm.
J. S. Blomfield Esq. Collection of 19th Century Country and Sporting Paintings

The sugar-beet originally grew on the coasts of the Atlantic. In 1747 a German chemist was the first person to experiment on the extraction of sugar from the beet. 150 years later half the entire sugar output of the world came from sugar-beet. Both Frederick the Great and Napoleon fostered the early development of the sugar-beet as a crop.
Production involved massive capital expenditure which had to come from public authorities.
The sugar-beet provided the farmer with a new source of income and East Anglia was the great centre of the new crop and it is believed that sugar-beet saved arable farming in those counties from complete collapse in the slump between World War I and II.

474
Model of the Prince of Wales' Bull, 1932
JOHN SKEAPING, R.A.
Bronze, 23 x 13 x 28cm.
The Worshipful Company of Goldsmiths

Modelled at the farm of the Prince of Wales, later King Edward VIII for the Buenos Aires exhibition in 1932 where it formed part of the collection of modern silver representing different aspects of this industry exhibited by the Company of Goldsmiths. This was a trade exhibition of industrial art arranged by the Board of Trade and Federation of British Industries in Buenos Aires.
The Prince of Wales had been active in South America and his enthusiasm was of great value at this time in stirring up exporters.

475
Embroidery representing the first 2,000 gallon lactation British Friesian Cow, Macknade Musgun, prize winner 1922 and 1923
32 x 42cm.
Basil Neame, Esq

Friesian cattle were exported from Holland, in large numbers, to Great Britain as early as the 17th Century. Valued for their high milk yields Friesians are more numerous than any other dairy cattle.

476
Fowls, 1929
THOMAS SAUNDERS NASH (1891-1968)
Oil on paper, 35.4 x 25.5cm.
Manchester City Galleries

The domestic fowl, it is generally believed, derives from the four main varieties of 'jungle fowl': *Gallus ferruginum*, *Gallus Stanleyii*, *Gallus sonneratii* and *Gallus furcatus*.
It was with the introduction of the feather-legged breeds from Asia during the 19th Century which saw a change in attitudes to keeping poultry in Britain. Prior to this hens were scavenging inhabitants of farmyards.
The new attitudes brought proper henhouses into being, the hens laying ability was better and winter eggs laid and fetched high prices and so the first commercial poultry farms were set up.

477
Straw Weathercock, 1930's
THOMAS HENNELL (1903-c.1945)
Wye College, University of London

During the war Thomas Hennell produced many watercolours and drawings of the farming world for the Pilgrim Trust's scheme 'Recording Britain'.
Between 1941-43 the War Artists' Advisory Committee purchased studies of workers on the land and commissioned Hennell to record the harvest of 1941. In 1943 he was invited by the Ministry of Information to take the place of Eric Ravilious who had gone missing over Iceland. In 1945 he was sent to the Far East with the Air Ministry visiting Rangoon, Singapore and Java. He disappeared in November, 1945. He sketched thousands of agricultural items and activities, a fine collection of which are kept at Wye College in Kent.

478
Gleaners Knots, 1930's
THOMAS HENNELL
Wye College, University of London

A mowing team, before binders and reapers or the combine-harvesters, might have consisted of two scythemen, two gatherers, two bandsters and one woman raker.
The bandsters were responsible for putting the open sheaves of corn into bound sheaves when they would use a knot such as this shown by Hennell. They would then set the grouped sheaves into a stack.

479
Rick Dollies, Topknots or Crows, 1930's
THOMAS HENNELL
Wye College, University of London

Many ricks were once thatched to secure protection against the elements and some were embellished with decorative dollies, topknots or crows.

480
The Mullion Wireless, 1921
CHARLES GINNER ARA (1878-1952)
Oil on canvas, 51.5 x 61.5cm.
Mr. and Mrs. Peyton Skipwith

Marconi's centre for the transmission of wireless messages across the Atlantic set in the Cornish landscape, where the harvest is being gathered in.

481
'Fallen Mill Sails', 1931
S. R. BADMIN, R.W.S.
Etching
Dr Chris Beetles

From the 1880's and up to 1939 the English countryside, as a result of the profound agricultural depression, fell into a gradual reversion to nature. The land took on a pleasing appearance of dilapidation; many similar scenes were documented for the Pilgrim Trust's "Recording Britain" scheme.

482
Shell Advertising Poster
and
483
Original painting: 'Farmers Prefer Shell', 1934
DENIS CONSTANDUROS
Shell (UK) Ltd.

One of the famous series of posters from the 1930's "You can be sure of Shell", to which artists such as Paul Nash, Duncan Grant, Tristram Hillier, Graham Sutherland and 'Zero' constructed informative interpretations on a wide range of subjects. Another well-known Shell poster was that designed by I. Shepheard of an owl and its prey with the slogan 'A Friend to the Farmer'.

484
Old Farm Implements
LESLIE DONOVAN GIBSON, B.A., A.R.C.A. (1910-1969)
Ink and wash drawing
Phillip Gibson, Esq.

Born in 1910 at Heaton, Newcastle-upon-Tyne, Leslie Donovan Gibson was awarded a Royal Exhibition to the Royal College of Art where he studied under Sir William Rotherstein, Professor Gilbert Spencer and Percy Horton. In 1936 he married Mary Wilde who founded the School of Costume and Dress Design at the Royal College of Art which later became the School of Fashion. Chiefly a landscape artist, he worked in a variety of media.

485

485
Hop Picking Granny—a portrait of Granny Knowles, c. 1938
DAME LAURA KNIGHT, D.B.E., R.A. (1877-1970)
Oil on canvas, 62.5 x 49cm.
The Royal Museum and Art Gallery, Canterbury

Hops are used in the brewing of beer; they improve the flavour and keeping quality.
Hops are grown in 'gardens', each year the plant sends vines or climbing stems which twine around the high poles. The hop is harvested in September. The great hop county is Kent. Kilns or oast houses are used for drying the hops.

486
Hop Tokens and Talleys
Wye College, University of London

Talleys were wooden slats used for recording the numbers of baskets of hops picked by cutting notches into the side.
A hop token was a stamped metal token piece issued by the grower from the late 18th to early 20th Century to guarantee payment to pickers. Denominations range from one to 120 baskets or bushels.

486

487

487
Sheet Iron Hat
Wye College, University of London

A hat which would protect the wearer from noxious sprays used on the hops: for example nicotine.

488
Hop Stilts
Wye College, University of London

A pair of wooden poles having foot-rests three or four feet from the top; used for elevated working.

489 a

489a
The Farmyard, 1928
THOMAS SAUNDERS NASH (1891-1968)
Oil and Pencil, 40 x 58cm.
Manchester City Art Galleries

A painting which like Gilbert Spencer's "A Cotswold Farm" (1930, Tate Gallery, London) seeks to create a sense of idyll; the figures drenched in strong light are part of a hot summer's day on a farm.

489b
"Looking them over", n.d.
ROBERT DUFF
Etching, 24 x 32.2cm.
Goldmark Gallery, Rutland

490
Water Cart
L. D. GIBSON
Phillip Gibson, Esq.

The provision of water for livestock in far distant fields has always been a problem.

491
'Potato Clamps', 1932
S. R. BADMIN, R.W.S.
Etching
Dr Chris Beetles

The normal procedure of storing a potato crop is 'clamping'. The tubers are heaped in as dry a place as possible in the field, covered with straw, which, in turn is covered with turves cut from the base of the heap, which tends to keep the heap drained. The failure of the harvest of 1794 and 1795 saw a circular sent out by Arthur Young, editor of the *Journal of Agriculture* asking leading farmers, clergymen and local landowners about the condition of corn crops, potatoes in store, what substitutes could be or were being used for wheat. The response was that stored potatoes were in good condition, many of which had been stored in the cellars of the house.
The Board of Agriculture adopted a policy of attempting to persuade people to substitute potatoes for bread, even to incorporate it in the baking of bread and published a recipe.

492
Downs in Winter, c. 1934
ERIC RAVILIOUS (1903-1942)
Watercolour on paper, 44.9 x 55.7cm.
Towner Art Gallery and Local History Museum, Eastbourne

An artist whose work has had tremendous impact on applied art in Britain despite his early death in 1942, when he disappeared over Iceland on an air-sea rescue mission. In this work a perfect synthesis is achieved between Ravilious's interest in patterning and that of the land he examines.

493
Jug and Mug, 1939
ERIC RAVILIOUS
21 x 22cm.
11.5 x 13cm.
By courtesy of the Trustees of the Wedgwood Museum, Barlaston, Stoke-on-Trent

Cream coloured earthenware (Queen's Ware) transfer printed and hand enamelled in purple lustre with the pattern "Garden Implements".

494

494

Sow and Litter
SIR ALFRED MUNNINGS, P.R.A. (1878-1959)
Oil on canvas, 39 x 42cm.
Private Collection

White, long-bodied and lop-eared the Long White Lop-eared
pig is a native breed or landrace. Munnings painted this work
in Cornwall.

495

The Percheron, 1940.
C. F. TUNNICLIFFE
Wood engraving on Japanese paper, 27 x 51cm.
Royal Academy of Arts, London.

The Percheron derives its name from the old French district
of La Perche. Found in Northern France, the Percheron has
a hard blue hoof evolved from many generations of the creature
working as a draught horse on rough stone roads.
First introduced into Great Britain during the First World War
it is a small horse with a short, compact body. The head is
refined and with a dish which indicates its strain of Arab blood.

496

The Plough, 1940
S. R. BADMIN, R.W.S.
Pen, ink and watercolour
Dr Chris Beetles

An appropriate image for 1940. Between 1939 and 1944 the area
under the plough in Britain increased from 12,900,000 to
19,400,000 acres and the output of food increased by over 70
per cent.
However it should be noted that it was tractor hauled ploughing
tackle which broke up the land. In 1938 there were about 60,000
tractors in Britain, by the end of the war there were 260,000.
Combine-harvesters, of which there were about 1,000 in 1941
rose to over 11,000 by 1950.

497

'Clamping Spuds', 1942
STANLEY ANDERSON
Line Engraving on white wove paper, 29.4 x 23cm.
Visitors of the Ashmolean Museum, Oxford.

498

The Wheelwright, 1941
STANLEY ANDERSON
Line engraving, 60 x 50cm.
Royal Academy of Arts, London.

499

Market Carts, c.1940
HAROLD WORKMAN (1897-1975)
Oil, 65 x 77.5cm.
Manchester City Art Galleries

500

A Threshing Team, 1941
THOMAS HENNELL
Watercolour on paper, 35 x 48cm.
The Trustees of the Imperial War Museum

Edward R. Stettinius, Jr., who took over the administration
of the land-lease programme in 1941 wrote in detail of the
massive effort made in Britain to increase agricultural output;
recorded his observations in "Lend Lease" published by
Penguin in 1944:

"The several times I flew over Britain, I looked down on a country
where almost every acre of land was being used. Forests that had
been carefully tended for centuries were being cut down, not only
to meet the pressing need for timber but also to make room for more
farms. Golf courses and the parts of great estates were being
ploughed up and tilled. Marshes were being drained and hilly land
... was being made to produce food. Family Victory Gardens had
been planted on every vacant piece of land round the cities. Farms
large and small were everywhere. But increased production alone
could not solve Britain's food problem. To cut their diet to fit their
larder, the British had to introduce rationing at levels which at times
have only barely sustained their fighting strength.
Tractors are in large part government owned and are shifted about
constantly from farm to farm as they are needed. Just before I left
Britain, the Ministry of Agriculture launched a campaign for even
more intensive use of farm machinery. An increase in farm acreage
was demanded, but the tractors in Britain were already being worked
from dawn to dusk. Since few new tractors were to be had, there
was only one answer—those already on the job would have to be
worked around the clock. The new inexperienced farmhands would
plough by day, the old hands after dark. But this raised difficulties
in a country which is blacked out every night ... a method was devised
of giving farmers enough light without sending a glare into the sky
visible to enemy bombers."

501

Silver Fruit Bowl, designed C. J. Shiner
presented by Worshipful Co. of Goldsmiths to the Women's
Land Army, 1940
The Worshipful Company of Goldsmiths

Silver fruit bowl, 1939, designed by C. J. Shiner, made by
Wakely & Wheeler Ltd. Inscribed "This bowl was presented
by the Worshipful Company of Goldsmiths to the Women's
Land Army in the presence of Her Majesty Queen Elizabeth
at Goldsmiths' Hall on March 14th 1940." The Queen inspected
a representative gathering of the Land Army under the direction
of Lady Denham, their leader, who gave the bowl to the
Company at the end of the war when the Women's Land Army
was disbanded.

502

502
Milking practice with artificial udders, 1940
EVELYN DUNBAR (1906-1960)
Oil on canvas, 61.5 x 76.5cm.
The Trustees of the Imperial War Museum

A painting produced for the War Artists' Advisory Committee, showing work at a training centre for women who were to work on the land. A similar painting by Evelyn Dunbar showed a milkmaid mastering the knack of moving milkchurns by rotating them.

503
Girl Milking
EVELYN DUNBAR (1906-1960)
Oil on canvas 22.5 x 22.5cm.
Wye College, University of London

This superb painting by Evelyn Dunbar, was presented by her husband Dr. Roger Folly to Wye College. Also at the College where Dr. Folly taught there is a window dedicated to her memory. Born in Strood, Evelyn Dunbar studied at the Royal College of Art during the 1920's. In 1939 she was sent to Sparsholt agricultural college in Hampshire to produce paintings for the W.A.A.C. where she painted several works on dairy practice. Many of her paintings are among the most outstanding works of World War II and of 20th Century English painting.

503

504

504
Sprout Picking, Monmouthshire, 1944
EVELYN MARY DUNBAR (1906-1960)
Oil on canvas, 24 x 25cm.
Manchester City Art Galleries

505

505

Potato Sorting, Berwick, c.1942
EVELYN MARY DUNBAR (1906-1960)
Oil on canvas, 30.7 x 76.2cm.
Manchester City Art Galleries

506

A 1944 Pastoral: Land Girls Pruning at East Malling, 1944
EVELYN MARY DUNBAR (1906-1960)
Oil on canvas, 91.3 x 121.8cm.
Manchester City Art Galleries

507

"The Hop Pickers", 1945
JOHN MINTON, R.B.A. (1917-1957)
Panel, ink and watercolour, 50 x 60.5cm.
Collection of Lord and Lady Irvine

Reproduced in "The English People" by George Orwell, published by Collins in 1947.

508

Map of Kent: Battle of Britain
R.A.S.E.

509

Selection of W.W.II Posters
The Trustees of the Imperial War Museum.

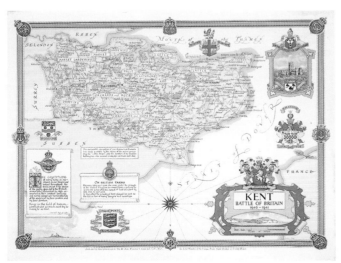

508

509

510

510
'Chilterns, Top Hambledon and Sawmill from Middle Asenden,
March 1948', 1948
S. R. BADMIN, R.W.S.
Pen, ink and watercolour, 16 x 22cm.
Dr. Chris Beetles.

511
Farm Crops in Britain, 1955
Puffin Picture book by Sir George Stapledon illustrated by S.
R. Badmin
S. R. BADMIN ESQ., R.W.S.

A beautifully produced book with meticulous illustrations by
Stanley Badmin and a clear, highly informative text by Sir
George Stapledon.
Activities illustrated include silage making, grass drying,
combine-harvesting, four-course rotation, the lifting and
clamping of mangolds, potato sorting, sugar beet topping,
harvesting beans for fodder, picking, weighing and packing
peas, tending, picking and packing watercress, pruning,
earthing-up celery, the machinery of cultivation, hop picking,
cider-making, collection of onion seeds.
Agriculture in the British Isles changed enormously after World
War II. Robert Trow Smith writes in "Power on the Land"(A
Centenary History of the Agricultural Engineers Association
1875-1975):

> "In 1947 the Labour Government stabilized war-time farming
> prosperity by implementing the protective legislation which
> the Ministry of Agriculture had been designing since the closing period
> of the war. Minister Tom William's Agriculture Act of that year
> turned farming almost overnight into a cosseted industry, working
> virtually on a cost-plus basis. Almost the only hazard which remained
> to threaten the British farmer was the British weather.
> Between 1947 and the time when Britain became a member of the
> European Common Market this umbrella of guaranteed prices for
> agreed outputs remained, to provide agriculture with a prosperity
> which ranged from modest to magnificent. It additionally provided
> its machinery suppliers with an unprecedented home market to
> supplement the export sales which grew rapidly with a developing
> world which stretched from China to Chile and from Iceland to
> Iraq."

512
'September Harvest Festival', 1947 for *Country Bouquet*
S. R. BADMIN, R.W.S.
Pen and ink
Dr Chris Beetles

Stanley Roy Badmin was born on the 18th April at Sydenham
in East London. He studied at Camberwell Art School and in
1924 won a Studentship to the Royal College of Art where he
studied under Randolph Schwabe and William Rothenstein. He
has continued to paint throughout his life; amongst his many
commissions are those from The Pilgrim Trust for the *Recording
Britain Scheme;* Puffin Picture Books including *Village and
Town, Trees in Britain,* and *Farm Crops in Britain* which was
written by Sir George Stapledon (exhibit no. 511).

513
Harvesting
JOHN NASH
Lithograph, 49.5 x 76.2cm.
Goldmark Gallery, Rutland

514
Eardley-End-Farm, Audley, 1960
C. W. BROWN (1882-1960)
City Museum and Art Gallery, Stoke-on-Trent

515
Cartoon
MAURICE MCLOUGHLIN
Published in "Punch" October 1st, 1947
The Farmers Club, London

Two agricultural types look at a bowler-hatted Ministry of
Agriculture official emerging from a cornfield: caption reads
"We haven't come across quite so many Ministry officials this
year."

516

'Old Fashioned Harvest; near Luscomb', c.1950.
S. R. BADMIN, R.W.S.
Watercolour on paper, 23 x 36cm.
Dr. Chris Beetles.

One of the paintings S. R. Badmin was commissioned to do by Odhams Press.
It depicts both the new form of storage (Dutch barn on the left) and the old method where the hay or straw was cut, left to dry, stacked in the fields to be collected. The ricks were then built with a stock of sheaves in the middle to create a funnel, held in place by tightly packed layers of sheaves all around. This pattern was repeated in several layers. The funnel prevented spontaneous combustion. The rick was then thatched for protection during the winter.
On the right are the 'modern' bales of hay or straw which replaced the old stacking method. The hens peck at fallen grains of corn.
The sheaves would be threshed throughout the winter.

517

'First Time Around'
S. R. BADMIN, R.W.S.
Watercolour on paper
Dr. Chris Beetles

The combine-harvester is perhaps responsible for some of the greatest visual changes to the countryside. Nigel Harvey in 'The Farming Kingdoms', first published in 1955 described the wide-ranging implications of the rising use of the combine during the late 1940's and early 1950's:

> "The combine delivers the crop as grain, not as sheaves of unthreshed corn, and therefore eliminates the rick from the routine of harvest. It does not eliminate the needs, which the rick met, on the contrary, it increases and intensifies them. The rick is an ingenious form of aerated store, which both protects and dries the corn it houses. The combine neither stores nor dries the corn it cuts. It merely delivers a sudden mass of grain and, under the climatic conditions of this country, often needs drying as well. It creates, therefore, a new problem and it created it on the farm. The warehouses of the merchants and millers were designed for the steady flow of grain from the ricks which the farmer threshed at his leisure in the winter months; and, despite expansion they cannot cope with a flood of grain at harvest time. So the farmer has turned once more to the engineer, who has produced equipment of a type never before seen on a British farm—driers of various shapes and sizes to rid the grain of surplus moisture, huge bins to hold it and cunning conveyors to move it cheaply from place to place. The combine, in short, has sired a sort of mechanical rick ... which can sometimes be fitted conveniently into one of the old barns where the flailers once threshed corn by hand. The grain-job has returned to its ancient home. But it has returned in a new form and in this there is an important parable. The corn-crops, like the old barn which serves them, have been adapted under the pressure of events to new purposes."

Model of combine-harvester by permission of Massey Ferguson (UK) Ltd.

518

518

Photograph of Winston Churchill watching demonstration of the TE20 "little grey Fergie" at Chartwell, 1950
Massey Ferguson (UK) Ltd.

The famous TE20 "little grey Fergie" tractor being demonstrated at Chartwell in 1950 for Winston Churchill, Anthony Eden and Christopher Soames (later to become Minister of Agriculture).

The revolutionary Ferguson System tractor went on to pioneer modern farm mechanistion on a global scale, and the name of its inventor, Northern Irishman Harry Ferguson, lives on today in the millions of Massey-Ferguson tractors at work in the UK and around the world.

Ferguson's contribution to Britain's economy through the world-wide export of his Coventry-made tractors caused Sir Winston Churchill to propose in 1953 that he should be offered a knighthood. Ferguson's reply reveals much about his complex character and rise to world-wide fame from humble beginnings on a small farm near Belfast.

The main body of his letter said:

"I am greatly touched by the Prime Minister's thought. I most deeply appreciate his kindness. I wish I were more worthy of such a recommendation.

I feel I should give you the reasons why I should not accept this honour.

"For great and brilliant statesmen like Sir Winston, who serve their country in the highest sense, no honour could be too great. Also for great soldiers, such as Lord Alexander, the Honours List is a splendid thing.

"I have the feeling, however, that the Honours List for industrialists may not be a good thing for the country. Unfortunately, many people in the industrial world do things, which they ought not to do, for financial gain. My experience is that the same kind of people will do even worse things when seeking to be included in an Honours List. It is substantially for this latter reason that I believe industrialists should not be recommended for Honours.

"Industrialists have the opportunity to become famous. If that is what they seek. They also have the opportunity to amass wealth and all that wealth can bring them. That should be sufficient for them!

"I fear I have seen, so often, the harmful effects of an Honours List for industrialists, that I believe I have come to the right decision when I ask that the Prime Minister would not submit my name to the Queen in this connection."

519

Portrait of Sir John Russell, D.Sc., F.R.S. (1872-   ), 1958
EDWARD HALL
Oil on canvas
Wye College, University of London

520

520

Royal Show, 1951: Festival of Britain Year, 1951
TERENCE CUNEO
Oil on canvas, 61 x 113cm.
R.A.S.E.

The Royal Show of 1951 was held at Cambridge from the 3rd to 6th of July. Prizes offered for horses totalled £5,690, for cattle £6,222, sheep £3,515, pigs £2,183, goats £225.

The Festival of Britain itself had a pavilion dedicated to the 'Land and the People'. Divided into various areas in the Country Pavilion; the variety of the land, science and the land, livestock and breeding, milk, mechanisation, planning the use of the land, the farmer today, rural crafts. The aims, pointed out in the festival brochure was to bring two groups back into step:

"Our theme is the Land and the People; and such a theme is bound to bring to light some awkward facts. Here, in this pavilion, we come upon the first of those—the fact that in making what they have from the land, the people have become divided. By and large they are now either countrymen or townsmen.

It is easy enough to see how the growth and demands of industry in the last hundred years have brought this about, and how the two groups have got out of step with each other. By now the difference in their occupations has compelled them into different ways of life. So, if these two groups are again to march in step, it is essential that each should understand the conditions in which the other lives and works."

519

521
Two 'Hooky' Rugs: Herdwick Sheep; Cow, Calf and Dairymaid
Abbot Hall Art Gallery & Museums

Rugs made in the early 1960s under the auspices of Winifred Nicholson who was responsible for the revival of an old Lakeland craft.

522
Butchers Shop No. 2, 1955
PETER COKER, b. 1926
Oil on board, 181 x 119.5cm.
Doncaster Museum and Art Gallery

In Medieval times October was the month when great herds of pigs were driven into oak woods to feed on acorns; carvings of the swineherd and his charges are found at Lincoln, Malvern, Ripple and Worcester. The acorn season lasted about six weeks from the end of September, the swineherd would hold up a hooked stick and bring down the acorns. Then came November, the great month of Slaughter, particularly of the 'family pig'. Spencer wrote in the Faery Queen:
"Next was November; full of gross and fat
As find with lard, and that night well might seem,
For he had been fattening hogs of late."
The post-war period has been one where many methods of raising animals, so far removed from those early methods, have been devised.

523
Hanging Pig, 1955
PETER COKER
Drawing on paper, 75 x 35.5cm.
Doncaster Museum and Art Gallery

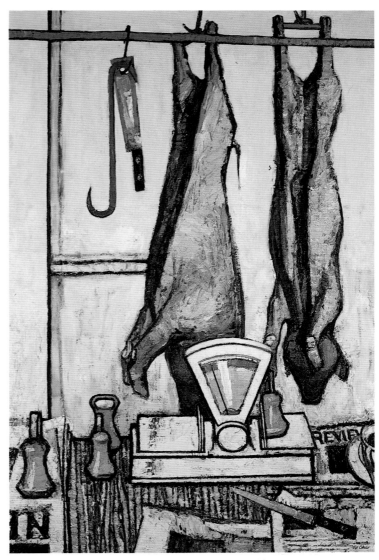

522

524
Collection of Milk Bottles
Miss Elizabeth Creak

524

Up to the mid 19th Century most milk was manufactured on the farm into butter, cheese and cream. The rising urban population and rising prosperity increased the demand for fresh liquid milk. Up to around 1860 every town drew its supplies from the immediate neighbourhood. As Professor J. A. Scott Watson and May Elliot Hobbs noted in "Great Farmers", where the town was large the cattle were mostly kept in it, rather than around it, being fed mostly on farm produce carted in and partly on brewers' grains, oil cake, bran and other by-products. As late as 1864 practically the whole of London's supply came from within a radius of some seventeen miles from the City. But the London cowsheds were nearly emptied by the cattle plague of 1865-6, and a great impetus given to change which had already begun.
In 1850 a business had been set up by Mr. George Barham, who initiated the method of cooling milk before its despatch. The development of the railways and the speeding-up of train services greatly increased the possibilities of the new trade. In 1865 only 3,000,000 gallons of country milk were brought to London. In a year the quantity had doubled. In 1937 the figure exceeded a 100,000,000 gallons. In 1987 the total figure for the Metropolitan Police district of London was 173,500,000.
Perhaps one of the best slogans to be found was "No milk for seven days makes one weak".

173

525
Cutting and Loading Silage, Bignor, 1960
S. R. BADMIN, R.W.S.
Watercolour & Pencil
Dr. Chris Beetles

The feeding of livestock in winter has always been a problem
for English agriculture. The introduction of the turnip in the
18th Century improved the position, as did the importation of
concentrated foodstuffs from abroad during the late 19th and
early 20th Centuries. H. Ian Moore in 'Silos and Silage'
commented that "in the ten years before the outbreak of war
in 1939, imported feeding stuffs were so cheap that it was held
to be uneconomical to grow arable crops at all. Thus a large
acreage of plough land was sown away to grass, livestock
numbers were increased and for winter feeding farmers relied
to an increasing extent on cheap imported feeding stuffs."
That situation came to an end with the war. Silage making
offered a solution to winter feeding. The process of "ensilage"
consists of preserving green forage crops in a sufficient condition
for use out of season.
Silage is the name given to the product so obtained and a "silo"
is the container in which silage is made. The process is of great
antiquity but not adopted in England until the 19th Century.

526
Sir R. George Stapledon, C.B.E., D.Sc., F.R.S., 1957
ALAN GWYNNE-JONES
Oil on canvas, 96 x 80cm.
By kind permission of the A.F.R.C. Institute for Grassland and
Animal Production, Hurley, Berkshire

Sir George Stapledon (1882-1960), a native of Devon, was the
founder of agricultural grassland science. He pioneered the
breeding of grasses and the improvement and scientific
management of agricultural grassland. In the late 1930s he
initiated and progressed the ploughing up of old virtually useless
grassland and brought about a massive increase of food
production from British agriculture. His efforts before and
during the war have been said to be very largely responsible for
saving Britain from starvation. In 1919 he was appointed first
Director of the Welsh Plant Breeding Station, Aberystwyth and
in 1940 he also became the first Director of the Grassland
Improvement Station, (later to be the Grassland Research
Institute). Both are now part of the Agricultural and Food
Research Council's Institute for Grassland and Animal
Production. Sir George was Knighted and elected FRS in 1939,
having been awarded the CBE in 1932.

527

527
"Starting the Stubble Burning. Tuppers from Bignor", 1979
S. R. BADMIN, R.W.S.
Watercolour heightened with white, 12 x 23cm.
Dr. Chris Beetles
Inscribed: 'Burning was started on the forward side of the field'.

528

528
Sheep Study: Sheep with Lamb III, 1972
HENRY MOORE
Etching and drypoint, 14.6 x 19.8cm.
The Henry Moore Foundation

529
Hop Garden and View of North Downs, Wye College Estate,
1973
GORDON DAVIES
Oil on board, 25 x 33.75cm.
Wye College, University of London

Wye College is the School of Agriculture and Horticulture of
the University of London. It has about 420 undergraduates and
220 postgraduates who work in various areas; agriculture and
the environment, economics, animal sciences, applied plant
sciences, rural environment studies and countryside
management. The college is also a centre for research into hops.
There is an agricultural museum on the college estate housed
in a 14th Century Tithe Barn and early 19th Century Oast
House.

530
'Monoliths', 1976
S. R. BADMIN, R.W.S.
Watercolour on paper, 13.5 x 23cm.
Dr. Chris Beetles

Standing bales seen by Badmin as monoliths.

531

Grow Food medal, 1974
JACQUELINE STIEGER
Cast bronze, 6 x 7cm.
The Worshipful Company of Goldsmiths

Grow Food medal, 1974, cast bronze, designed, modelled and cast by Jacqueline Stieger. Obverse, abstract design of peas bursting out of their pods. Reverse, back of same organic theme. Winner of a competition sponsored by the Paris Mint and exhibited in *Revival of Medal* 1974.

532

Kitty Fisher and the Mountain Ewe
DENNIS CURRY
Oil on canvas, 61.2 x 73.5cm.
The Duchess of Devonshire

532

533

"The End of New Barn, Glatting", 1980
S. R. BADMIN, R.W.S.
Watercolour on paper, 13.5 x 23cm.
Dr. Chris Beetles

534

Engraved Glass Bowl: "Farmyard Birds", 1988
Jacqueline Allwood

535

The Great Yorkshire Show, 1987
RUTH GIBBONS
Oil on canvas, 86 x 122cm.
By permission of the Council of the Yorkshire Agricultural Society.

Founded in 1837 the Yorkshire Agricultural Society had as one of its aims: "the promoting of good farming generally, and that not merely to the large farmer, but more especially to the small farmer, who has not always been equally considered, though in greater need of encouragement." Vance Hall in his "History of the Yorkshire Agricultural Society" puts forward an interesting theory that the hiatus in railway promotion and speculation (between 1837 and 42) made money available from which the new agricultural associations such as the Yorkshire and Royal Agricultural Society of England benefitted. He supports this theory convincingly by pointing out that several of the founders of these societies had substantial interests in railways.

536

British Simmental Bull
JAMES LYNCH, b. 1956
Oil on canvas, 58 x 80cm.
T. R. Pearce, Esq.

The Simmental is the world's most numerous pedigree breed with 42 million animals. The breed originated in Switzerland. A large creature, red and white in patches, the red varying from a dark dun to ochre. The head, legs and top of the tail are white. The Simmental was introduced to Britain in 1970.

537

Harvest Moon, 1986
MICHAEL CHALWIN, b. 1943
Pen with earths and acrylic on paper, 60 x 74cm.
Collection of the artist

538

Ploughman's Lunch, 1985
STEPHEN FARTHING, b.1950
Oil on canvas, 106 x 120cm.
Courtesy of Edward Totah

539

New Crop Borage, 1985
STEPHEN FARTHING, b. 1950
Oil on canvas, 132 x 132cm.
Courtesy of Edward Totah

The genus *Boraginacae* contains only one agricultural crop, Russian Conifery, which has been recommended as a forage crop. It is not in general cultivation.

539

540
Five Sheep, 1988
Photograph by GEOFF TOMPKINSON
G. TOMKINSON, ESQ

A photograph of five cloned sheep

541
A set of four stamps marking Food and Farming Year, the 150th Anniversary of The Royal Agricultural Society of England and the Centenary of the Ministry of Agriculture
35 x 35mm.
Designed by SEDLEY PLACE
Printed by HARRISON AND SONS IN photogravure

These are new square format stamps. 1st Class (19p) features fruit and vegetables, 27p meat and fish, 32p (Air Mail to U.S.A.) dairy foods and 35p (Australia) cereal crops.
The Royal Mail.

542
The Iron Stranger, 1988
Peter de Francia, b. 1921
Charcoal on paper, 58.5 x 91.5cm.

Collection of the artist

543
Ditching on a January Afternoon, Warwickshire, 1988
DAVID MYNETT, b. 1942
Pastel, 75 x 17.5cm.
Collection of the Artist

This work is one of the illustrations from ''England's Pleasant Land'' by Anthony Rosen.

Artists' Biographies

James William Booth (1867-1953) was both a figure and a Rustic painter, who practiced in both oil and watercolour. In the early stages of his career he lived and worked in Middleton, Manchester (1886) and Scalby, Yorkshire 1902 and eventually moved to London. He exhibited at the Royal Academy between 1896 and 1935.

Raymond Coxon b.1896 was known as a writer and lithographer as well as a painter who exhibited from 1928 until 1940. He was born in 1896 and studied at the Leeds School of Art and then at the Royal College of Art. He was a member of the London group in 1981.

Charles Ginner was born in France (Cannes) in 1878 (d.1952) He studied in Paris, and eventually settled in London in 1910, after having travelled to Buenos Aires. He was a founder member of the London Group, and is known both as a painter and a wood engraver of the Neo Realist School, alone with Harold Gilman (1914). He exhibited between 1900 and 1939, and was perhaps best known for his street scenes. He was an official war artist in World War I.

John Nash (1893-1977) is possibly best known for his painting of English Landscapes in watercolour, as an illustrator he produced finely detailed drawings of flowers for botanical publications. He taught Design at the Royal College of Art and was assistant Master at the Ruskin School of Drawing. He was an official war artist in World War I.

Thomas Saunders Nash (1891-1968) lived for a time at Pangbourne in Berkshire. A figure painter he exhibited at the R.A. and N.E.A.C.

Harold Workman (1897-1975) painted landscapes, marine subjects, architectural subjects and occasionally interiors, working both in oil and watercolour. He was born at Oldham and studied at Oldham and Manchester Schools of Art. He moved to London in 1934 and exhibited work at the Royal Academy, the New English Art Club and leading London and provincial galleries. He was elected R.B.A 1937, R.O.I 1948, he was also president of the United Society of Artists.

George Gregory was born in 1849 at Newport on the Isle of Wight. The majority of his pictures are marine paintings and dated between 1870 and 1910. His father Charles Gregory (1810-1896) was also a well known marine painter. Although Gregory painted the occasional landscape or continental town scene his fascination was with the sea and in particular with lifeboats and sea rescue. He painted a great deal in the Solent, Southampton and Portsmouth areas. He died in 1938.

John Harris the Younger (Fl.1720-1755) was the son of a like-named topographical painter of the early18th Century. The four-bird's-eye view of Durham Massey are by his hand and the view of the City of Worcester is attributed to him.

John Linnell (1792-1882) was a landscape artist, and also a portrait painter and engraver until 1845. He studied under John Varley who was perhaps one of the most influential teachers of landscape painting of his day, his pupils included Samuel Palmer (Linnell's son-in-law) and William Holman Hunt). He also taught at the Royal Academy Schools. He became Blake's life-long Patron, giving help and encouragement, and introduced artists such as Varley, Palmer and Calvert into his circle. Linnell lured and worked at Redhill in Surrey and it was the Surrey landscape, albeit in idealized form, which became the subject matter of many of his works.

Taylor Longmire (1841-1914) was a landscape and animal painter. He was born in the Lake District, and studied under Mr. Howe. He worked and lived at Ambleside (from 1874), he did not however make a good living from his art.

Henry J. Boddington (1811-1865) was known as a landscape painter and in particular, for his ability to convey atmospheric conditions and the moods of the seasons. His subjects were chiefly from the Thames and Welsh Rivers. He was, in fact, a member of the 'Williams Family' of painters and changed his name in order to distinguish himself. He was a member of the Society of British Artists in 1842 and contributed exhibits both to this and the Royal Academy (where he exhibited all his life). He died in London, aged 54.

George Vicat Cole (1832-1893) a landscape and genre painter born in Portsmouth, the son of George Cole. He was made an A.R.A. in 1870 and R.A. in 1880.

George Cole (1810-1883), father of George Vicat Cole, was a landscape, portrait and animal painter. For the early part of his career he showed great interest in animal painting, after a job painting posters for a travelling circus called 'Wombwell's Menagerie'. Although he showed great promise as a sporting painter he turned to landscape painting instead. He was born in Portsmouth and moved to London in 1853.

Fredrick William Watts (1800-1862) was a landscape painter and a contemporary of Constable. He painted the inland scenery of England, visiting many countries, and exhibited at the Royal Academy, the British Institution and the Royal Society of British Artists. He lived in Hampstead at the same time as Constable and imitated, even copied, his work on a number of occasions. However, he is now recognised as having his own, individual style.

Benjamin Williams Leader (1831-1923) was known as a landscape and coastal painter who worked mainly in oil. He was born at Worcester, 'Leader-Williams' but reversed the names to distinguish himself from the un-related Williams family. He studied at Worcester School of Design at then at the Royal Academy Schools. He exhibited at the Royal Academy regularly from 1854 and won a gold medal at the Paris Exhibition 1889. He worked in Scotland, Wales and the Midlands and was elected A.R.A 1883 and R.A. 1898.

Richard Cosway (1740-1821) a miniature painter, was born in Tiverton where his father was a school master. He showed early drawing ability and was sent to London as a pupil of Hudson and 'soon became a pupil in Shipley's School. In 1755 he received a premium for drawing from the Society of Arts. Member of the Incorporated Society of Artists in 1766 admitted as a student to the R.A. in 1769. In 1770 he was elected A.R.A. and in 1771. R.A. It was said that his miniatures were "not only fashionable, but the fashion itself."

John Minton (1917-1957) was a 20th Century painter of both landscapes and town scenes. He worked in oil, watercolour and pen and ink. He was born near Cambridge and studied in London in the 30's at St. Johns Wood Art School, under P.F. Millard and Kenneth Martin, and at Colarossi's in Paris. His first one man show was held in London in 1945 and he exhibited during the late 40's. During this time he also taught at Camberwell and the Central Schools of Art, and at the Royal College until his early death, 1957.

Reginald Fairfax Wells (1877-1951) was a sculptor and a Potter. Born in Brazil, he came over to England, and studied at the Royal College of Art. He exhibited between 1899 and 1933, living near London (Home Counties) throughout this time.

Walter Tiffin exhibited between 1844-67 at the Royal Academy and the British Institution.

Benjamin Blake (c.1780-1830) was primarily a still life painter who exhibited the occasional landscape, especially of Dunford, nr. Salisbury where at one stage he lived. Few details are known of his early life, the earliest mention of him being when he first exhibited at the Royal Academy in 1807. He painted mainly for dealers, sending a few works to the R.A. and the Society of British Artists, of which, in 1824, he was a founder member.

William Henry Bartlett (1807-1854) was known as a topographical landscape painter. He was born in London but spent his life travelling. Initially sketching many views and buildings in the Southern and Home Counties, and churches and monastries of England and France, he subsequently travelled further afield to the middle east; Syria, Palestine and Egypt. He also voyaged several times to America, recording all these trips in his drawings.

Robert Hills (1769-1844) was a watercolour painter who was born, and died, in London. He was a founder member of the Old Watercolour Society, and was its secretary for many years. He exhibited with the society almost constantly, with a short break from 1818 to 1823 when he exhibited at the Royal Academy. He is credited with a large number of drawings and numerous etchings of animals. Most of his work was painted in the studio, using drawings of animals and scenery which had been painstakingly sketched direct from nature.

William Henry Pyne (1769-1843) devoted the early part of his career to producing watercolour landscapes (often with figures) and rural subjects. He exhibited at the Royal Academy from 1790 and was an original member of the Watercolour Society, in 1804. He later became connected with Ackermann the publisher and the remainder of his life was devoted to literary pursuits. He wrote articles for a number of 'society magazines and gazettes and a book "The Twenty Ninth of May: A Tale of Restoration". He was closely connected with the literary and artistic world.

Stephen Farthing was born in London in 1950. He attended St. Martins School of Art and the Royal College of Art. Now head of painting at West Surrey College of Art and Design at Farnham. He has exhibited widely in this county and abroad.

Dame Laura Knight (1877-1972) was an English painter, Alabastor and engraver. She studied at Nottingham School of Art, and exhibited at the Royal Academy from 1903. She spent over ten years from 1907-1918 in Cornwall, at Newlyn, painting coastal scenes with figures. As little coastal painting could be done during the war, the Knights moved to London. Here she painted Ballet and Theatre subjects during the 20's, and the circus and gypsies in the following years. In 1936 she was the first female academician since the original women members, and was created D.B.S. in 1929.

James Pardon (op.1800-1850) painted portraits, landscapes, still lifes and sporting paintings, according to demand although he exhibited only portraits and landscapes at The Royal Academy. He lived in London (1811), then at Canterbury until 1825 where he painted the local landscape and the church. He was also in Suffolk (1828) and possibly in Birmingham for a time.

Peter Leslie was a landscape and portrait painter. He was born in London (June 3rd 1877). His father was George Dunlop Leslie (1835-1921) a landscape and genre painter who had exhibited at the Royal Academy 1857 and had been elected A.R.A 1868 and R.A. 1876, who had also been born into a 'painting' family. Leslie studied at the Herkomer School, and under his father. He lived at Linfield in Sussex.

John Dalby (op.1838-1857) was the son of David Dalby of York, both were animal and sporting painters. The first record of a John Dalby as a painter is 1838, when he was living in York (two years after David's death) Although there is no painting signed John it is assumed that the later pictures signed Dalby are his. They are different in style from his father's, and consisted predominantly of hunting scenes, painted in fine almost minaturist, detail.

Alfred Mayhew Williams (1832-1905) was a London based painter. He was taught by William Bennet, and exhibited around 1882, four works at the Royal Academy and one at the Society of British Awards. He visited Northern Italy and Switzerland, where he sketched the alpine scenery, in 1854.

Richard Dodd Widdas (1826-1885) Son of John Widdas animal portrait. R.D. Widdas specialised in animal and marine painting.

Samuel Spode (op.1825-1858) was a sporting and animal painter. Little is known of his origins, although it is known he painted in both England and Ireland. His style has been described as slightly naive, an impressive example of his work being ''Coursing at Stonehenge'' He also painted horse portraits. His work does not appear to have been exhibited, but was working between 1825 and 1858.

Martin Theodore Ward (1799-1874) was an animal and sporting painter, who studied under Landseer. He is known to have exhibited at the Royal Academy from 1820 and also at the British Institution, contributing portraits of dogs and horses. He took up residence in Yorkshire after 1840, where his work is well known, and where it is said, he lived a rather eccentric life style.

Henry Bernard Chalon (1770-1849) was a well established animal and sporting painter. He exhibited many works at the Royal Academy although he was never elected Associate. Nevertheless he enjoyed a number of distinguished patrons including the Duke of Beaufort, the Duke of Devonshire, the Duchess of York, the Prince Regent, and William IV. Not only were his works reproduced in the Sporting Magazine and 2 other publications but he also published two books of his own, both animal studies, one, ''Studies from nature'' showing the influence of Stubb's work on the anatomy of a horse.

Sir Augustus Wall Callcott (1779-1844) was a fashionable landscape painter, who became a Royal Academician in 1811, and was Knighted in 1837. He was a pupil of Hoppner, and eventually adopted a style which was reminiscent of Turner but fashionably adapted. He worked in both oil and watercolour, but was more prolific in oil and his work is represented in a number of large public collections including the National Gallery and The Victoria and Albert Museum.

Charles Fredrick Tunnicliffe (b.1901-   ) was a painter and etcher of animals and birds. He was born and lived in Macclesfield and studied at Macclesfield and Manchester Schools of Art from 1915 to 1921 and at the Royal College of Art 1921 to 1925. He exhibited between 1928 and 1940 at the Royal Academy, in the provinces and abroad. He also published a few books on local fauna for example the countryside and many of his best known works are the illustrations for ''Both Sides of the Road.''

Joseph Mallord William Turner (1775) was a landscape and seascape painter, who was born in London and studied for a short while at the Royal Academy Schools in 1789. Although he disregarded its reading, the Academy supported him, recognising his talent. He became A.R.A. in 1799, R.A. in 1802, Professor of Perspective in 1807 and deputy President in 1845. In 1792 Turner began a career of sketching tours which took him all over Britain and Europe. He worked with Girbin at Dr. Monro's house (c.1795) and up to 1796 was exclusively a watercolourist, exhibiting his first oil at the R.A. in this year. His trips to Italy in 1829, 1833 and 1840 had a marked affect on his oil paintings which displayed the effects of light so characteristic of his late works and watercolours.

Stanley Anderson (b.1884-   ) was a painter and live engraver. He studied at Bristol Municipal School of Art in 1908 and was awarded the British Institute of Engraving Scholarship in 1908. He also studied at The Royal College of Art under Frank Short 1909 to 1911 and at Goldsmiths under Lee Hankey.

Edward Hall was born in 1922 at Barwell, Leicestershire. He studied at Wimbledon School of Art and at the Slade School of Fine Art, London. He has exhibited at The Royal Academy, mostly as a portrait painter, becoming R.P. in 1959 and the Honourary Secretary of the Royal Society of Portrait Painters. His works are mainly in oil and pastel.

Thomas Hennell (1903-1945) was a painter of landscape and figure subjects in watercolour. He was born at Ridley in Kent, where he was later to settle (1936) and to paint the local scenery. He studied at Regent Street Polytechnic from 1921 to 1926. He then moved to Bath, where he became an art teacher (also at Bristol) from 1928 to 1932. He suffered a nervous breakdown and spent 1932 to 1935 in a mental hospital, (later he was to publish an autobiographical account of this experience—''The Witness'' 1938.) He was appointed official war artist, and was posted at a number of stations abroad before disappearing, presumed killed in the Far East, in 1945.

James Lynch was born in 1956 at Hitchin. He was educated at Devizes School, and is a self taught artist in gouache and watercolour. He has exhibited at the Royal Academy, the Royal Watercolour Society, and Odette Gilbert. He has had several one man shows at Linfields, Bradford on Avon in 1982-83, at Nevill, Bath 1984 and the Odette Gilbert Gallery in 1988. In 1983 he won The Greenshield Foundation Award, and The Pimms Prize at the Royal Academy in 1986. He lives in Somerset.

John Augustus Atkinson (b.1775-18??) is chiefly known for his military paintings although he did exhibit rustic and classical subjects as well. For the early part of his career he lived and worked in Russia, gaining the patronage of the Empress Catharine and later the Emperor Paul. He returned to England in 1801 where he exhibited (and later published) his Russian subjects and also Rustic and Classic subjects, Battle Pieces and Camp scenes in both oil and watercolour, at the Royal Academy.

William Heath (1975-1840) was a draughtsman of The English School. There exist many humorous domestic subjects by him and also some drawings of military costumes. He drew and etched for Sir John Bowring's 'Minor Morals' in 1834. He died, aged 45, in London.

Sir Thomas Lawrence (1769-1830) was an English portrait painter. He succeeded Reynolds as 'Painter in Ordinary' to the King in 1792, and became president of the Royal Academy in 1820. He was born in Bristol, and came to London in 1786 to study at the Royal Academy Schools. He was Knighted in 1815, and was commissioned by the Royal Family to paint the 'Waterloo chamber series' commemorating the overthrow of Napoleon. From 1818 to 1820 he worked abroad, among these works which established an international reputation, was a portrait of Pope Pius VII.

John Cranch (1751-1821) an amateur painter, was born in Devon, and came to London, leaving his office job, to become a painter. He was noticed and befriended by Sir Joshua Reynolds, and painted portraits, although he never exhibited at the Royal Academy. He was multi-talented, and published a work in 1794 'On the Economy of Testaments' and wrote on the promotion of Arts.

Nicholas Pocock (1741-1821) was a marine painter, born in Bristol, the son of wealthy merchant. His early years were devoted to a military career which he gave up to pursue art as a profession. He drew portraits, landscapes and sea pictures but he mostly painted and exhibited marine books. He received encouragement from Sir Joshua Reynolds, 1780, and continued to exhibit at the Royal Academy until 1815. He was one of the original members of the Watercolour Society from 1805 to 1813, and also contributed the occasional Welsh landscape.

Mary Ellen Best (b.1810-?) was a self taught, amateur watercolour painter. Her subjects included views of Yorkshire, where she was born and reared, and German Interiors, portraits and still lifes. In 1840 she married Johann Sarg and they moved to Germany.

William Shiels (1785-1857) was a native of Berwickshire, and practiced in Edinburgh. He is best known for domestic, and country scenes and animal paintings including horses. He painted a series of pictures of different breeds of horses for the Agricultural Museum of Edinburgh University, which were used as illustrations in a book by David Low. He occasionally exhibited at the Royal Academy 1813-1814, and at many London Exhibitions (between 1808-1852) where he lived for a while before returning to Scotland where he lived for the remainder of his life.

Alexander Nasmyth (1758-1840) was born and educated in Edinburgh. He moved to London and became a pupil of Allan Ramsay. He subsequently travelled to Italy where he studied historical and landscape painting, although it was the latter which eventually preoccupied him. He settled in Edinburgh, beginning his career as a portrait painter, and was privileged to paint a number of distinguished sitters. Soon he painted only landscapes; exhibiting Scottish scenes at the Royal Academy between 1813 and 1826 and was a member of the original Society of Scottish Artists.

Peter De Wint (1784-1849) was born in Stone, Staffordshire of Dutch-American descent. He was an English landscape painter, and one of the first to be master of both oil and watercolour. In his formative years he was a pupil of J.R. Smith and helped by Varley, as well as being patronised by Dr. T. Monro, through he was influenced by Girbin. De Wint exhibited 12 oil landscapes (English) at the Royal Academy from 1807-1820 and 417 works at the Old Watercolour Society of which he was a member and then an exhibitor. He specialised in painting the flat countryside around Lincoln which lent itself well to his wide-format paintings.

Thomas Gainsborough (1727-1788) was born at Sudbury, Suffolk. He went to London in 1740 and worked under Cravelot. Among early influences were 17th Century Dutch landscape paintings, by Ruisdael and Hobbema. Although Gainsborough's chief concern was landscape painting he painted portraits for a living. He moved to Bath in 1759 then a very fashionable Spa, in order to find patrons. In 1774 he came to London when Reynolds reputation was at its highest, and exhibited at the Society of Artists. His relationship with the newly formed Royal Academy was turbulent. From the more arcadian (French style) landscapes of the Bath period, his late landscapes were Rubenesque in handling.

William Needham (1801-1849) (signed 'Nedham') was a provincial painter working in the Leicestershire area. He was born, it is believed, at Syston, on December 8th 1801, and studied under J. Ferneley snr. He painted a number of Equestrian scenes and among his patrons was a Mr. V. R. Pochin of Barkby Hall. He does not appear to have exhibited anywhere.

Eric Ravilious was a painter, designer and engraver. He was born in London in 1903 and studied at Eastbourne School of Art. He received a Scholarship from the Royal College of Art (1922-25) where he studied under Paul Nash. He travelled, on a scholarship, to Italy, in the same year, 1925, he was proposed for membership of the Society of Wood Engravers. He was commissioned to paint a mural at Morley College with Edward Barrden, which was later destroyed in the war. He had his first one man show at Zwemmers in 1933 and was also offered work by Wedgwood, amongst other design commissions. He was appointed official war artist in 1940, but two years later disappeared while with the R.A.F. observing a rescue operation over Iceland.

John Dunthorne (1798-1832) of Bergholt was a landscape painter who became a friend and neighbour of John Constable. He worked for Constable as an assistant until an early death aged 34. He exhibited six works at the Royal Academy and three at the British Institution.

F. E. Große (fl.1888-1919) lived in Colchester where he worked as a figure and landscape painter. In 1903 he was made R.B.A., he died in Dulwich in 1919.

Thomas H. Hair (fl.1838-1849) was a Northumbrian painter of towns, landscapes and industrial subjects. Notably, he made a series of views of Northumbrian coal mines, which were later published (1839). He exhibited at the Royal Academy from 1841-49 and the British Institution from 1842-49.

George Smith of Chichester (1714-1776), as he was known, was an artist of many talents. He, and his brother, were landscape artists, painting the surrounding rural scenery and pastoral compositions. He became a fashionable and successful artist since he painted 'Ideal' landscapes in the manner of Claude and Poussin, and his work was engraved by many fine engravers in 1760 the Society of Arts awarded him their first premium in competition with Richard Wilson, and in 1763 he was made a member of the 'Free Society of Artists'. He was a talented poet and musician, and also etched and engraved his own work which he published jointly with his brother.

W. Frank Calderon (1865-1943) was born in London and was educated at University College School. Aged 14 he obtained the Trevelyan Goodall Scholarship and later the Slade Scholarship. In 1881 he exhibited his first picture at the Royal Academy. In 1894 he founded the 'School of Animal Painting' which was a great influence, attracting horse painters and already established painters who went there especially to study animal painting. The school only closed because of the war which forced the family to move from London.

John Duvall (1816-1892) was an animal painter. He is thought to have been born in Kent, then the family moved to Ipswich. In 1855 he is recorded as an art teacher, he also illustrated the Suffolk Horse Society Stud Book. He may have begun his career as a portrait painter but the advent of photography possibly caused him to reconsider his career. Col Barlow commissioned him to paint 'Suffolk Show' in Christchurch Park, Ipswich in 1868 which established Duval as an animal painter. His other patrons include the Duke of Hamilton and the Princess of Wales. He exhibited regularly at the Ipswich Art Society from 1875 to 1889, and was one of the two men who conceived of the Ipswich Fine Art Club in 1874.

Thomas Hearne (1744-1806) trained as an engraver and worked for a few years as a draughtsman before establishing himself as a topographical and 'picturesque' watercolourist. He specialised in painting antiquities and views of countryside seats, for example, he collaborated with William Byrne on 'The Antiquities of Great Britain' 1777 and painted Downton Castle for Payne Knight. His work was collected by his friend Dr. T. Monro.

Harry Becker (1865-1928) was a painter of Genre, landscape and portrait. An engraver and lithographer, he exhibited at the Royal Academy from 1885 and the New Watercolour Society, having studied at the Antwerp Academy and Paris.

Gertrude Elisabeth Rogers (1837-1917) was a 19th Century photographer. His work is usually dated between 1860 and 1861 and is largely genre subjects. These were shot on location in Southern England, and in the studio. Her works are exhibited in print form. She was obliged to give up photography on her marriage.

Valentine Green (1739-1813) was born in Shropshire. He was intended for the law but decided to take up engraving. He moved to London in 1765 where he experimented with and developed an original mezzotint technique. He began exhibiting in 1766 at Spring Gardens and soon became successful, being among the first artists to use the technique for historical subjects instead of portraiture. He engraved plates after many well known artists including Reynolds, Zoffany, Van Dyck and the Italian masters. He became a member of the Encorporated Artists Soc. 1767 and was elected A.E. and appointed engraver to George III in 1775. In 1805 he became keeper of the British Institution, until his death in 1813.

Ferdinand Jean Joubert (1810-1884) was a French engraver, who spent some time in London, and exhibited at the Royal Academy from 1855-1881. He studied at the 'ecole des Beaux Arts in 1829, and began to engrave illustrations around 1830. He made his debut at the Salon in 1840, engraving portraits and genre subjects after artists such as Murillo, Winterhalter, Lejeune and Greuze.

Thomas Rowlandson (1756-1827) draughtsman and caricaturist, was born in London and studied in Paris. He also studied at the R.A. schools. Much of his work was produced for the print publisher Ackermann.

John Boultbee (1747-1812) a painter of sporting pictures. He painted many portraits of livestock including those of Robert Bakewell and a portrait of Bakewell on his horse.

Richard Ansdell R.A. (1815-1885) was born in Liverpool and educated there at the Blue Coat School. He became President of the Liverpool Academy. Ansdell exhibited at the Royal Academy and the British Institution and painted a wide range of animal subjects.

Hubert Herkomer R.A. (1849-1914) a major graphic illustrator and portrait painter who was made a member of the Royal Academy in 1890. During the late 1860's he illustrated many periodicals such as the Graphic' in which his portraits of working men appeared.

Richard Whitford (1854-1887) lived at Evesham and Northleach and specialised in the portraiture of prize farm animals.

Sir Godfrey Kneller (1646-1723) was born in Lübeck. He arrived in England c.1676 and became the leading portrait painter. Knighted in 1692 and in 1715 was the first painter in England to be made a Baronet.

Sir Alfred Munnings (1878-1959) was president of the Royal Academy 1944-9. He painted a wide range of animal subjects, often in an impressionist manner. Many of his works may be seen to contrive the life of sporting paintings represented in an earlier period by Stubbs or Marshall.

George Morland (1763-1804) was born in London. His father Henry Robert Morland was a painter who also dealt in paintings. Morland exhibited at the R.A. from the age of 15. He was married to James Ward's sister. He worked on rustic subjects which included a vast array of detail.

David Cox (1783-1859) born in Birmingham and trained as a scene painter, he moved to London where he was taught by John Varley. He travelled extensively in the Low Counties and Northern France and was much influenced by Bonnington.

Randolph Schwabe (1885-1948) one time Professor of Painting at the Slade

Evelyn Dunbar (1906-1960) was trained at the Royal College of Art in the 1920's, Commissioned to record work on the land during World War II, she continued to paint up to the time of her early death, in addition to rural scenes she also worked on allegorical subjects.

James Stark (1794-1859) was a member of the Norwich School, founded in 1803.

J. F. Herring Senior (1795-1865) an enormously successful artist in his own life time. His subjects included sporting and rustic scenes. He worked for George IV, William IV and Queen Victoria. He exhibited at the R.A., the British Institution and the R.S.B.A.

George Garrard (1760-1826) studied with Sawrey Gilpin and at the Royal Academy. As a partner he produced images of sport, animals and landscapes. From 1795 he worked as a modeller and used accurate anatomical measurements for his models and engravings.

Thomas Weaver (1774-1843) born in Shropshire and possibly the greatest artist of the age of the English agricultural revolution.

John Frederick Herring Jnr. (1820-1907) the eldest of J. Herring's three sons (Charles 1828-1856) and Benjamin (1830-1871). The Herring family worked in close co-operation and many works display several different hands. He exhibited at the R.A. between 1863-1873.

D. Dalby of York (1794-1840) resided in York and painted mainly horses.

J. Dalby (op.1826-1853) resided in York and painted many hunting scenes and portraits of horses.

James Ward (1769-1859) perhaps best known as the painter of the massive canvas "Gordale Scar" (Tate Gallery). Ward was to a certain extent influenced by the work of his brother-in-law George Morland, and also from 1903 by the painting "Chabean de Steen" by Rubens.

Sir George Clausen (1852-1944) was born in London of Danish descent and attended the South Kensington School of Art. Influenced by Whistler and subsequently Bastienn Lepage, he was a major figure in British Post-Impressionism he became an R.A. in 1908.

Thomas Bewick (1953-1828) was born near Newcastle. A museum at his birth place Cherryburn has recently been opened. A wood engraver his work displayed great refinement of detail and tonal gradation. He illustrated many books including his "General History of Quadrupeds" (1970).

Samuel Palmer (1805-1881) was a painter of pastoral landscapes, best known for the works of his 'Shoreham Period' of 1826-35. The most important follower of William Blake.

Peter Coker was born in 1926 in London. He studied at St. Martin's and at the Royal College of Art. His work is to be found in all the major British galleries. His more recent work has included many Scottish Landscapes.

Peter de Francia was born in 1921 in France. From 1972-1986 he was Professor of Painting at the Royal College of Art. The author of a major study of the works of Leger (1983) his most recent exhibition was a retrospective at Camden Arts Centre in 1987.

Selected Bibliography

Discovering Farm Livestock, Nigel Harvey, Shire Publications, 1975.
The Observer's Book of Farm Animals, Lawrence Alderson, Warne, 1978.
The Farmers Tools, G. E. Fussell, Bloomsbury Books, 1985.
Smithfield Past & Present, Alec Forshaw, Heinemann, 1980.
English Farming, Sir John Rusell, Collins, 1946.
Lend-Lease, E. R. Stetinius, Jr., Penguin Special, 1944.
British Farm Animals in Prints & Paintings, Walter Shaw Sparrow, Walker's Quarterly, 1932.
Richard Ansdell, R.A., Exhibition Catalogue: Malcolm Innes Gallery/Richard Green Gallery, 1985.
A History of English Farming, C. S. Orwin, Nelson, 1949.
Great Farmers, J. A. Scott Watson & May Elliot Hobbs, Selwyn & Blount, 1937.
Art and the Industrial Revolution, Francis D. Klingender Paladin, 1972.
Sharpen the Sickle, Reg Groves, Merlin, 1981.
The Village Labourer Vols I & II, J. L. & Barbara Hammond, Guild Books, 1948.
A History of the Yorkshire Agricultural Society, 1837-1987, Vance Hall, Batsford, 1987.
The Drovers, Shirley Toulson, Shire Album (45), 1980.
Power on the Land, Robert Trow-Smith, Agripress, 1975.

The Farming Kingdom, Nigel Harvey, Turnstile Press, 1955.
Thomas Sidney Cooper of Canterbury, Brian Stewart, Meresborough Books, 1983.
One Thousand Years of Devon Beekeeping, R. H. Brown, The Devon Beekeepers Association, 1975.
Prints and Paintings of British Farm Livestock, 1780-1910, D. H. Boalch Rothamsted Experimemtal Station Library, 1958.
British Craftsmen, Thomas Hennell, Collins, 1943.
A Classic of English Farming: Hodge & His Masters, Richard Jefferies, Faber & Faber, 1936.
British Breeds: Extant & Extinct, C. M. A. Baker & C. Manwell, Westburn Press, 1989.
Sir Joseph Banks, H. B. Carter, British Museum (Natural History), 1988.
His Majesty's Spanish Flock: Sir Joseph Banks and the Merinos of George III of England, H. B. Carter, Sydney, 1964.
John Betjeman's Collected Poems, Murray, 1980.
The Earth/La Terre, Emile Zola trans., Douglas Parmée, Penguin Classics, 1980.
The Georgics, Virgil trans. L. P. Wilkinson, Penguin Classics, 1982.

Index

ROYAL AGRICULTURAL SOCIETY OF ENGLAND

The Royal Agricultural Society of England, founded nearly 150 years ago by a group of leading landowners, seeks to encourage the effective communication of new ideas and developments in agriculture and provide a platform for the promotion of British agricultural expertise and practice.

The History

It is nearly 150 years since a number of the country's leading landowners combined forces to establish the first corporate national body for the farming community in England—the English Agricultural Society—with the prime objective of improving agriculture by sharing knowledge and experience.

The year was 1838; and in 1839 this new Society held the first national agricultural show at Oxford on 17 July, followed in 1840 by the granting of a Royal Charter giving the Society its new name The Royal Agricultural Society of England.

In that it took just three years to achieve such official approval is a measure of the efforts and enthusiasm of those founder members, as well as the obvious need for some form of 'umbrella' organisation over such a widespread and largely uninformed industry.

The Royal Charter set down a number of main objectives broadly summarised as '. . . to encourage good husbandry, agricultural craftsmanship and forestry; to confer and co-operate with other societies and governments at home and abroad; to exchange views and information and generally encourage the dissemination of knowledge'.

Given this brief, the Society considered the best way of fulfilling it was to invite the country's farmers to meet at a selected place each year to see the latest developments in farming. In this way, the Royal Show was able to reach a new audience each year and soon became a valuable technical and social meeting ground, as well as an educational exercise, attracting a rapidly growing membership as it travelled the country.

The Society played a pioneering role in agricultural education in the nineteenth century administering, for example, the National Diploma in Agriculture examinations for the National Education Board of the Joint Societies, which was only superseded by a new examination structure in the 1970s.

At the same time, the Society was venturing into the field of agricultural research, launching the country's first experimental station at Woburn. The Society was responsible for Woburn for the first 44 years of its existence, from 1877 to 1921. Even earlier, in 1872, the Society's chemical and botanical work was recognised as being extremely beneficial.

Another significant step was taken by the Society in 1928 when it opened the first quarantine station, which some six years later was taken over by the Ministry.

The 1920 tractor trials enabled the Society to help establish the tractor in general farm use and provided information on which the farmer could base his choice of model—the forerunner of the OECD and Nebraska Test Reports—information on which is published by the AFRC Institute of Agricultural Engineering in 'Agricultural Tractors'.

By the 1950s it became clear that a permanent venue had to be found for the Royal Show, not only for economic reasons, but also to enable the Show to meet the demands of the vastly changed and sophisticated agricultural industry. Hence, in 1963 the Royal Show settled permanently at Stoneleigh, close to the acknowledged centre of England.

The ability to build up permanent pavilions and exhibition facilities, and the space to introduce practical demonstrations of growing crops and machinery at work, has helped to give the Royal Show a unique appeal and advantage over international shows.

At the same time, a fact-finding committee concluded that the permanent base of the RASE must evolve into 'The Agricultural Centre of England'. What the committee envisaged as 'a Centre with all that is best in agricultural practice, in science, in technical development and reflecting new ideas all year round' is now a fact recognised throughout the UK and much further afield.

After the basic facilities such as roads, water and power services had been installed, work began on technical demonstration units. There are now six such units based at the NAC: beef & calf, dairy, pig, sheep and poultry on the livestock side and an arable unit embracing a wide field of crop technology interests.

In creating such a Centre, the Society is pleased to have attracted over the years many other organisations involved in the industry who now have permanent offices at the NAC. The showground is also widely used by many 'outside' organisations who find the blend of permanent buildings and open exhibition facilities ideal for staging practically any type of event.

While the Royal Show remains the Society's major event of the year, the Society has extended its 'event' programme to include a number of specialist technical demonstrations each year, both at the NAC and at locations throughout the country. Each winter, the Society also combines with ADAS to present a conference programme on a wide range of current topics and developments. The Conference Unit is also involved in organising a number of international symposia and conferences attracting worldwide interest and debate. Communications also extend to the non-farming community, interpreting farming to schools and the general public through a number of events and open days. Perhaps the best known of these is the Town and Country Festival.

Recognising the Centre's value to international visitors, the Society's International Relations Department organises group visits and technical tours to the NAC Demonstration Units, and also offers information, in a variety of languages, to international visitors about the Society's events and in particular the Royal Show.

The mechanisation of agriculture, leading to lower direct employment on the farm, is having a significant effect on the prosperity and welfare of the rural community as a whole. The Society has always seen its responsibilities in this wider context, and therefore, has been involved for many years in initiatives concerning aspects of the rural economy. One such initiative is the NAC Rural Trust which has encouraged the development of low-cost housing in rural areas from its inception in 1975.

Similarly, the Society has been concerned in drawing greater attention and resources to the training and employment needs of rural areas, through the work of the Rural Employment and Training Unit. Other aspects of the Society's work, in generating economic activity in rural areas, include the development of the Farm Holiday Bureau. Countryside conservation continues to develop both within the NAC and on the Society's farms at Stoneleigh and Sacrewell, Cambridgeshire and Stowford, Devon.

The 1987 Royal Show saw the opening of the Conservation Centre Pavilion by HRH The Princess Royal—the final stage in the development of the Site from its beginnings in 1983. The site itself continues to develop—now to the stage where management of the various habitats is essential.

On the land, management of the farm wildlife habitats is given an increasing degree of emphasis. At Stoneleigh, where woodlands comprise—with the ponds—the most important sector, additional planting has been completed. These new woodlands take the form both of conventional hardwoods with planting at close spacing and agroforestry. This is a new concept in Britain with wide spacing of young trees to allow sheep grazing and is experimental. During 1988 the Society also introduced the John Eastwood Farm Conservation Trail at Stoneleigh, designed to demonstrate some of the practical aspects of conservation and management of woodlands, ponds and hedgerows on a modern, productive farm.

At Sacrewell, with its great diversity of habitats, emphasis is given to the care of herb-rich meadows and wetlands. Fencing, to protect limestone pastures and banks, is under way and a programme of scrub clearance and maintenance of the new reservoir banks is being prepared.

An important part of the Society's role as a communicator is met through its various publications, the best known of which is 'The Journal', one of the very first enterprises the founder members of the RASE embarked upon. The early reputation of 'The Journal' as a record of discovery and invention, was unrivalled, and it remains today an important document of record on agricultural matters.

Also long established is 'Fream's Elements of Agriculture', first published by the Society in 1892, and recognised as a standard agricultural textbook since that time. Now, sixteen editions later, re-titled and completely re-written for the 1980s, 'Fream's Agriculture' was re-launched in 1983.

Other Society publications include the 'National Calendar of Events', regular reports and newsletters from the livestock and arable units, and the quarterly 'RASE/NAC News' which brings together news, features and pre-event publicity and information for the RASE's 18,000 members.

The Society, a registered charity, is governed by its Council. The President for the year is The Earl of Selborne, KBE, DL. The Chairman of Council is Mr C. M. T. Smith-Ryland.

Further copies of the 'This Land is our Land'' exhibition catalogue are available by post for £12.50 plus £2.50 postage and packing. Cheques should be made payable to RASE (1989) and sent to 35 Belgrave Square, London SW1X 8QN.

NAME ....

ADDRESS ....

....

Please send me .... copies of the catalogue at £15 each.

History Gathered In

A new History of the Royal Agricultural Society of England—*Harvests of Change*—is being published to help celebrate our 150th anniversary. It is written by Dr Nicholas Goddard, senior lecturer in Geography at the Cambridgeshire College of Arts and Technology, and traces the Society's progress from its foundation in 1838 by a group of landowners, agricultural journalists and other sundry 'enthusiasts', through to the present day and its management of the National Agricultural Centre, which provides the industry with a national and international focus.

The story of how the Society's founders carried through their aims, often in the face of intense scepticism from people outside the organisation, is graphically related.

In writing the book, Dr Goddard took great care to identify the Society's role in the agricultural community, as he explains:

"Although it is a history of the Society—which it is important to record—it is not an inward-looking book. The Society is presented in the broadest context, with material being drawn from the widest possible range and number of sources, including the contemporary agricultural press".

Personalities and families who have featured prominently in its affairs are profiled, such as the Voelckers. Three generations of the family were its consultant chemists for nearly 120 years between them. Augustus Voelcker served from 1857 to 1884, being succeeded by his son J Augustus, who held the post until 1936, and his nephew Eric, who retired in 1976.

The book also describes the Society's role in founding scientific services for farmers, like its pioneering of feed testing in the wake of scandals over adulterated farm supplies, when attempts to prevent merchants profiteering led to complicated legal actions.

One thing Dr Goddard discovered during his research is that there is really nothing new in the industry—most ideas in vogue today have been tried in the past.

Alternative crops—for instance—are no newcomers. Under that part of its Charter which charges the Society to investigate the potential of new crops, researchers during the great depression conducted trials on tobacco, teasels and buckwheat.

And while some people find the backcombing and shampooing used by today's stockmen to improve their animals' looks for the show ring extraordinary, some unusual ones were practised in the 19th Century.

Pigs' teeth were filed to give an impression of youthfulness, sheep were carefully trimmed to give an impression of symmetry and to hide faults while the essential ingredients of one of the popular diets—formulated to give animals that extra show-ring bloom—were aniseed, gin and treacle.

The machinery stands on show at those early events were also a far cry from today's highly developed, professionally styled presentations, although to be fair to the exhibitors, their cause was not helped by their steam engines' tendency to blow up!

Humorous incidents in the Society's history are also recounted, such as that which occurred at the 1947 show at Lincoln. Anticipating a large turnout, Sir Archibald Weigall was despatched to investigate the availability of additional accommodation at what the Society's records call, 'the Butlins Hotel at Skegness'.

Please send me _____ copy/copies of *Harvests of Change, The Royal Agricultural Society of England 1838-1988*. I enclose payment of £18.50 per copy (£16 plus £2.50 postage and packing). Cheques and postal orders should be made payable to the RASE.

NAME ....

ADDRESS ....

....

Please return to: The Members Shop, Royal Agricultural Society of England, National Agricultural Centre, Stoneleigh, Warwickshire, CV8 2LZ.

Mall Gallery

The concept of this unique exhibition "This Land is Our Land" grew out of the plans and activities being developed over the past few years for British Food & Farming Year.

British Food & Farming Year is being celebrated by all sectors of the industry. The objective is to focus public attention on the immense contribution of the food and farming industry to the economy and to our whole way of life, from food and drink to our architectural and landscape heritage.

It also has an historical relevance. 1989 marks the 150th anniversary of the Royal Agricultural Society of England and the centenary of the Ministry of Agriculture, Fisheries and Food. So, what better time to celebrate our oldest industry? And how better to celebrate than with an exhibition exploring the rich and varied influences of aspects of agriculture in art over the centuries?

At whatever period one looks, the impact of farming on the culture of Britain has been enormous. The landscape is created by different farming systems in different parts of the country. Much of our architectural heritage whether in houses or churches, is the result of agricultural prosperity. The visual and fine arts—as so wonderfully demonstrated by this exhibition—have constantly reflected farming and the rural scene.

This Land is Our Land is the first activity during British Food & Farming Year. It sets the scene and puts the Year in perspective in a way guaranteed to attract many people—not just those from a farming background. It is appropriate that the Royal Mail have decided to launch the Food & Farming Year commemorative stamps (issue date 7 March 1989) at this exhibition. The stamps are, after all, yet another aspect of agriculture in art!

Other activities during the Year include a travelling exhibition to provincial museums; fashion shows highlighting British Wool as a fashion fabric; the ASDA Festival of Food & Farming—a three day event in London's Hyde Park from 5-7th May; the opening of a new model farm at Alton Towers, Staffordshire; special features and television programmes; new publications including a superb new cookery book, "The Dairy Book of British Food"; school visits to farms up and down the country; country fairs and shows; farm open days, farm walks and exhibitions at rural museums, and much more. If you want to know more about the Year please send a stamped addressed envelope to BFFY, 35 Belgrave Square, London SW1X 8QN.

So many people have helped us by putting tremendous time, energy and devotion into this exhibition. We would particularly like to thank all the lenders of the works of art, Andrew Singleton of Phillips, John Hearth of the RASE and last, but by no means least, Demelza Spargo without whom it would quite simply not have happened.

Judith Shallow
Peter Jackson
British Food & Farming Year

The Rare Breeds Survival Trust

More than 40 breeds of farm animals are now receiving support from the Rare Breeds Survival Trust because there are so few of them left that their continued existence cannot be taken for granted.

The threat of extinction

A large proportion of these breeds, for example Gloucester cattle and Cotswold sheep, were popular no more than 30 years ago. Yet by 1973, when the Rare Breeds Survival Trust (a registered charity) was formed, many were in danger of extinction.

The danger is real. Already this century, more than 20 unique breeds of British farm animals have died out. None have been lost since the Trust started work.

Preserving the species

Preservation of breeds that are part of our living heritage is valuable for more than sentimental reasons; once lost, an extinct breed can never be brought back to life. The Trust works to extend our understanding of the genetic make-up of individual breeds, and to ensure the preservation of the widest possible range of characteristics for potential future farming use.

This work entails paying for surveys, blood typing and other scientific investigations, as well as the formulation of sound breeding policies, the maintenance of a semen bank for unique genetic material and the provision of grants to breeders, where necessary, for the maintenance of small groups of animals.

The value of this work

Current farming techniques in Britain favour a relatively narrow range of breeds and hybrids. But in future, breeders of commercial farm stock will inevitably need the widest possible selection of genetic material on which to draw to improve such factors as vigour, disease resistance and food conversion performances.

The preservation of a diverse genetic pool of our rare breeds is vital.

Members, playing an active part

As the membership has built up, the Trust has been able to offer growing support to endangered breeds, nearly all of which have increased in number. Several breeds which were once seriously depleted are now out of all danger and off our lists.

Since its formation, the Trust has been successful in reversing the trends of the previous century.

That success has in large part been due to our members. Their support had enabled us to identify endangered species, to publicise our cause, to attract grants, sponsorship and bequests.

Yet we cannot be complacent. Our work has shown the need for further scientific studies; for more practical help for rare breeds. Many are still threatened.

A strong membership (we already have over 8,000 members) means that we are more able to respond to urgent requests for help—and to attract generous grants towards the costs of registering, studying and supporting rare pig, cattle, sheep, goat and horse breeds.

RARE BREEDS SURVIVAL TRUST, National Agricultural Centre, Kenilworth, Warwickshire, CV8 2LG. Tel: Coventry (0203) 696511.

THE FUTURE. NOW.

THE NEW VAUXHALL CAVALIER 4x4.

VAUXHALL. ONCE DRIVEN, FOREVER SMITTEN.

HELPING BRITISH FOOD AND FARMING EVERY YEAR.

The National Trust owns over half a million acres in England, Wales and Northern Ireland. With its tenants it has made a contribution to food and farming every year since 1895 – and of course to nature conservation too.

We are proud to be associated with British Food and Farming Year 1989.

The National Trust

MINTON®

Dynasty

LEADING BRANDS ON THE LAND.
LEADING BRANDS IN THE HOME.

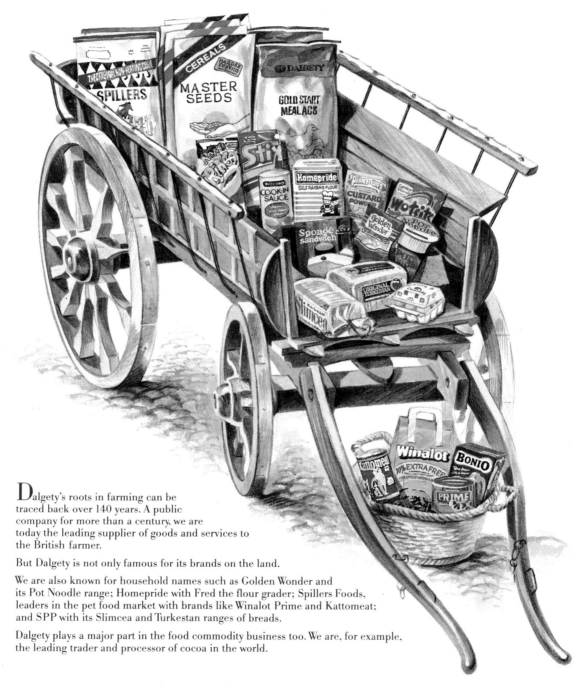

Dalgety's roots in farming can be traced back over 140 years. A public company for more than a century, we are today the leading supplier of goods and services to the British farmer.

But Dalgety is not only famous for its brands on the land.

We are also known for household names such as Golden Wonder and its Pot Noodle range; Homepride with Fred the flour grader; Spillers Foods, leaders in the pet food market with brands like Winalot Prime and Kattomeat; and SPP with its Slimcea and Turkestan ranges of breads.

Dalgety plays a major part in the food commodity business too. We are, for example, the leading trader and processor of cocoa in the world.

DALGETY ■

Dalgety PLC · 19 Hanover Square · London · W1R 9DA · Tel: 01-499 7712

AGRIBUSINESS · FOOD · FOOD COMMODITIES